How To Teach
ORIGINS
(Without ACLU Interference)

How To Teach
ORIGINS

(Without ACLU Interference)

Dr. John N. Moore

MOTT
MEDIA

Acknowledgements

In writing this book on my methods of teaching about origin questions I am primarily indebted to the hundreds of students at Michigan State University who experienced various classroom procedures. I always appreciated and profited from their comments received at the close of each teaching term. I am indebted to many departmental colleagues who afforded guest lecture opportunities in their classes, and through private discussions helped me sharpen communication in the evolution/creation confrontation teaching approach. Also many correspondents have helped, especially in reading and commenting upon early forms of manuscript chapters.

I appreciate permission to include quotations granted by the following: Allan and Bacon, Inc.; Dr. Henry M. Morris, Director, Institute for Creation Research; Editors of *Origins*, publication of the Geoscience Research Institute; Field Museum of Natural History; Harcourt Brace Jovanovich, Inc.; Macmillan Publishing Co., Inc.; and McGraw-Hill Book Company.

Development of these teaching methods was broadened while I was summer visiting professor at Tennessee Temple College in 1974, and also as invited instructor in special volunteer study modules on "Evolution/Creation" for senior education majors in the College of Education at Michigan State University in 1975 and 1976. I am fully indebted to my wife who typed the original manuscript, which was prepared in 1977 during a sabbatical from Michigan State University and while I was a guest lecturer at Christian Heritage College, San Diego. I have benefitted from technical assistance by editors and other personnel of Mott Media for which I am most grateful.

HOW TO TEACH ORIGINS (Without ACLU Interference)

Copyright © 1983 by Mott Media, Inc., Publishers

Manuscript copy edited by Ruth Schenk and John Tiner
Typeset design by A. G. Smith
Typeset and cover design by Frieda Bohn and Joyce Bohn

Manufactured in the United States of America

ISBN 0-915134-88-8

Contents

Classroom Teaching Aids

Figures

Page

PREFACE

This book is written for the many who have asked, "How do you teach creation in a public educational institution?" Even more particularly this book is written for those who have asked, "How do you teach creation in a science course?"

Often, scientific colleagues have reacted with the thought, "But evolution is scientific, and creation is religious; so how can you teach religion in a science course?" A specific answer to this question depends upon clear consideration of two vital questions: 1) What is religion? and 2) What is science? It is sufficient for the moment to say that religion commonly involves worshipful relationship to an almighty being, while science involves the identification and classification of knowledge through use of scientific processes. These questions will be discussed at great length in the Introduction and in chapter 1. It is not our goal to teach students how to worship God, but to concentrate instead upon explanation and illustration of scientific methodology and subject matter content.

This book affords scientific assistance to teachers presenting alternate points of view on the multifaceted topic of first origins; that is the *origin of the universe, origin of life on the earth*, and *origin of humankind*. The focus of this book will be upon *first* origins, in contradistinction to the origin and birth of a human being, or the beginning of a new commercial product, or the commencement of a new educational institution. In each of these latter instances, which occur during the "present", direct *scientific* study can be initiated with all the common checks and double-checks of proper research methods.

Prior to the nineteenth century, the predominant position held about *first* origins was that God created the universe: the galaxies, the stars, the comets, the planets—and life on the earth, including humankind. For centuries, people had been taught that Jesus Christ was the Creator of all things.

> For by him were all things created that are in heaven, and that are in earth, visible and invisible, whether they be thrones, or dominions, or principalities, or powers: all things were created by him, and for him: (Col. 1:16)

All things were made—created—by Jesus Christ. This is the answer that John, Peter and Paul, have given to the question of first origins. They along with Moses, Isaiah, and the Psalmist had revelation from God. No human being was present to witness any first origin events. Yet, since the time of Charles Darwin, it has become more and more fashionable to believe in supposed natural causes for the existence of all things: the universe, life on the earth, and for humankind. In the United States, the creation explanation for first origins continued in science textbooks to some degree until the mid-1940's. Yet all practical reference to a creationist point of view regarding first origins was excluded from science textbooks after the mid-1940's. However, no systematic treatment of evolutionary thinking on first origins was included in high school science textbooks until the mid-1960's.

In regard to *first* origins, certain questions must be raised. Can scientific research be applied? Is it possible to scientifically study the origin of the universe? Is it possible to scientifically study the origin of life on the earth? Is it possible to scientifically study the origin of humankind? According to the majority of the scientific community, the answer to each of these questions is "Yes." In actual fact, the most rigorous answer to each of these questions about first origins is a definite "No."[1] It is the responsibility of the science teacher to fully examine, review and test all ideas.

The science teacher should be especially able to help others to understand that *no* question about first origins can be answered scientifically. First origin questions involve events that are forever past. The very beginnings of the universe, of life on the earth, of humankind are *not* repeatable. Proper scientific research requires multiple, direct or indirect observations of repeatable events. From a rigorous metaphysical position, *all questions* of first origin should be considered more opportunely within the subject matter areas of philosophy and theology. Realistically, first origin questions—about ultimate cause—are within the purview of philosophers and theologians. Thus, they could more properly be included in humanities or social studies.

However, fully qualified scientists do not omit discussions of ultimate origin of the universe, life on the earth, or humankind from their science courses. Thus, in the last 100 years, at various levels of education in the United States, and in varying degrees, emphasis in science teaching has been upon evolutionary thinking. It is shocking to realize that the colossal impact of evolutionary thinking can be identified and traced across the entire range of academic pursuits in the twentieth century. Attention to the impact and infusion of evolutionary thinking into all academic disciplines has become more and more explicit in the present decade. It permeates all the major disciplines of human knowledge.

Significantly, ever since the mid-1960's spokemen for the creationist point of view about first origins have become quite active. Confrontations have become common at both the university and high school levels as a consequence of campus debates between scientists and declarations by authors in professional science education journals.[2] Thus some teachers at all levels of education are interested in using the growing evolution-creation confrontation as a viable medium to stimulate individual student participation and to increase attention to methods of scientific inquiry.[3]

Thus a need exists for a book in which particular attention is given to methods of systematic pro- and con- examination of scientific data used in current confrontations between evolutionist scientists and creationist scientists. Since this book is not intended as a science textbook in biology or in any of the physical sciences, the level of discussion centers upon those principles that can be applied at any level of education. Although details are included for meaningful treatment of the topics, this book is designed to be used as a teaching aid and supplement to regularly adopted science textbooks. Some problem of vocabulary may become evident depending upon the specific level of the educational endeavor at which the principles discussed are applied. For instance, teachers at the elementary level must use their own ingenuity, intuition, and skill to simplify and orient ideas treated in this book into word form usable at their level.

To provide specifically functional means for presenting ideas in the science classroom, Classroom Teaching Aids are included in the text. These teaching aids have been employed successfully in my own evolution/creation confrontation teaching approach at Michigan State University since

1973. They have been utilized with undergraduate students, graduate senior education majors, and with citizen participants in public lectures and seminars. Their usefulness has been well tested. By means of these Teaching Aids, science teachers can develop personal teaching approaches; give positive assistance on teaching strategies to other teachers, and to local school board memebers on policy making with respect to teaching about *first* origins. Initial recommendations on the use of Classroom Teaching Aids will be found in the Note To Teachers.

In the book, we will discuss 5 major questions:
  1. **What is science?**
  2. **Is it possible to scientifically study the origin of the universe?**
  3. **Is it possible to scientifically study the origin of life on earth?**
  4. **Is it possible to scientifically study the origin of mankind?**
  5. **What difference does it make?**

The Introduction, entitled "Impact of Modern Evolutionary Thought" is provided to make most explicit the profound extent of evolutionary thinking in *all* major disciplines of human knowledge. The very real scope of selected indoctrination is given specific treatment.

In the Note To Teachers, consideration is given as to how to use this book regarding teaching aids. Some legal and conceptual aspects of the confrontation technique in the classroom are also discussed.

Chapter 1 contains a multifaceted answer to the question, "What is science?" Many processes of inquiry and *17* aspects of scientific activities, as well as recognizable limitations are made fully evident by means of operational definitions.

In chapter 2 the question, Is it possible to scientifically study the origin of the universe?" will be examined through consideration of cosmology and cosmogony. Extra emphasis is given to the real differences between them, a topic so relevant to considerations about the origin of the universe.

In chapter 3 the question, Is it possible to scientifically study the orgin of life on the earth?" will be analyzed with respect to historical ideas about the origin of life, and to processes of *synthesis* of components of living substance as developed in accordance with a reductionist approach to life studies.

In chapter 4 the question, "Is it possible to scientifically study the origin of humankind?" is treated thoroughly in light of the latest archaeological and paleontological findings, as background to full confrontation of ideas of evolutionists and creationists regarding the appearances and changes of humankind.

Chapter 5 provides a summation of the main themes of this book.

Finally chapter 6 tackles the question, "What difference does it make?" in the light of social, ethical and moral ramifications.

Quite often persons who doubt the propriety or objectivity of the evolution/creation confrontation teaching approach, have asserted that no fair testing could be effected in such a teaching plan. Many ask how it is possible to objectively examine students about such controversial topics as are associated with evolution and creation? The importance of examination and evaluation in education has not been ignored in this book. Quiz questions have been incorporated after the Introduction and chapters 1-4, and a final examination follows chapter 6. Keyed answers to all questions are also provided for the teacher. In this manner, the proper close correlation between instruction and evaluation is clearly manifested.

Additional useful materials for teachers are included in the various Appendices. They include summary of operational definitions, list of audiovisual materials, and an extensive annotated bibliography of creation/evolution books.

I hope that these chapters contain clear elucidation of my frequently repeated public claim that creation concepts *can be* objectively presented and evaluated in meaningful testing, and my claim that no new legislation or special rules are needed. Further, I trust that many readers will be strengthened in their faith in God, and that all readers will be led to think more deeply on these matters. It does make a significant difference how we teach first origins, especially in regard to the spiritual status and future life of every human being on this earth. May all of this book be for the honor and glory of Jesus Christ, the Creator.

January, 1983
East Lansing, Michigan

FOOTNOTES

[1]By the way, the practice of testing all ideas is fully consistent with Biblical context according to Paul to the Thessalonians, and according to Jesus Christ: "Go . . . tell John what things you have seen . . . " (Luke 7:22)," . . . "which we do know, and testify . . . " (John 3:11), "Behold, the fowls of the air . . . " (Matt. 6:26). Christ taught exact observation. Christians are to speak what they know, what they have heard and seen. Christ can be considered the founder of modern scientific thought.

[2]Multiple reports of campus debates have appeared in the monthly publication, *Acts and Facts*, available from the Institute for Creation Research, 2100 Greenfield Drive, El Cajon, CA 29021; see also "Evolutionist—Creationist Roundtable", L. P. Lester, W. W. Anderson, J. N. Moore, and R. D. Simpson, *The Science Teacher*, Vol. 43 (8), Nov. 1976.

[3]See unpublished doctoral thesis by Richard Bliss, Curriculum Director, Institute for Creation Research, entitled, "A Comparison of Two Approaches to the Teaching of Origins of Living Things to High School Students in Racine, Wisconsin" (1978). Bliss shows that students using a two-model approach in an inquiry context will show significant improvement in concept development and cognitive skills compared to those studying evolution only. Also with regard to value judgements, interpretations of data and formulation of questions and hypotheses, students taught in a two-model fashion will be more critical and willing to change ideas as new data are presented.

ADDENDUM

Effective July 1, 1982 Dr. John N. Moore accepted an early incentive retirement offer from Michigan State University. Therefore he is now available to discuss objective, scientific evidence regarding first origin questions in a calm, legal and constitutionally sound manner. He offers pros and cons of ideas about teaching about origin questions in lectures, seminars and in-service sessions to teachers, parents, school board members, ministers, and lawyers.

Dr. Moore has developed an effective strategy to meet representatives of the American Civil Liberties Union (ACLU) as an important basis for presentation of data and argumentation about origin questions. To begin any such discussion Dr. Moore regularly states that the modern scientific discipline "came out of" the world view of Theism and the Judeo-Christian belief pattern. The historically factual basis of this assertion is supplied by the thoroughly documented works of award-winning scholar-physicist Stanley L. Jaki, by Alfred North Whitehead, by Robert Oppenheimer, and by many others.

These scholars document that modern science, as a discipline, was "stillborn" in the Greek, Arabian, Chinese, Babylonian, and Egyption cultures. Modern science began when the basic Hebrew world view on creation was taken seriously, in varying degrees of commitment, by such as Roger Bacon, Robert Grosseteste, Francis Bacon, Copernicus, Galileo, Versalius, Tycho Brahe, Linne Linnaeus, John Ray, Robert Nuttall, Johannes Kepler, and Isaac Newton.

ACLU representatives have no legal basis to prevent public school teachers from telling taxpayers sons and daughters about the fully historical basis of modern science. Furthermore by such an opening approach to origin questions students gain a proper perspective. By such an approach taxpayers sons and daughters realize that early scientists believed that the universe, including the earth and life on the earth, had been created by a reasonable God. They believed that God had created an orderly universe (uniformity of natural events), that they could look for explanation of any event in terms of earlier events (cause and effect), that objective reality existed—there was something "there" that could be studied successfully, and that the natural environment was worth studying for to do so was to investigate God's creation. Early scientists believed that such investigations were possible because human beings had been created in the image of God; human beings could find out about natural things because they had been given dominion, as God's creations, over all things.

ACLU representatives cannot prevent taxpayers sons and daughters from hearing about the fact that there was continued impetus for implementation of the basic belief that the orderly universe was contingent upon the very creative acts of God. Robert Boyle, Michael Faraday, James Clerk-Maxwell, Gregory Mendel, Louis Pasteur, and many others held this view. These leading scientists did their scientific work within the thought forms derived from the Judeo-Christian world view; and their special methods of inquiry resulted in discovery of many lawful relationships, which they believed were established by God, the Law-Giver.

REFERENCES

Stanley L. Jaki, 1974, *Science and Creation* (From Eternal Cycles to Oscillating Universe). NY: Science History Publications; 1978, *The Road to Science and the Ways to God*. Chicago: The University of Chicago Press; and 1978, *The Origin of Science and The Science of Its Origin*. South Bend: Regnery/Gateway, Inc. (See also Alfred North Whitehead, 1926, *Science and the Modern World*. NY: Macmillan; and J. Robert Oppenheimer, "On Science and Culture", *Encounter*, October, 1962.)

Wendell R. Bird, "Freedom of Religion and Science Instruction in the Public Schools", *Yale Law Journal*, 87: 515-570, January, 1978; and "Freedom from Establishment and Unneutrality in Public School Instruction and Religious School Regulation", *1979 Harvard Journal of Law and Public Policy*, pp. 125-205, June, 1979.

Henry M. Morris, 1982, *Men of Science—Men of God* (Great Scientists Who Believed the Bible). San Diego: Creation-Life Publishers.

Introduction | Impact of Modern Evolutionary Thought

Many scientists consider creation to be religious and evolution to be scientific. A straightforward presentation of the creation point of view *and* the evolution point of view about first origins is fully within responsible education of the young. No new laws are necessary. There is no possible violation of so-called separation of church and state, since *no religious* teaching is involved.

In presentations of modern creationism, no theistic "religion" or sectarian teaching is involved. This point may be clarified by defining the term "religion". It may be defined as (1) "belief in a divine or superhuman power or powers to be obeyed and *worshipped* as the creator(s) of the universe"; (2) "expression of this belief in *conduct* and *ritual*"; and (3) "any specific system of belief, *worship or conduct*".

Clearly two main facets of meaning are incorporated in these definitions of "religion": (1) the facet of belief, and (2) the facet of worship. Of paramount importance is the fact that *no* attention at all is given to worshipful conduct or ritualistic procedure in the evolution/creation confrontation teaching approach about first origins. Use of prayer beads, a prayer rug, head covering, certain wearing apparel, or facing toward the east are examples of specific procedures and characteristic practices of religious worship, ritual or conduct by the many peoples of earth.

But these procedures and practices are *not* part of any recommended evolution/creation confrontation teaching approach. Rather, exclusive attention is given to consideration of the *facet of belief* held by different people. Teaching *about* the beliefs of people is fully legal and consistent with the U.S. Supreme Court rulings.[1] The Supreme Court has clearly designated only three acts that violate the First Amendment in public schools: (1) state-required prayer (Engel); (2) state-required Bible reading

(Schempp); and (3) state-required on-premises religious training (McCollum). None of these practices are part of any recommended evolution/creation confrontation teaching approach.[2]

Furthermore, federal court action clearly illustrates that "religion" is not a reasonable classification.[3] The broad classification of "religion" cannot be used as a proper basis for exclusion of curricular material in public educational institutions. To do so violates the rights of non-students to a public forum and equal protection under the laws. The important point to grasp is the fact that the evolution/creation confrontation teaching approach involves *beliefs* that people have had and do presently hold with regard to *first* origins. The evolution point of view entails one set of beliefs about human beings, and the creationist point of view entails another set of beliefs about human beings.

In fact a certain way of guaranteeing that one pattern of beliefs is not favored above another set of beliefs is to assure fair and open treatment in a multi-model approach that teaches both the evolution view *and* the creation view regarding first origins. (See fig. 1 for contrast of basic points.)

"Cover Word"
(Beware Semantic Confusion)

Religion: often used without proper clarification of the fact that both beliefs and worshipful practices, procedures, and conduct are included in connotation of the word.

For centuries people were taught that *all* things were created by God. Charles Darwin, who laid the foundation for modern total evolutionism, accepted the theistic explanation of first origins. Young Darwin prayed to God for support and guidance. He referred to the Bible as an "unanswerable authority".[4] But in his maturing years Darwin changed. His faith in God seemed to shrivel as he placed greater emphasis upon natural laws and neglected the spiritual laws of God. He began his studies of the natural environment with belief in the special creation of all things by the Creator. His initial turning from belief in special creation came while on board ship, the *H.M.S. Beagle*, on a voyage around the world. There he studied very thoroughly the two volume work on geological changes

Figure 1
EVOLUTION AND CREATION MODELS CONTRASTED

From Henry M. Morris, Ed., *Scientific Creationism, Public School Edition*
(San Diego: Creation-Life Publishers, 1974), p. 13.

BASIC POINTS OF

Category	Evolution Model	Creation Model
Structure of Natural Law	Constantly Changing	Invariable
Galactic Universe	Galaxies Changing	Galaxies Constant
Structure of Stars	Stars Changing into Other Types	Stars Unchanged
Other Heavenly Bodies	Building Up	Breaking Down
Types of Rock Formations	Different in Different "Ages"	Similar in All "Ages"
Appearance of Life	Life Evolving from Non-Life	Life Only from Life
Array of Organisms	Continuum of Organisms	Distinct Kinds of Organisms
Appearance of Kinds of Life	New Kinds Appearing	No New Kinds Appearing
Mutations in Organisms	Beneficial	Harmful
Natural Selection	Creative Process	Conservative Process
Age of Earth	Extremely Old	Probably Young
Fossil Record	Innumerable Transitions	Systematic Gaps
Appearance of Man	Ape-Human Intermediates	No Ape-Human Intermediates
Nature of Man	Quantitatively Superior to Animals	Qualitatively Distinct from Animals
Origin of Civilization	Slow and Gradual	Contemporaneous with Man

authored by Charles Lyell. He studied first hand geologic features of South America and the Galapagos Islands in the Pacific Ocean; and he read a book on food consumption and human population by Thomas Malthus. Apparently Darwin did not continue his study of the Scriptures.

All of these ideas were synthesized in Darwin's thinking in such a manner that he discarded his *belief* in special creative acts of God as the origin of living things. Darwin replaced it with his own *belief* that competitive interactions of many variations of living things in natural environments resulted over lengths of time in changes of organism—some becoming extinct and others producing new varieties that presumably became new kinds of organisms. He called his imagined process natural selection. His explanation of this presumed means whereby changes of living things supposedly came about on the earth was read by his contemporaries, such as the noted British philosopher Herbert Spencer. They adopted the phrases, "survival of the fittest", or "struggle for existence", to express Darwin's ideas. Victorian Englishmen knew much about wars, diseases, famines, and weather conditions, and the idea of competitive struggle was easily understood. They believed Darwin had explained how living things had evolved.

Thus Darwin's own turning from belief in special creation, because he became insensitive to the Bible and spiritual laws of God, was evidently more or less characteristic of many leading English scholars. Darwin set an example for all "free thinkers". Many of the scholars attracted to Darwin's ideas were likewise unpracticed in close study of Genesis and reading about the special creative acts of God regarding origin of heaven and earth. Evidently they were not personally armed with the unchangeable answers about ultimate origins in the Bible. Hence, most English scholars were "susceptible" and became confused by the various speculative ideas and imaginations of Darwin and his followers. They were vulnerable to so-called naturalistic, non-supernatural ideas.

Victorian Englishmen were easily persuaded that natural selection of living things occurred analogously to selection of domestic organisms, to groups of human beings with "class" status, to nations competing in world economies and to warfare. *But Darwin never established scientifically that natural selection was a means whereby evolution occurred.* He only published a lengthy series of persuasively presented arguments. In actual fact, *no scientist* has ever been able to scientifically study the origin of any new kinds of organisms. (Recall, *scientifically* entails either direct or indirect observation of repeatable events.)

No other author in the nineteenth century influenced human thought around the world more than Charles Darwin when he published his two books: *The Origin of Species* and *The Descent of Man.* The "lineage" of Darwinism in scholarly thinking is brought out in two excellent reference works: *The Comparative Reception of Darwinism*, edited by Thomas F. Glick and *Darwin in America (The Intellectual Response, 1865-1912)* by Cynthia Eagle Russett.[5] Darwinism was later replaced by Neo-Darwinism which has since been replaced by the Modern Synthetic Theory of Evolution. Today the evolutionary viewpoint is so broadly applied, that one can speak most accurately of *total evolutionism* as including steller evolution, molecular evolution, organic evolution, and cultural evolution.

However, this broadened viewpoint of total evolutionism that has developed in a little over a century since Darwin is *without* any significant repeatable empirical data from naturally occurring events. On the contrary, evolutionists speak glowingly and write ingeniously about numerous *supra-natural concepts.* These include the "big bang" explosion of a dense particle, spontaneous generation of living substance, mountain building due to movement of dry rock masses, division of one land mass into existing continents, and appearance of new physical traits through mutational changes. But all of these ideas are totally *without* any conclusive empirical support from studies of naturally occurring events of the magnitude involved in such concepts. Total evolutionists commonly do *not* deal with natural events, but with imagined *supra*-natural events.

Yet the circumstantially grounded megaevolutionary* point of view involving total evolutionism is *the* world view that has been adopted by influential scholars in every major academic discipline of human thought. Evidently what Darwin wrote was just what the mainstream of academia in England and elsewhere were waiting to read. Today, evolution is the *supreme* overriding world view adopted in most major academic disciplines. Some idea of the colossal scope of this situation is obtained from study of Classroom Teaching Aid 1.

The full range of research in the history of ideas substantiates that selected indoctrination among the intellectuals of the world has increased ever since

---

* See Glossary for definition.

Classroom Teaching Aid 1
IMPACT OF MODERN EVOLUTIONARY THOUGHT

IF research in the history of ideas can substantiate that the position of

1. Marx and Keynes in economics and social studies

2. Beard in American history,

3. London and Shaw in modern novels,

4. Becker in political science,

5. Nietzsche, James, and Positivists in modern philosophy,

6. Camus, Sartre, and Heidegger in existential thought,

7. Freud in psychology and psychiatry,

8. Dewey in modern education,

9. Fosdick and "higher" biblical critics in modern theology,

10. White in sociology,

11. Pound, Holmes, Frankfurter in modern jurisprudence,

12. Simpson, Dobzhansky, J. Huxley and P. Teilhard de Chardin in paleontology, modern genetics and evolutionary humanism.

depends upon Darwinism, Neo-Darwinism and/or Modern Synthetic Evolutionary World View,

THEN

selected indoctrination has been and is the lot of many modern intelligentsia, since 1860 to the present.

Positive affirmation of each of the antecedents in the above complex material implication is gained through full examination of the history of ideas.

Therefore, modern secular educational content results in selected indoctrination of many of the intelligentsia of the United States and of Western Civilization.

publication of Charles Darwin's *The Origin of Species* in 1859. Darwin did not invent evolution, but his books *seemed* to provide support for a world outlook desired by the intelligentsia of his day. In another manner the colossal scope of this empirically unfounded, selected indoctrination can be illustrated by representing the flow of acceptance of the "struggle for existence" or "survival of the fittest" concepts by specialists in social studies, sociology, anthropology and humanities, as well as in science. This situation is diagrammed in the flow chart in Classroom Teaching Aid 2. The next nine sections of this chapter contain specifics to help teachers of every subject matter interested in the evolution/creation confrontation teaching approach, to make a significant contribution toward student understanding of general interconnection of ideas. It clarifies the impact of evolutionary thinking in the subject matter areas of economies, political science, American history, literature, philosophy, psychology, education, theology, and science.

Economics

Karl Marx was a prime leader among the intelligentsia of the world who utilized Darwin's concept of "natural selection", or "struggle for existence". Marx wrote his associate Friedrich Engels that he considered Darwin's ideas about competition of living things in the natural environment to be relevant to their material on the competition between classes. For Marx the concept of "struggle for existence" became translated into "class warfare"[6]

As the acceptance of the idea is traced into other countries, the concept of "might makes right" seemed to be sanctioned from the writings of Darwin and the thinking of Marx. In Germany, Darwin and Marxism were broadly adopted. These two philosophies are easily identified as basic to the superman concept of Nietzsche and the superior Aryan race concept of Hitler.

In fact the dictatorial actions of Hitler, Mussolini, Lenin, Stalin, Krushchev, as well as many current dictators, have all been sanctioned supposedly by Darwin's natural selection through "struggle for existence" and "survival of the fittest". Leaders of the Fascist nations believed themselves most "worthy" of survival. Similarly, the Communist nations are currently claimed by their theoreticians to be most worthy of survival.

Classroom Teaching Aid 2

THE "FLOW" OF DARWIN'S INFLUENCE

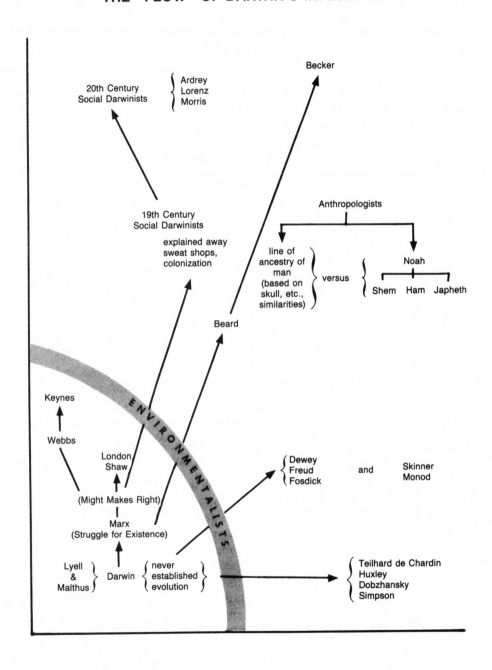

Empirical evidence is abundant that coexistence with Communist nations does not occur. The formerly free nations of Afghanistan, Bulgaria, Czechoslovakia, Cuba, East Germany, Estonia, Hungary, Latvia, Poland, Romania, Tibet and Ukrania are mute evidence to this point.

Particularly in England, a political group called the Fabian Socialists, under the leadership of Sidney and Beatrice Webb, interjected the "struggle for existence" concept into a political frame of reference. For Fabian Socialists, the struggle was in terms of voting for gradual social change rather then fighting with guns for radical revolution. They thought in terms of "social revolution" that seemed to be a consistent extention of supposed biological evolution. Of course there have been multiple extensions of Marx's thinking regarding his presumption of class warfare, as can be traced in the works of John Maynard Keynes on economics and his American followers as democratic socialism became established in the United States after 1932. Repeatedly, Darwin's evolutionary thinking has become a root sanction for governmental intervention. It sanctions government to intervene for the survival of what is "best", according to the reasoning of the elite few, be they Fabian Socialists, Communists, or Democratic Socialists, for the "benefit" of the many ordinary citizens.

Political Science

Impact of evolutionary thinking in political science can be traced, similar to the force of such thinking in economics, through analyzing the position taken by those who were influenced by and become followers of Karl Marx. These include men such as Carl Becker, the noted historian, and many others.[7] Becker encouraged the use of Marxian ideas and influenced several decades of graduate students by his evolutionary thinking which was oriented along the struggle for existence line in modern society. Eventually he recognized the logical consequences of that thesis (in the form that might makes right) when he learned of the savage, cruel rape of Europe by Hilter's troops. That there are really no philosophical differences between Fascist Germany and Communist Russia can be documented quite easily by tracing acceptance of Marxism by Lenin and the eventual development of Bolshevism and Leninism. The thinking of the leaders of the U.S.S.R. is deeply rooted in an evolutionary outlook.[8]

American History

The impact of evolutionary thinking in American history can also be traced to the acceptance of the ideas of Karl Marx. Marx used the concept of struggle for existence to support and excuse his thesis of class warfare. According to Marx, society was the context for the struggle for survival of "class" human beings.

In American history this relationship of struggle for existence and supposed class warfare was applied by Charles A. Beard[9] to the adoption of the Constitution of the United States of America. According to Beard, passage of the Constitution in each of the thirteen colonies was the result of class warfare. In his analysis the landed gentry and noblemen were for the Constitution, while farmers, the poor, and indigent were against the Constitution. Thus indirectly Beard's ideas were a basis for selected indoctrination in Darwin's struggle for existence from the time Beard's ideas were published in 1913 until some forty years later. In the 1950's his thesis of class warfare in the colonies was shown to be completely invalid by the research and analysis of actual records of voting practices and land ownership by two independent investigators, Robert Brown and Forest McDonald.[10] They accomplished the research that Beard *never* completed!

Literature

The novels of Jack London, the plays of George Bernard Shaw, and even the poetry of Alfred Tennyson contain a seemingly convincing basis for belief in the "evolution" of humankind.[11] Tennyson actually expressed an evolutionary viewpoint some time before Darwin's book appeared in 1859. But the writings of these "greats" for literature and others as well, were strongly instrumental in adding to the impact of Darwin's second book, *The Descent of Man*. They helped convert nineteenth century intellectuals to acceptance of the concept of the evolution of human beings.

Actually both London and Shaw were English socialists and followers of the thinking of the Fabian Society. This society came into existence due to the work and effort of Beatrice and Sidney Webb, who in turn were followers of Karl Marx in England. Collectively these people created a subtle "web" of selected indoctrination into literature for an evolutionary viewpoint. Both London and Shaw used their literary works to present Marxian socialistic views as most plausible and to illustrate the concept of struggle for existence. London especially popularized the "red tooth and claw" phrases through the struggles he wrote about in *White Fang* and *The Call of the Wild*. Continued use of evolutionary thinking by novelists can be shown in the works of Veblen, Norris, Dreiser and Michener. For instance, the early chapter's of Michener's *Contennial* is a *par excellence* example of misapplication of "historical" geology. Here author Michener uses the "geolical column" to write about supposed coastal changes as "history" of the Colorado region of the United States. He refers to mountain formation, glacial action, and river formation as if such discussions are founded upon proper scientific findings. Of course such origin concepts about possible past events in the Colorado areas are plainly imaginative narratives as we will see in the chapter on the nature of science.

Philosophy

In philosophy, the impact of evolutionary thought can be traced through the increasingly broad criticism of nineteenth century classification systems. These systems involved archetypes as possible created kinds of plants or animals. According to the evolutionists' position there has been a slow, gradual change between organisms as one kind supposedly had joint ancestry with another kind, and all present kinds that are known today gradually came into existence over a great expanse of time.

As if that position were grounded in proper, orderly science, philosophers have mistakenly accepted that viewpoint and used it as a basis for their attitude that categories cannot be clearly defined and that absolutes are not identifiable. Thus all things are relative. Hence confusion has been introduced into logic. Basic Aristolelian principles of thinking have been challenged by systems of multi-valued logic. Further confusion has been fostered in ethics and aesthetics by acceptance of evolutionary thinking in philosophy. Mention must be made especially of the importance of the writings of John Dewey, who fully accepted evolutionary thinking.[12] His views were very influential in development of the "new" philosophy of the twentieth century. This philosophy has strongly contributed to the despair that comes with existentialism, the New Consciousness, and has encouraged "openness" to the mysticisms of Eastern religions.[13]

Psychology

By tracing acceptance of the concept of inheritance of acquired characteristics by Sigmund Freud, a good beginning is made toward showing the impact of evolutionary thinking in psychology and psychiatry. In the late edition of his book, *The Origin of Species*, Darwin utilized the concept of inheritance of acquired characteristics fostered by Lamarck, who believed that characteristics acquired during the lifetime of an individual were transmitted to offspring. Although this idea is now fully discredited and completely rejected by leading biologists and geneticists, Freud's acceptance of the idea gave significant impetus to the environmentalist's inclination so prominent in psychology. According to environmentalists, an individual's behavior is the consequence of the environment in which growth and development have occurred. Today prominent scientists such as B.F. Skinner, Robert Ardrey, Konrad Lorenz and Desmond Morris reflect broad acceptance of the environmentalist approach which is based upon the unscientific idea of an evolutionary origin of humankind.[14]

Education

The prime innovator of modern education, John Dewey, showed a broad acceptance of Darwinism in his extensive writings. He viewed the human being as a product of evolution that was slowly improving physically and mentally. According to Dewey, the environment in which schooling occurred was most important. Because Dewey stressed an evolutionary outlook in his writings and because generations of educators have followed his philosophy in one form or another, environmentalism has become a strong viewpoint in the development of educational principles and policies in the public schools. The human being has been treated as an intelligent animal developing as a consequence of interaction with the environment, as a "survior" by use of its wits.[15]

Theology

Even the modern-day study of theology has been influenced by evolutionary ideas. According to the Graff-Wellhausen "hypothesis", Bible content has evolved. This idea regarding criticism of Biblical texts is evidence of the broad impact of evolutionary thinking. A most influential spokesman for the view of evolution of the Bible was Harry Emerson Fosdick.[16] He wrote extensively on the theme that man's worship of God evolved from the worship of a sun god and moon god, to a mountain god and river god, to a crop god, to a tribal god, to an Omnipotent God. Actually, polytheistic worship is a degenerate deviation of ancient, initial monotheism as can be shown by reference to outstanding present-day scholarship.[17] The whole position of higher criticism in the twentieth century is rooted in an evolutionary viewpoint.

Science

In the multiple sub-fields of the scientific discipline the impact of evolutionary thought has been almost complete. The influential writings of such leaders as Julian Huxley, Theodosius Dobzhansky and Pierre Teilhard de Chardin, in support of the infusion of evolutionary thinking into all facets of biology and associated sciences, still have great impact in the training programs of young scientists and in the mass communication media as well. In addition to their influence, G.G. Simpson still serves as a strong guide to almost uniquitous application of evolutionary thought.

However, weaknesses and deficiencies in Darwinism, Neo-Darwinism, and even the Modern Synthetic Theory of Evolution have been published by scientists in every decade since *The Origin of Species* was published in 1859.[18] Yet such criticisms have not been included to any significant extent in science textbooks. Specific impetus inaugurated in the 1960's to expand and augment the teaching of evolutionary origins in the secondary schools in the United States has really been an important cause in the 1970's for the development of creation teaching; that is, explanation of the scientific basis or support of the creation account of origins.[19]

Another approach to the matter of impact and inter-connection of evolution and other major groups of ideas might be gained through use of Classroom Teaching Aid 3. Interrelationships of the thinking of Darwin, Freud, Dewey and various "isms" can be visualized through the use of this page. It is very interesting to note that so-called naturalistically oriented scholars always turn to some other *human being* as a source of thought to be propounded into one system of ideas or even a philosophical panacea.

Followers of Marx emphasize that human beings should be considered

Classroom Teaching Aid 3
IDEAS FOR YOUR VALUE SYSTEM

Given: Scholarship should be an attempt
   a) by an informed and disciplined mind
   b) to achieve an accurate statement of what the evidence is
   c) accompanied by an objective evaluation of what the evidence *implies*:
      1) not merely in relation to all similarly derived knowledge, but
      2) in relationship to both theistic and non-theistic thinking as part of Basic Beliefs.

Taking the above *given* and in the spirit of *Academic Freedom*, you might note:

Science cannot understand man in his completeness; for man is a person, and science is equipped to handle only the impersonal—the generalized, not the unique or singular.

Application of the scientific method in impersonal terms brings into focus
   a) man and ecomonic relationships—Marxism
   b) man's natural instincts—Freudianism
   c) man, a clever animal—Darwinism

BUT, man is *all* these things, and to say that man is *nothing but* an economic or intellectual animal is to commit the fallacy of reduction.

Man is not only an object, *but also a subject.*

Therefore, be aware of changes in historical time from theistic to non-theistic thought, or from science to scientism.

The problem of first cause (the beginning) still remains:

Pragmatism	lead to	which can put
Utilitarianism	Agnosticism	science in the
Logical Positivism	(which Engels called	place of God
	"polite atheism")	

Therefore, be aware of things that matter, and look sharply to the *consequences* of ALL ideas. After all,

| a new trinity | $\left\{ \begin{array}{c} \text{science} \\ \text{machine} \\ \text{dollar} \end{array} \right\}$ | has led to a | $\longrightarrow$ | new secular religion |

which can lead to: a) "economic man"—Marxism
                        b) "faceless man"—Nazism
                        c) "hollow man"—Skepticism who believes in
                             nothing, often not even himself—Nihilism

Is it any wonder that we see parallelisms of East and West?

Western Culture today:		Communist Societies today:
$\left\{ \begin{array}{c} \text{Secularism} \\ \text{Standardization} \\ \text{Commercialism} \end{array} \right\}$	PARALLELS	$\left\{ \begin{array}{c} \text{Atheism} \\ \text{Regimentation} \\ \text{Economism} \end{array} \right\}$

Root of Trouble:
       Failure of modern thought to understand man and the
       human situation in the fullness of their being

(See: D. R. G. Owen, *Scientism, Man and Religion* (Philadelphia: Westminister Press, 1952).

economic animals. Followers of Freud emphasize that human beings should be considered sex animals. Followers of Darwin more or less emphasize that human beings should be considered clever animals. All such compartmentalizing of thought by focusing attention on primarily one facet of human behavior is quite in keeping with the old absolutistic thinking of early Greeks, who proposed that the basic element of matter or existence was air, water, fire, or earth.

Particularly characteristic of such old and modern absolutistic thinking is the need for proponents of a philosophy to rely on the ideas of some *human being*, who is in the same predicament of all other human beings seeking ultimate answers. Of course, *if naturally-minded people will not accept answers by revelation on ultimate origin, identity and future distiny, then they must go to another human being in the same predicament.*

Yet Godel[20] has shown so very well that the basic tenets, assumptions, postulates, or presuppositions of a thought system can never be fully authenticated or documented by that same thought system. Therefore Marxism, Freudianism and Darwinism can only be validated against principles from outside those systems. Thus, it follows that the creation medel, which is based fundamentally on the Judeo-Christian belief system, is the *only* thought system that can claim and offer validation from without that thought system. God's answers on ultimate origins, identity, and future destiny are presented as coming from the First Cause, from the Author of heaven and earth and all that is therein. The authentication and documentation of the Judeo-Christian thought system is available in the historically accurate Bible, preserved over the centuries that anyone might read and know.[21] Of course faith commitment is involved, but such is also true of the proponents of Marxism, Freudianism, Darwinism—each of which have come from individuals in the "human predicament".

The creation model is *the* frame for reference whereby all of human existence can be brought into a coherent, integrated whole. The human being is a whole person who has economic, sexual, intellectual, biological, physical and psychological needs. As the one life form who is both subject and object of study, the human being can gain solutions to problems of identity, alienation, and relevance within the context of relation to the Creator God. This may be aided by studying contrasts between the evolution model and the creation model which are brought out so strikingly through use of Teaching Aids 4 and 5.

For a still deeper approach to the impact of evolution, Classroom Teaching Aids 4 and 5 will be useful as diagrammatic representations of the grand scale of evolutionism and the full scope of creationism. Total evolution clearly envolves the imagined continuity from stellar evolution to one-world utopianism. All in this evolutionary triangulation in Classroom Teaching Aid 4, could be looked upon as a type of "Tower of Babel". Here is seen diagrammatically the human pride tendency worked out at the ideational level.

Total evolutionists feel that they have succeeded in building a "tower of explanation'' for *all* reality. In their thinking, they have done so by emphasizing only matter and energy, while at the same time overstepping bounds of their adopted naturalism by intrusion of *supra*-natural ideas: explosion of a dense particle, spontaneous generation, dry rock mountain building, continental breakup, and mutational improvement through error of replication.

In contrast to the diagram of total evolution is the triangulation of total creationism (Teaching Aid 5) which might well be considered representative of a fallen tower of ideational constructs. A specific beginning and ending are part of this formulation, and *all* of the careful and proper scientific data available today can be fitted into this frame of reference. All empirical data obtained by careful and proper scientific methodology repeatedly corroborated can be fit into the creationism diagram. All careful research and data from genetics, paleontology, comparative anatomy, embryology, serology, biochemistry, physics and thermodynamics can be meaningfully interpreted by means of the creation model.

At this point I would like to acknowledge a typical problem that, the science teacher can expect because of the possible wide range of belief patterns with regard to first origin questions represented by students. Some deeply sensitive Christians have uncritically accepted ideas about first origins that are essentially speculations presented by evolutionary, naturalistically-minded scientists. Some Christians seem to think in a dialectical manner in this area. They hope that an interaction of the thesis of evolution (total evolution, megaevolution) with the antithesis of creation (special, instantaneous creative acts by Christ) will lead to a synthesis called theistic evolution. The science teacher should be prepared to meet the earnest, seeking student who feels that some compromise or fitting together of the evolution model with the creation model is possible, desirable, and even necessary in this scientific age.

Some students have read material prepared by scientists who are professing Christians, but who are also proponents of the theory of theistic evolution (also variously called Christian evolution, progressive creation, threshold creation, or biblical evolutionism). Or some other types of possible accomodation or harmonization between material written by scientists and biblical content may be a part of student thinking under other labels, such as gap theory, day-age theory, ruin-reconstruction theory (sometimes called creation-reconstruction), or days of revelation theory.

Classroom Teaching Aid 4
DIAGRAM OF TOTAL EVOLUTION

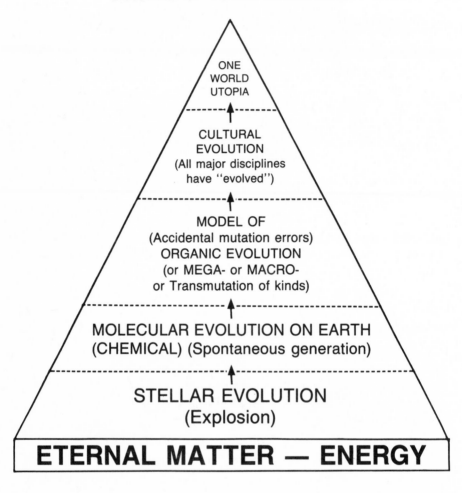

Reference to these labels or titles of positions may entail writings prepared by scientists who are Christians. It may not be wise to challenge the Christian posture or position of any proponent, student or parent, of any of these thought patterns.

However, I should like to reiterate that we are considering the *ideas of men*. We are *not* dealing directly with Scripture, though some of these thought patterns may be found as part of marginal notes, or in the reference materials of some Bibles. Nevertheless, from the theory of theistic evolu-

Classroom Teaching Aid 5
DIAGRAM OF TOTAL CREATIONISM

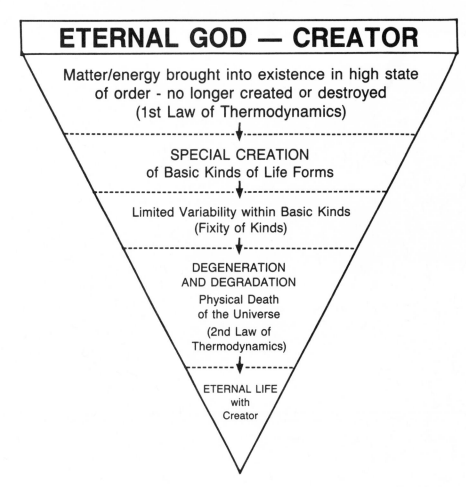

ETERNAL GOD — CREATOR

Matter/energy brought into existence in high state of order - no longer created or destroyed (1st Law of Thermodynamics)

SPECIAL CREATION
of Basic Kinds of Life Forms

Limited Variability within Basic Kinds
(Fixity of Kinds)

DEGENERATION
AND DEGRADATION

Physical Death
of the Universe

(2nd Law of
Thermodynamics)

ETERNAL LIFE
with
Creator

tion through days of revelation theory we have only human ideas. We will now give brief attention to each pattern of thought. All are variants or variations of the main theme of the evolution or creation model.

Theory of Theistic Evolution

(Christian evolution, progressive creation)
(Threshold creation, or biblical evolutionism.)

It is difficult to gain a firm definition of theistic evolution. Some have defined it as an evolutionary philosophy of origins involving God. The degree of involvement of God depends upon the proponent consulted. The combination of God with evolution may be intended to create matter, to create first life, or to establish lawful relationship of things in the universe. It may even mean to change kind to kind in which God changed an anthropoid into a human being with soul and spirit (mind) as well as body. Clearly, a proponent of such thinking is an "evolutionist" first and a "theist" second: the latter word is an adjective modifier of the noun category in the expression: theistic evolution.

There are some difficulties that can be pointed out regarding theistic evolution. Even if teleological, or purposeful, intent is understood to be a point of this thought pattern there are several superficial flaws:

1. The majority of evolutionists will have nothing to do with theistic evolution. They either ignore or laugh at it.
2. Theistic evolution seems like a device to obtain the "best of two worlds" —to be accepted and appreciated by both evolutionist and theist. Commonly the many difficulties with evolutionary thought are glossed over or ignored.
3. There is a vagueness about the role of "God" in theistic evolution.
4. Although there is a seeming orientation to the Bible, no clear reconciliation or means of harmonization is conclusive in direct reading of Biblical authors.

To bring a more detailed analysis to bear on the thinking of theistic evolutionists, Classroom Teaching Aid 6 might be used. The evolution/creation confrontation teacher can use this aid to emphasize the "problems" which render evolution unreasonable and to highlight detected order, pattern and design in the natural environment through an intelligent Creator God. The creation model is more reasonable. Evidence about God is, in fact, obvious. (Romans 1:20) Actually there is no empirically repeatable evidence that megaevolution has ever occured; hence the theistic evolutionist is primarily an evolutionist possibly persuaded so by desire for acceptance by peers.

That megaevolution and the revelatory sequence of the creation model are *mutually exclusive* can be demonstrated quite successfully be means of Classroom Teaching Aid 7. This teaching aid can be used to show that theistic evolutionists, in accepting many precepts of so-called naturalistic evolutionists, violate the biblical basis for unchanging answers about the

Classroom Teaching Aid 6
IS THEISTIC EVOLUTION REASONABLE?

EVOLUTION IS UNREASONABLE BECAUSE

1. Nothing about "big bang" of some dense particle to start universe is scientific or probable.

2. Nothing regarding spontaneous generation of life on earth is scientific or probable.

3. Nothing regarding chance, accidental changes of genes, to cause man to come from some animal is scientific or at all probable.

CREATION IS MORE REASONABLE BECAUSE

the order, pattern, and design observed make belief in God the Creator as the First Cause most rational.

---

ultimate origin of living things on the earth. As the two columns are studied, certain similarities and differences become evident. The evolution/creation confrontation teacher should ask, "If there was an agreement between megaevolution and Revelation, then what should the chart look like?" Of course the answer is that maximum one-to-one correlation would be indicated by straight lines joining entries opposite each other in the two columns from bottom to top. Careful examination requires a most candid conclusion that *no significant correlation* exists. Any synthesis of the theistic evolutionists is no more than a figment of imagination.

Gap Theory

(Ruin-Reconstruction Theory
and Creation Reconstruction Theory)

These theories assume a gap of millions of geological ages between the first two verses of Genesis or place several gaps in the geneological lists

Classroom Teaching Aid 7
IS THE ORDER OF APPEARANCE COMPARABLE?

Evolution (Mega-evolution)	Revelation (Genesis of Life)
Placental mammals and early man	Man (male and female)
Marsupial mammals, angiosperms	
Dinosaurs, birds, egg-laying mammals	
Mammal-like reptiles	Living creature (land), cattle, creeping things, beasts of the earth
Reptiles, fern-like plants, gymnosperms	Moving creature, fowl, great whale (fish), every living creature (water) that moveth
Amphibians, vascular plants	
Insects	Greater light (sun), lesser light (moon), stars
Fishes, some land plants	
Primitive vertebrates and proto-chordates	Grass, herb yielding seed fruit tree yielding fruit
Some algae, fungi, modern invertebrates	Light
Galaxies, stars, planets	Heaven and earth
Explosion of dense particle	
Eternal matter	Eternal Creator (Jesus Christ)

IS THERE ANY SIGNIFICANT CORRELATION?

of Genesis 5 and 10, so as to consider human history as extending over more than six thousand years. Proponents suggest in the first variation that five billion years of geologic events may have followed the first primeval creation of Genesis 1:1 and then a great worldwide catastrophe or cataclysm occurred such that the earth "became without form and void." Both geological and scriptural reasons for debating this theory are available in Henry M. Morris', *Biblical Cosmology and Modern Science* (Grand Rapids, Michigan: Baker Book House, 1970). Numerous difficulties and contradictions are enumerated by Morris.

Days of Revelation Theory

According to this idea, God took six days in which to reveal His creative acts to Moses. In other words the ultimate origin of the heaven and earth and all that is therein was related to Moses in six days of discussion or teaching about creation. This is clearly an idea of men imputed to the Genesis record. In no direct manner does the author of Genesis convey the concept that revelations about creation took six days.

The many ramifications of these various modifications of the creation model cannot be discussed to meet the expectations of all proponents. To do so would be beyond the scope of this book. Nor is there room to review the many authors who have written about the fragile tower of hypotheses upon hypotheses that evolutionists have built as part of their pursuit of the "Tower of Babel" of total evolution.

Moral and ethical consequences are enumerated to some degree in Chapter 6 through recitation of the inhumanity of human beings "doing good" through the sanction of "might makes right", when applied to war, concentration camps, ballot box conquests, or similar competitive means of "natural selection".

The bedrock contrast between evolution and creation may be clearly portrayed in the manner found in Classroom Teaching Aid 8. A point by point comparison and contrast will undoubtedly be a useful means of highlighting the fundamental spiritual problems involved in evolution/creation discussions of first origins: origin of the universe, origin of life on the earth, and origin of humankind. My prayer is that the reader will realize the opportunity and responsibility of bringing this challenge to each student so that full and complete realization of the confrontation meaning will be clearly apparent.

Each student should be aware that even in the twentieth century real choices still exist. Elijah asked his people, "How long halt you between two opinions?" (I Kings 18:21). [And Joshua likewise had urged his people, "Choose you this day whom ye will serve" (Joshua 24:15).] Or, in the New Testament context of Colossians 1:14-17, Is Christ the Creator or is He not? (Col. 1:14) And the possibility exists today that people will be enticed to violate the first commandment of God: "You shall have no other gods before me". (Exodus 20:3).

When people give serious thought to acceptance of evolutionary estimates of the age of the universe and/or the age of the earth, will they be following the "god" of time? When people give serious thought to acceptance of evolutionary speculations about the accidental beginning of life on the earth, will they be following the "god" of chance? The moral implication of turning toward men's ideas about time or chance are grave, and have direct bearing on a frame of mind that seeks to honor God.

Classroom Teaching Aid 8
IMPORTANT CONTRASTS

Four Evolutionary Propositions

1. Man is an accident and has no purpose

2. Man never had a relationship with God.

3. Man has no need of a Saviour

4. No reconciliation is needed. Man will build "perfect" society

Four Scriptural Propositions

1. God made man for a purpose

2. Man is separated from God

3. Jesus' sacrifice reconciled man and God.

4. Each person must accept Jesus to be reconciled to God.

Introduction
Impact of Modern Evolutionary Thought

General Discussion Questions
1. Explain some of the different aspects of the concept "religion".
2. Which three actions in public schools would violate the First Amendment according to Supreme Court rulings?
3. What is the evolution view?
4. What is the creation view?
5. Discuss at some length the fact that Charles Darwin changed from a theist to an agnostic; and explain how some people interpret that position as "practical atheism".
6. Just how broad has been the impact of evolutionary thought in modern intellectual endeavors?
7. What is meant by "absolutistic thinking"?
8. What is meant by "total evolutionism"?
9. Explain Godel's position that science is possible only within a larger framework of nonscience issues and concern.
10. What is meant by "Christotheism"?
11. What is meant by "theistic evolution"?
12. Compare and contrast "Gap Theory", "Day-Age Theory", and "Days of Revelation Theory".
13. Explain why discussion of the contrast of the Four Scriptural Propositions with the Four Evolutionary Propositions is fully constitutional.

Class Projects or Individual Assignments
1. Prepare a topical outline of this chapter.
2. List "cover words" that could cause semantic confusion.
3. Prepare a large chart of basic aspects of the contrasting positions of the evolution view and the creation view.
4. Prepare a list of human disciplines impacted by modern evolutionary thought, and locate cut-out pictures of leading spokespersons in each of the nine disciplines discussed in this chapter.
5. Prepare a large flow chart of the influence of Charles Darwin's ideas about "survival of favored races".

6. Prepare a table of comparison of main ideas of alternative crea-
    tionist positions.

7. Work out a set of answers for the evaluation items provided at the
    close of this chapter. Now prepare a set of similar evaluation items
    for this general subject matter area.

Read:

Duane T. Gish, "Creation, Evolution and the Historical Evidence",
American Biology Teacher, March 1973, pp. 132-141.

Lane P. Lester, Wyatt W. Anderson, John N. Moore, and Ronald D.
Simpson, "Evolutionist-Creationist Roundtable", *The Science Teacher*,
November 1976, pp. 34-39.

John N. Moore, "Evolution, Creation, and the Scientific Method",
American Biology Teacher, January 1973, pp. 23-26.

Henry M. Morris, *The Twilight of Evolution*. 1963. San Diego: Creation
—Life Publishers.

Henry M. Morris, *The Troubled Waters of Evolution*. 1974. San Diego:
Creation—Life Publishers.

L. Duane Thurman, *How to Think about Evolution*. 1977. 1978. Downers
Grove, IL: Inter Varsity Press.

On the Use of Scripture in Parochial Schools

1. Ask students to read Isaiah 55:8 and Psalm 118:8. Now ask them
    to explain how these verses could be applied to the contrast of the
    theistic evolution and theistic creation.

2. Ask students to read Genesis I:11, 20-21, 24-36. Have students
    list the order of appearance of different forms of matter and dif-
    ferent life forms about which they have just read.

3. Now have students list the order of appearance of forms of matter
    and life according to evolutionists.

4. What position do theistic evolutionists take in regard to the order
    of appearance of forms of matter and life? How do these relate to
    the Biblical record?

5. Examine the whole of Genesis 1 and Genesis 2 as a basis for discuss-
    ing the "time theories" mentioned in this chapter as alternatives
    to theistic evolution.

6. Ask students to search for Scripture verses for the Four Scriptural
    Propositions listed at the close of this chapter.

Evaluation Questions

Creation scientist authors write in their books about aspects of what they label two models of origin of living things. Select from the key the entry which is *most closely* associated with each item 1 through 11:

KEY: 1. Evolution model of origin of living things
                2. Creation model of origin of living things
                3. Characteristic of each of these models of origin

1. Some integrative and innovational principle or principles have been involved in changes of living things. (1)
2. Variation and speciation has been and is limited to changes within possible kinds. (2)
3. Basic plant and animal kinds with ordinal characteristics resulted from acts of a Supreme Being. (2)
4. Some conservational and disintegrative principle or principles have been involved in changes of living things. (2)
5. Gradual changes have occurred of least complex kinds into more complex kinds with transitional series linking all kinds with no systematic gaps. (1)
6. Origin of all living things from a single or very few living sources which came from inanimate matter because of inherent properties of inanimate matter. (1)
7. This model is untestable directly, but primarily only by analyzing logical reasonableness. (3)
8. Sharp boundaries exist between major classification groups with no transitional forms between higher categories. (2)
9. Geologic column is evidence of a vast history of the earth. (1)
10. Only local sedimentary columns exist and worldwide destruction is evidenced by worldwide distribution of sedimentary rocks. (2)
11. Some forces of origination and integration have been involved in changes of living things. (1)

Select from the key the entry which is *most closely* associated with each item 12 through 23:

> KEY: 1. Part of design argument for Creator origin
> 2. Part of order out of disorder (higher from lower) argument
> 3. Major gap in observational data
> 4. Specific *supra*-natural event imagined by some scientists

12. Orderly pattern(s) of constellations, planet, comet motions (1)
13. From no matter to matter (3)
14. Mountain building from movement of dry land masses (4)
15. Complex patterns of left handed amino acid structure, organelle and organ interactions (1)
16. Spontaneous generation of living substance (4)
17. From no living substance to living substance (3)
18. Similarities of chemicals and body parts (2)
19. Personality and reflective, symbolic, conceptual thought (1)
20. From unicellular to multicellular (3)
21. Animallike behavior in reaction to signals, signs and perceptual thought (2)
22. New physical traits from accumulation of mutational changes (4)
23. Synthesis of amino acids and urea, rubber, fibers. (2)

At this time you should be able to draw from your study of natural science to explain to another person what might be called the main themes of positional statements associated with the so-called evolution model and/or creation model of first origins. Therefore, select from the key the entry which is *most closely* associated with each item 24 through 41:

> KEY: 1. Evolution model of first origins.
> 2. Creation model of first origins.
> 3. Either of these models of first origins.
> 4. Neither of these two models of first origins.

24. Matter that existed eternally somehow generated into a whole series of elements, stars and planets. (1)
25. The physical universe was specially created (by a Creator). (2)
26. The universe was created complete and stable in essentially the present state. (2)
27. Mutations are evidence of increased disorder and only changes within limits of kind result from mutations and/or recombinations of genes. (2)

28. A catastrophic flood shaped the geologic column according to scientific evidence. (2)
29. Organic matter came spontaneously from inorganic matter. (1)
30. No initial observations of events can be used as basis of any first origin model. (3)
31. Mankind is related to the ape through an unknown common ancestor. (1)
32. No common ancestry exists between man and apes according to scientific evidence. (2)
33. Forces of origination and integration exist such that order comes from disorder. (1)
34. All human beings belong to the same race, and languages are merely tribal differences. (2)
35. Original kinds have been stable. (2)
36. Changes in evolutionary sequence of life forms are due to random mutational changes in genes. (1)
37. The law of entropy applies generally to the solar system and living organisms. (2)
38. Apparent land features resulted from specific causes of vulcanism, diastrophism and gradation. (1)
39. The earth and life were created relatively recently according to scientific evidence in comparison with the billions of years of uniformitarianists. (2)
40. Races of man resulted from mutations and segregation in early manlike forms. (1)
41. Fossils of genus *Homo* are immediate ancestors of modern man. (1)

For items 42 through 55 select from the key the entry which you could use to help another person understand about creationism and super- and supra- natural events such as we have talked about during this term:

KEY: 1. Associated most closely with biblical creationism
      2. Associated most closely with the creation model (scientific creationism)
      3. Associated most closely with the evolution model (total evolutionism).
      4. None of the above.

42. Present matter came from explosion of dense eternally existing particle. (3)
43. No common ancestry exists between man and apes according to scientific data. (2)
44. Worldwide catastrophic changes modified greatly the land surface of the earth. (2)
45. New physical traits have occurred from accumulation of mutational changes and new kinds of organisms have appeared. (3)
46. Adam did not have any common ancestry with animals but was directly created by God from inorganic matter according to Genesis. (1)
47. Life appeared as a result of spontaneous generation. (3)
48. Movements of dry rock masses resulted in mountain building. (3)
49. A worldwide flood occurred in which only Noah and his family were preserved in an ark according to Genesis. (1)
50. The curse caused a general tendency toward sin and deterioration. (1)
51. Stable groups or kinds of living organisms were established in the beginning. (2)
52. Break up of one land mass resulted in the present continents. (3)
53. The law of entropy applies generally to the solar system and living things. (2)
54. The earth, life, and Adam were created about 6,000 years ago according to the book of Genesis. (1)
55. The earth and life were created relatively recently according to scientific evidence in comparison with the several billions of years of uniformitarianism. (2)

Select from the key the particular aspect of total evolution which is *most closely* associated with each item 56 through 59:
KEY: 1. Molecular evolution
        2. Organic evolution
        3. Societal evolution
        4. Stellar evolution
56. Through accretion of particles of matter elements became combined into stars and planets. (4)
57. Some time in the distant past subvital parts of matter combined into the DNA code material and into organic entities which in turn became cellular. (1)

58. Grand scale changes in living things occurred over great expanses of time such that present forms of life came from other forms which came from a unicellular origin. (2)
59. Groups of human beings have changed their patterns of organization with resulting improvement and progress. (3)

In this course you have *not* been asked to state what you believe about origins of human beings. Rather you are expected to have an *understanding* about human beings as products of megaevolution or societal evolution. For items 60 through 75 select from the key the entry by which you show that you have a clear understanding:

KEY: 1. Part of current majority understanding of human beings as products of biological (mega-) evolution.
2. Part of current understanding of human beings as product of cultural (societal) evolution.
3. Part of current minority understanding of human beings as products of biological (micro-) evolution.
4. Not part of understanding fitting either of the above.

60. In the past there has been kind to kind change involving change of all populations. (1)
61. So-called cave people are considered ancestors of modern human beings. (1)
62. The progress toward some utopia as the coming of a classless society. (2)
63. The idea of fixity of basic kinds which still had potential for variation within kind. (3)
64. The pattern of change over time has been essentially unilinear. (1)
65. Charles A. Beard and Carl Becker influenced many people in many decades to believe in class warfare as a type of struggle for existence between human beings. (2)
66. John Dewey was specifically influenced regarding application of an evolutionary outlook in both psychology and education. (2)
67. No true, genetically demonstrated transitional kinds can be established. (3)
68. Freud laid the basis for adoption of the importance of the environment supposedly for the development of the human being. (2)

69. Marx was happy at reading Darwin's book as supposedly containing evidence for class warfare concept applied to human beings. (2)

70. Change of living things over time has been essentially within limits of kind or only involving change in one population of some kind over time. (3)

71. So-called cave people are considered descendants of earliest survivors of some worldwide catastrophe from which very few survived. (3)

72. Darwin more or less set the pattern for the 19th and 20th century intellectuals when he replaced his belief in special creation of life by God with his own belief about living things and so called natural selection. (2)

73. Religion of human beings changed from polytheistic to monotheistic pattern according to Fosdick. (2)

74. The concept of struggle for existence (or survival of the fittest) so popular to 19th century social Darwinists is once again a central part of the thinking of 20th century social Darwinists who try to explain human behavior. (2)

75. Relationship of ''races'' of human beings from centuries have been along the line of ''superior'', ''accomplished'' whites over ''lower races'' and ''inferiority'' of blacks. (2)

FOOTNOTES

[1]Some people might hold that information about Genesis (or any part of the Bible) cannot be used in the public schools. Contrary to this position is the interpretation made amply clear by Supreme Court rulings which affirmed that the Bible can and should be used as a reference book where applicable—and the subject areas of first origins, history, language, culture study, religion, and even English literature could be considered appropriate subject matter areas.

[2]Engel v. Vitale, 370 U.S. 421 (1962). School District of Abington Township, Pa. v. Schempp, 374 U.S. 203 (1963). McCollum v. Board of Education, 333 U.S. 203 (1948).

[3]Stacy v. Williams, 306 F. Supp. 963, 1977 (1969); aff'd., 446 F. Supp. 1366 (1971).

[4]Gertrude Himmelfarb, *Darwin and the Darwinian Revolution* (Garden City New York: Doubleday and Company, Inc. 1962) (Anchor Books A 325). Sherwood Wirt, ''Charles Darwin's Other Voyage'', *Decision Magazine*, 3 (1): 8 and 19, 14 Jan.

[5]Austin: University of Texas Press, 1974. San Francisco: W. H. Freeman and Company, 1976.

[6]Conway, Zirkle, *Evolution, Marxian Biology, and the Social Scene.* (Philadelphia: University of Pennsylvania Press, 1959 and H. Selsam, ''Charles Darwin and Karl Marx'', *Mainstream* 12 (6): 28 and 36, June, 1959.

[7]Robert E. Brown, *Carl Becker on History and the American Revolution* (East Lansing, Michigan: The Spartan Press, 1970).

[8]Zirkle, *Evolution, Marxian Biology, and the Social Scene.*

[9]Charles A. Beard, *An Economic Interpretation of the Constitution of the United States.* (N. Y.: Macmillan Company, 1913). See also Robert E. Brown, *Charles Beard and the Constitution* (A Critical Analysis of "An Economic Interpretation of the Constitution"). (Princeton, N. J.: Princeton University Press, 1956).

[10]Robert E. Brown, *Middle-Class Democracy and the Revolution in Massachusetts, 1691-1780* (Ithaca, N.Y.: Cornell University Press for The American Historical Association, 1955); Robert E. Brown and B. Katherine Brown, *Virginia 1705-1861: Democracy or Aristocracy?* East Lansing, Michigan: Michigan State University Press, 1964). Forest McDonald, *We The People: Economic Origins of the Constitution.* (Chicago: The University of Chicago Press, 1958).

[11]Roderick W. Conner, *Cosmic Optimism: A Study of the Interpretation of Evolution by American Poets from Emerson to Robinson.* (Gainesville, Florida: University of Florida Press, 1949); Leo J. Henkin, *Darwinism in the English Novel* (N.Y.: Corporate Press, Inc., 1940); Bert J. Loewenberg, *Darwinism: Reaction or Reform?* (N.Y.: Holt, Rinehart and Winston, 1964); Stow Parsons, *Evolutionary Thought in America.* (N.Y.: George Braziller, Inc., 1956); George Roppen. *Evolution and Poetic Belief* (Oslo, Norway: Oslo University Press, 1956); Lionel Stevenson, *Darwin Among the Poets* (N.Y.: Russell and Russell, 1963). See also Zirkle, *Evolution, Marxian Biology, and the Social Scene,* especially Chapter 10, "Marxian Biology in the Communist World".

[12]See various Dewey books such as *Reconstruction in Philosophy* (1920) and *The Quest for Certainty* (1929).

[13]Francis A. Schaeffer, *Escape from Reason* (Chicago: Inter-Varsity Press, 1968) and James W. Sire, *The Universe Next Door: A Basic World View Catalog.* (Downers Grove, Illinois: Inter-Varsity Press, 1976).

[14]B. F. Skinner, *Beyond Freedom and Dignity* (N.Y.: Knopf, 1971); Robert Ardrey, *The Social Contract* (N.Y.: Atheneum, 1970) and *African Genesis.* (N.Y.: Atheneum, 1962); Konrad Lorenz, *On Aggression* (N.Y.: Harcourt, Brace and World, 1966); Desmond Morris, *The Naked Ape* (London: Cape, 1967). See Francis A. Schaeffer, *Back to Freedom and Dignity* (Downers Grove, Illinois: Inter-Varsity Press, 1972) in which he responds to the Skinner book as well as to Jacques Monod, *Chance and Necessity* (N.Y.: Knopf, 1971) and to Francis Crick, *Of Molecules and Men* (Seattle: University of Washington Press, 1966).

[15]Morton White, *The Origins of Dewey's Instrumentalism.* (N.Y.: Columbia University Press, 1943). Among many books by John Dewey see his *Essays in Experimental Logic* (Chicago: University of Chicago Press, 1916) and *Logic: The Theory of Inquiry* (N. Y.: Henry Holt & Co., 1938). See also Zirkle, *Evolution, Marxian, Biology and the Social Scene.*

[16]Josh McDowell, *Evidence That Demands A Verdict* (San Bernardino: Campus Crusade for Christ, International, 1972). Also excellent on the Graff-Wellhausen thesis is Osward T. Allis, *The Five Books of Moses.* (Philadelphia: Presbyterian and Reformed Publishing Company, 1943); and Clifford Wilson, *Ebla Tablets: Secrets of a Forbidden City* (San Diego: Master Books, 1977).

[17]Wilhelm Schmidt, *The Origin and Growth of Religion: Facts and Theories.* Translated by H. J. Rose. (London: Methuen, 1931). See also Andrew Lang, *The Making of Religion* (London: Longmans Green, 1909) and *The Origin Of Religion* (London, Watts, 1908); Stephen H. Langdon, "Monotheism and the Predecessor of Polytheism in Summerian Religion", *Evangelical Quarterly,* (London, April, 1937); Paul Radin, *Monotheism among Primitive People* (London: n.p., 1924); W. H. Rule, "Monotheism, A Truth of Revelation and Not a Myth", *Transactions of Victoria Institute,* 12 (1878-79): 343-369; J. H. Titcombe, "Prehistoric Monotheism", *Transactions of Victoria Institute,* 8 (1873): 145; D. G. Whitely, "Traces of a Religious Belief of Primeval Man", *Transactions of Victoria Institute,* 47 (1915): 125-148; Samuel Zwemer, "The Origin of Religion: By Evolution or by Revelation", *Transactions of Victoria Institute,* (1935): 189 and *The Origin of Religion* (Nashville, Tenn.: Cokesbury, 1935).

[18]An accumulative computerized bibliographic compilation is available for one dollar upon request from Dr. Moore. These materials were gathered while using six research grants from Michigan State University over twelve years under the title, "Library Search for Representative Statements by Scientists on Organic Evolution, Natural Selection, and Related Topics since 1859".

[19]Books published by Creation-Life Publishers, such as Richard B. Bliss, *Origins: Two Models, Streams of Civilization,* Vol. I, *Ancient History to 1572 A.D.* by Albert Hyma and Mary Stanton; *Scientific Creationism* by Henry M. Morris, and John N. Moore and Harold S. Slusher, Eds., *Biology: A Search for Order in Complexity* (Grand Rapids, MI.: Zondervan Publishing House, 1974).

[20]*Ernest Nagel and James R. Newman, "Godel's Proof", Scientific American* 194(6): 71-86. June 1956. See also *Godel's Proof*, Ernest Nagel and James R. Newman. (New York: New York University Press 1958.) (Note: "It must be pointed out that science itself has its roots and origins outside its own rational realm of thinking. In essence, there seems to exist a 'Godel Theorem of Science' which holds that science is possible only within a large framework of nonscience issues and concerns. The mathematician Godel proved that a system of axioms can never be based on itself: in order to prove its validity, statements from *outside* the system must be used." (Emphasis added) Victor F. Wiesskopf, "Frontiers and Limits of Science", *American Scientist* 65 (4): 405-411, July-Aug. 1977.)

[21]I remind that Supreme Court Justices have taken the position that the Bible can and should be used as a reference in the public school classroom. Probably resistance toward use of the Bible in the public classroom stems from several sources; among which are impressions by many, generated by proponents of higher criticism in the nineteenth century, that the Bible is not reliable, is only a collection of myths and legends. Contrariwise the Bible is now established as a historically accurate account of human activities that holds for centuries before the Advent of Jesus Christ. Archaeologists have accumulated confirmation of biblical people and events as far back as Genesis 14. Thus there are good reasons to assert that all of the Bible is fully reliable.

Note to Teachers

The chapters that follow will show the science teacher how to present the concepts of creation as well as popular evolutionary concepts. Presentation of creation concepts regarding the origin of the universe will be found in Chapter 2; presentation of creation concepts regarding origin of life on the earth will be found in Chapter 3; and presentation of creation concepts regarding origin of humankind in Chapter 4.

Presentation of the creation model is frequently rejected in public schools on the basis that it cannot be proven scientifically and must be believed of the basis of religious faith. However, belief in total evolution is a philosophical system or world view and requires as much faith as creation. This is evident from the following facts.[1]

1. Evolution cannot be observed in operation. The small variations that can be seen taking place within species and genera are horizontal changes not vertical, and are equally to be expected according to the creation model. So-called "vertical" evolution must be accepted on faith. A horizontal change is variation within the same species or family such as the varieties of birds. A vertical change crosses family lines—the changes required for a fish to change into a bird, for instance.

> Evolution, at least in the sense that Darwin speaks of it, cannot be detected within the lifetime of a single observer.[2]

2. Evolution is not limited to biological concepts. Instead, it is a world view, a philosophy of life and meaning, and thus is a religion for many proponents.

> The Darwinian revolution of 1859 was perhaps the most fundamental of all intellectual revolutions in the history of mankind. It not only eliminated

man's anthropocentrism, but affected every metaphysical and ethical concept if consistently applied.[3]

3. Evolution is a most serious challenge to Christianity and other forms of theism, "theistic evolutionists" notwithstanding.

Darwinism removed the whole idea of God as the creator of organisms from the sphere of rational discussion . . . I think we can dismiss entirely all idea of a supernatural overriding mind being responsible for the evolutionary process.[4]

Here is a theory that released thinking men from the spell of a superstition, one of the most overpowering that has ever enslaved mankind . . . We owe to the *Origin of Species* the overthrow of the myth of creation.[5]

One of (Darwin's) greatest accomplishments was to bring the teleological aspects of nature into the realm of science . . . The teleology of nature can now be explained . . . without recourse to an eternal Creator or to spiritual or non-material forces.[6]

4. Evolution provides the philosophic framework of all non-theistic religions, including humanism and atheism. Evolution, indeed, is fundamentally humanistic and atheistic since it purportedly eliminates the need for a transcendent God and deifies man as the most advanced product of evolutionary process.

Humanism is the belief that man shapes his own destiny. It is a constructive philosophy, a non-theistic religion, a way of life . . . The American Humanist Association is a non-profit, tax-exempt organization, incorporated in the early 1940's in Illinois for educational and religious purposes.[7]

I use the word "humanist" to mean someone who believes that man is just as much a natural phenomenon as an animal or plant; that his body, mind, and soul were not supernaturally created but are products of evolution, and that he is not under the control of any supernatural being or beings, but has to rely on himself and his own powers.[8]

There are, no doubt, sufficiently profound distinctions between the ethical process and the cosmic process as it existed prior to man and to the formation of human society. As far as I know, however, all of these differences are summed up in the fact that the process and the forces bound up with the cosmos have come to consciousness in man.[9]

5. Like religious systems, evolution is the basis of a system of ethics— essentially the ethics of self-interest.

The foregoing conclusions represent, I believe, an outgrowth of the thesis of modern humanism, as well as the study of evolution, that the primary job for man is to promote his own welfare and advancement, both that of his members considered individually and that of the all-inclusive group in due awareness of the world as it is, and on the basis of naturalistic, scientific ethics.[10]

An ethical system that bases its premises on absolute pronouncements will not usually be acceptable to those who view human nature by evolutionary criteria.[11]

6. Evolution even involves a program for social action and a doctrine of future things.

We no longer need be subject to blind external forces but can manipulate the environment and eventually may be able to manipulate our genes. Thus, unlike any other species, we may be able to interfere with our biological evolution.[12]

Through the unprecedented "faculty" of long-range foresight, jointly serviced and exercised by us, we can, in securing and advancing our position, increasingly avoid missteps of blind nature, circumvent its cruelties, reform our own natures, and enhance our own values.[13]

Although science teachers may very well accept the previous six point analysis of the nature of evolution as part of their own individual thinking, there may still be a serious, sincere, and specific doubt about the *legality* of teaching the creation model as a viable alternative to the evolution model about first origins. The individual science teacher may choose to teach the creation model because of the plain fairness of doing so. Only in that way will those in the classroom have a true opportunity to make a choice or even be aware that a choice is possible. However, facing up to making a choice might prove painful in terms of application of patient thought and delicate discernment. Many question the legal basis for teaching creation in the public schools. However, to do so requires no new laws or special ruling. A straightforward presentation of the creation point of view *and* the evolution point of view about first origins is fully within responsible education of the young. *No religious worship is involved* in the teaching of the creation model. Thus there is no violation of so-called separation of church and state.

Since the creation model can be effectively discussed on scientific grounds (as is pointedly demonstrated in Chapters 2-4) and since evolution is fundamentally a philosophy or world view, it is clearly unsound educational practice and even unconstitutional, for evolution to be taught and promoted in the public schools to the exclusion or detriment of special creation. There are constitutional provisions which clearly protect children of parents whose religious convictions favor creation explanations of first origins against any imposition of exclusively evolutionary teachings. In effect, exclusive presentation of evolutionary explanations of first origins amounts to compulsory indoctrination in a state-endorsed religion. Note the wording of two important, relevant Constitutional Amendments:

> First Amendment, U.S. Constitution, Section 1: Congress shall make no law respecting an establishment of religion, or prohibiting the free exercise thereof; or abridging the freedom of speech, or of the press; or the right of the people peaceably to assemble, and to petition the government for a redress of grievances.

> Fourteenth Amendment, U.S. Constitution, Section 1: No State shall make or enforce any law which shall abridge the privileges or immunities of citizens of the United States; nor shall any State deprive any person of life, liberty or property, without due process of law; nor deny any person within its jurisdiction the equal protection of its law.

And section 202, the 1964 National Civil Rights Act means the following is unlawful:

> . . . discrimination or segregation of any kind on the ground of race, color, religion, or national origin at any establishment or place, if either purports to be required by any rule, order of any State or any agency or political subdivision thereof.

Just as racial and ethnic minorities are protected against discrimination of any kind in any state institution or agency thereof (such as a public school classroom), so are religious minorities. Thus any inference favoring evolution over creation by a teacher or textbook, unless balanced by an adequate presentation of the contrary evidence favoring creation, is illegally discriminatory against creationists.

Please note these further comments by Justices of the United States Supreme Court:

1. We agree, of course, that the State may not establish a religion of secularism in the sense of affirmatively opposing or showing hostility to religion, thus, "preferring those who believe in no religion over those who do believe." (From Justice Clark's majority opinion on the case of Abington School District vs Schempp)

2. It is said, and I agree, that the attitude of the State toward religion must be one of neutrality. But untutored devotion to the concept of neutrality can lead to invocation or approval of results which partake not simply of that non-interference and non-involvement with the religious which the Constitution commands, but of brooding and pervasive devotion to the secular, or even active hostility to the religious. Such results are not only compelled by the Constitution, but, it seems to me, are prohibited by it. (From Justice Goldberg's concurring opinion, with Justice Harlan joining, in the case of Abington School District vs Schempp.)

3. The fullest realization of true religious liberty requires that government neither engage in nor compel religious practices, that it effect no favoritism among sects or between religion and non-religion, and that it work deterrence of no religious belief. (Justice Arthur Goldberg, *Ibid.*, Justice Harlan joining.)

4. Government in our democracy . . . state and federal, must be neutral in matters of religious theory . . . It may not aid, foster, or promote one religious theory as against another. (Justice Abe Fortas, in connection with ruling striking down Arkansas anti-evolution law.)

It is obvious from the above judicial comments that it would be illegal for schools to teach only creation and ban evolution from their instructional program. Since the evolution model is not more scientific than the creation model, it is equally illegal for the instructional treatment to favor evolution instead of creation.

The only fair, legal, constitutional solution of this problem is to teach both evolution and creation as scientifically based models of origins, whenever and wherever the subject of first origins is under discussion.

An important and necessary means for clarification of the legal basis for teaching the creation model is available in the January 1978 "Note" in the *Yale Law Journal*, "Freedom of Religion and Science Instruction in Public Schools", by Wendell R. Bird.* Primary points of the argument in that singularly important investigation are as follows:

*See Appendix H

The Constitution prohibits governments from abridging free exercise of an individual's religion. An abridgement occurs when a state program has content contrary to religious precepts, imposes a burden on exercise of those religious beliefs of practices, and lacks a compelling interest justifying that burden.

Exclusive instruction by public secondary and elementary schools in the general theory of evolution abridges the free exercises of creationist students and parents. The general theory of evolution is totally contrary to creationist beliefs. Presentation only of the evolutionary theory imposes a burden on free exercise through undermining creationist beliefs, violating separatist practices, and compelling unconscionable declarations of belief. This burden is accomplished by coercion through prescription of some courses containing evolution, imposition of an unconstitutional condition on a public benefit (i.e., to study other material in a course a student realistically must study a theory violative of free exercise), influence from teachers, and pressure from other students. Government does not have a compelling interest in exclusive presentation of evolution, in any instruction at all in that theory, or even in instruction in biology, anthropology, sociology, and other subjects incorporating evolution.

Public schools must remedy this abridgement. Presentation of all scientific theories of origins, including scientific creationism along with evolution, is the preferrable method, instruction in creation in a scientific context without use of the Bible would not violate the establishment clause of the Constitution. Elimination of all theories of origin, including evolution, from public school classes is another constitutionally acceptable form of relief.

Bird summarized his 55 page article in his conclusion:

Comparison of these alternative remedies in light of their protection of religious liberty and impact upon state educational interests suggests that the preferred remedy in secondary schools is neutralizing instruction in the origin of the world and life or, in exceptional circumstances, exempting students from a block of classes (if the text and instructor present the general theory only in a single unit.) The preferred approach in elementary schools is neutralizing course material or excluding the general theory. These preferred remedies would alleviate the unconstitutional burden on free exercise from exclusive presentation of the general theory and counter substantial coercion against religious liberty, and yet would avoid the greater interference with governmental interests from elimination of biology instruction and steer clear from the prescriptions of the establishment clauses. (p. 570)

A further basis for examination of the validity of a two-way evolution/creation confrontation teaching approach about first origins can be gained through careful study of the following contrasting statements:

Humanist Statement
Affirming Evolution
as a Principle of Science

For many years it has been well established scientifically that all known forms of life, including human beings, have developed by a lengthy process of evolution. It is also verifiable today that very primitive forms of life, ancestral to all living forms came into being thousands of millions of years ago. They constituted the trunk of a "tree of life" that, in growing, branched more and more; that is, some of the later descendents of these earliest living things, in growing more complex, became ever more diverse and increasingly different from one another. Humans and the other highly organized types of today constitute the present twig-end of that tree. The human twig and that of the apes sprang from the same apelike progenitor branch.

Scientists consider that none of their principles, no matter how seemingly firmly established—and no ordinary "facts" of direct observation either— are absolute certainties. Some possibility of human error, even if very slight, always exists. Scientists welcome the challenge of further testing on any view whatever. They use such terms as *firmly established* only for conclusions founded on rigorous

Creationist Statement
Affirming Openness as
a Principle of Science

In recent years the origin of matter/energy, the cosmos, the solar system, and life on the earth have been presented in the classroom from the evolutionary point of view only. The traditional creationist point of view has been suppressed. We are concerned with the social, ethical, and scientific consequences of the current exclusive presentation of a humanistic evolutionary point of view regarding origins. The students have a right to know there is an alternative creationist point of view. They have a right to know the scientific evidences which support that alternative. They have a right to make the choice between evolutionary and creationist points of view so far as their understanding of origins is concerned.

Controlled experimentation may be applied only to a limited degree to problems dealing with the past or the future. For that reason, any conclusions regarding either the past or the future lack the scientific reliability of conclusions regarding present phenomena. Accordingly, it is especially important that there be openness in discussing matters related to origins.

evidence that have continued to with-
stand searching criticism.

The principle of biological evolution,
as just stated, meets these criteria
exceptionally well. It rests upon a
multitude of discoveries of very
different kinds that concur and com-
plement one another. It is therefore
accepted into humanity's general body
of knowledge by scientists and other
reasonable persons who have
familiarized themselves with the
evidence.

In recent years, the evidence for the
principle of evolution has continued to
accumulate. This has resulted in a
firm understanding of biological
evolution, including the further confirmation of the principle of natural
selection and adaptation that Darwin
and Wallace over a century ago
showed to be an essential part of the
process of biology evolution.

There are no alternative theories to the
principle of evolution, with its "tree
of life" pattern, that any competent
biologist of today takes seriously.
Moreover, the principle is so important for an understanding of the world
we live in and of ourselves that the
public in general, including students
taking biology in school should be
made aware of it, and of the fact that
it is firmly established in the view of
the modern scientific community.

Creationism is not scientific; it is a
purely religious view held by some

We therefore affirm a policy of openness as a principle of science with
respect to presentation of matters of
origins in the classroom. The
evidences support an evolutionary
point of view and the evidences supporting a creationist point of view
should be given proper presentation in
any classroom where the topics under
discussion relate to the origin of
matter/energy, the origin of the
cosmos, the origin of the solar system,
or the origin of life.

We are not asking that religious
dogmas be presented in the classroom,
but we are asking that scientific
evidences supporting both of these
alternative points of view be
presented. We call upon all local
school boards, manufacturers of textbooks and teaching materials, concerned citizens, and teachers and
educational agencies to resist pressures
toward scientific dogmatism and
presentation of only one point of view
on origins.

religious sects and persons and strongly opposed by other religious sects and persons. Evolution is the only presently known strictly scientific and nonreligious explanation for the existence and diversity of living organisms. It is therefore the only view that should be expounded in public school courses on science, which are distinct from those on religion.

We, the undersigned, call upon all local school boards, manufacturers of textbooks and teaching materials, elementary and secondary teachers of biological science, concerned citizens, and educational agencies to do the following:

*Resist and oppose measures currently before several state legislatures that would require creationist views of origins be given equal treatment and emphasis in public-school biology classes and text materials.

*Reject the concept, currently being put forth by certain religious and creationist pressure-groups, that alleges that evolution is itself a tenet of a religion of "secular humanism", and as such is unsuitable for inclusion in the public-school science curriculum.

*Give vigorous support and aid to those classroom teachers who present the subject matter of evolution fairly and who often encounter community opposition.

These two statements, side-by-side, give the science teacher the most striking basis for detecting aspects of the *confrontation* that really exists between proponents of the evolution model and the creation model. In *The Humanist* statement the science teacher can see the present opinions of the majority of science peers and in the Creationist statement the position of the minority of science peers.

As a further introduction to the evolution/creation confrontation teaching approach to be developed in the important chapters, "Origin of the Universe", "Origin of Life on the Earth" and "Origin of Humankind", I can think of no more appropriate question to arise than: Does evolution qualify as a scientific principle? An answer to this question is provided by Ariel A. Roth writing in *Origins*, Vol. 4 1977, pp. 4-10. The article, "Does Evolution Qualify as a Scientific Principle," is reprinted by special permission from the editors of *Origins*, a publication of the Geoscience Research Institute, Berrien Springs, Michigan.

DOES EVOLUTION QUALIFY AS A SCIENTIFIC PRINCIPLE?

The *Humanist*, an official publication of the American Humanist Association and the American Ethical Union, published a statement affirming evolution as a principle of science (January/February 1977). The statement, signed by 163 scholars, most of whom are biologists in leading universities of the United States, was prepared for distribution to major public school districts in the United States. Among its sponsors are such notables as Isaac Asimov, Linus Pauling, and George Gaylord Simpson.

The statement points out that "all known forms of life including human beings developed by a lengthy process of evolution." This broad perspective on evolution is what Kerkut (1960, p. 157) calls the "general theory of evolution," in contrast to the "special theory of evolution" which deals with small variations in organisms such as have been observed in nature and the laboratory. The statement in the *Humanist* also indicates that the principle of biological evolution meets "exceptionally well" the criteria demanded by science of being "firmly established . . . on rigorous evidence" and that in recent years more confirmation of the principle of natural selection and adaptation as proposed by Darwin and Wallace has continued to accumulate. The statement further asserts that "creationism is not scientific," while evolution is "strictly scientific."

On the other hand there has been an ongoing debate within the scientific community, largely among individuals who believe in evolution, about the validity of evolution as a scientific principle. The statement published in the *Humanist* suggests that under the pressure of current criticism leveled at evolution, basic scientific values may be overlooked or given secondary place over the other factors.

Much of the debate regarding the validity of evolution revolves around the elementary notion that science explains things on the basis of cause and effect. Simply stated, given certain conditions, certain results can be expected. This feature gives science its predictive qualities. For instance the statement "a magnet attracts iron" can be tested and used to predict what will happen when the two are near each other.

Hans Reichenbach in *The Rise of Scientific Philosophy* (1951, p. 89) emphasizes the necessity of a predictive quality for science:

> A mere report of relations observed in the past cannot be called knowledge, if knowledge is to reveal predictions. A radical empiricism, therefore, denies the possibility of knowledge.

The concept of predictability and subsequent testability has prompted the noted scientific philosopher Karl Popper to further emphasize that if an explanation cannot be adequately tested, it is not scientific. The concept must be testable (i.e., falsifiable) to qualify. Any kind of explanation will not do; it must be amenable to a testing process. If it survives testing, it can qualify. In our magnet example, we might propose that objects of only a certain color (and not a magnet) attract iron. If a red magnet were found to work, we could further test the notion by using a wooden block of the same color as the magnet and thus disprove the color theory. Popper in his book *The Logic of Scientific Discovery* (1968, p. 40) is emphatic on the matter of falsification. He states:

> But I shall certainly admit a system as empirical or scientific only if it is capable of being tested by experience. These considerations suggest that not the verifiability but the falsifiability of a system to be taken as a criterion of demarcation.

The idea that a genuine scientific idea must have the consistency that gives it predictive value, and the potential for falsification, has received a great deal of attention during the past few years among scientific philosophers and evolutionists. There is very little disagreement with this aspect of science as enunciated by Popper, and there is genuine concern as to how to apply this principle to the theory of evolution. The unrepeatable or untestable events postulated for evolution are not amenable to evaluation on the basis of consistency and prediction. Thus the concept of evolution as a principle of science is being questioned at a most fundamental level. Does it really qualify as a scientific principle? Some examples of deficiencies follow.

The concept of natural selection by survival of the fittest is the basic evolutionary mechanism. This concept does not qualify as a scientific principle, since fitness is equivalent to survival. Here we have a case of circular reasoning; no consistency or predictive value can be tested. According to this idea, organisms have survived through the evolutionary process because they are better fit, and the way one tells they are better fit is that they survive. A number of evolutionary scholars have labeled the principle of survival of the fittest a tautology (e.g., Waddington 1957, Eden 1967, Peters 1976). Popper (1963) attacks the unfalsifiable nature of the concept and concludes:

> If, more especially, we accept that statistical definition of fitness which defines fitness by actual survival, then the survival of the fittest becomes tautological, and irrefutable.

The concept of survival of the fittest of itself does not necessarily imply any evolution. Would not the fittest survive, whether they evolved or were created? The noted evolutionist Mayr (1976, p.3) speaks of "an all-powerful natural selection." Platnick (1977) wonders if there is any difference in this kind of explanation as compared to that of an all-powerful Creator.

Some evolutionary biologists are of the opinion that it is not necessarily the fittest that survive through the evolutionary process, but those that are best adapted to the requirements of evolution. Others have emphasized that survival of the organism is not as important as its fecundity [reproduction]. In both cases the problem of predictability remains. In a symposium volume celebrating 100 years of Darwinism the prominent geneticist Waddington (1960, p. 385) evaluates the matter of fecundity. He states:

> Natural selection, which was at first considered as though it were a hypothesis that was in need of experimental or observational confirmation, turns out on closer inspection to be a tautology, a statement of inevitable although previously unrecognized relation. It states that the fittest individuals in a population (defined as those which leave most offspring) will leave most offspring.

Another problem associated with the untestability of evolutionary theory is that the theory explains too much. Grene (1959) points out that "whatever might at first sight appear as evidence against the theory is assimilated by redefinition into the theory." Evolutionary theory is broad enough to accomodate almost any data that may be applied. Two ecologists Birch and Ehrlich (1967) emphasize this. They state:

Our theory of evolution has become, as Popper described, one which cannot be refuted by any possible observations. Every conceivable observation can be fitted into it. It is thus 'outside of empirical science' but not necessarily false. No one can think of ways in which to test it.

No matter what is observed, there usually is an appropriate evolutionary explanation for it. If an organ or organism develops, it has positive survival value; if it degenerates, it has negative survival value. If a complex biological system appears suddenly, it is due to preadaptation. "Living fossils" (contemporary representatives of organisms expected to be extinct) survive because the environment did not change. If the environment changes and an evolutionary lineage survives, it is due to adaptation. If the lineage dies, it is because the environment changed too much, etc. Hence the concept cannot be falsified. Platnick (1977) states that this type of situation "makes of evolutionary biologists spinners of tales, bedtime storytellers, instead of empirical investigators."

A few scientists (e.g., Williams 1970, 1973, Ball 1975, Ferguson 1976) have tried to show that evolutionary theory can predict. Their attempts, however, are concerned with the small changes of the special theory of evolution instead of the general one which is at issue and which is the main subject of the declaration published in the *Humanist*. These small changes do not prove large ones as Grene (1959) points out:

> By what right are we to extrapolate the pattern by which colour or other such superficial characters are governed to the origin of species, let alone of classes, orders, phyla of living organisms?

The question of the testability of the general theory of evolution remains.

Basic textbooks of biology usually illustrate evolution using the concept of homologous structures. Here we have another example of circular reasoning that would not pass the prediction test for science. Homologous structures are defined as comparable parts of different life forms that have a common evolutionary origin. The forelimbs of a salamander, crocodile, bird, bat, whale, mole and man all have the same basic bone structure and are considered homologous. Similarity does not necessarily imply evolution. A student commenting to an evolutionary professor put it aptly: "They find a muscle in an animal and give it a name; in another animal they find a muscle in a similar position and give it the same name and then call it evolution". Darwin himself used the argument of similarity of structure to support evolution.

Lee (1969) points out that the argument is logically invalid:

> He [Darwin] argued that morphological similarities were due to common

descent and yet offered no further really acceptable evidence for common descent save morphological similarities. A circular piece of reasoning if there ever was one.

Hull (1967) makes the same complaint:

> It is tautological to say that homologous resemblances are indicative of common line of descent, since by definition homologous resemblances are those resemblances due to common line of descent.

The same difficulty reappears when evolutionists attempt to classify living and fossil organisms so that their evolutionary relationships are revealed. One might select, for example, the group of invertebrates which most closely resembles the chordates and place the two groups near each other in a classification scheme. The classification is then often used as evidence for an evolutionary relationship.

Several widely divergent schools of thought have developed regarding the kinds of characteristics that are most important in determining evolutionary relationships. As a result opinions as to whether Popper's criteria of falsifiability can be satisfied also differ widely (e.g., Bock 1973, Wiley 1975). Perhaps the soundest conclusion expressed by a number of scholars is that from a practical standpoint the process of evolution is too complex and past events too unknown to permit a meaningful reconstruction of evolutionary phylogenetic patterns (Manser 1965, Barker 1969, Lee 1969, Platnick 1977). Orians (1973) and Slobodkin (1968) admit it is very difficult. An alternative is to adopt the view expressed by the prominent evolutionist Ernst Mayr (1976, p. 411) that classification of organisms is an "art." This would remove the problem altogether from the arena of science.

This brings us to another point: a number of scientists and scientific philosophers in attempting to reconcile the lack of rigor in evolutionary theory compared to current scientific standards have proposed that evolution be treated differently. This, of course, tends to alienate it from science and from being a "principle of science" as proposed in the *Humanist* statement. Such views have been proposed by Beckner (1959), Scriven (1959), Smart (1963), and Manser (1965), while Barker (1969) and Flew (1966) propose that evolution is more closely related to historical studies than to typical science. Ruse (1973) on the other hand suggests that evolutionary events are subject to the same scientific principles that apply to most of science. Platnick (1977) in the journal *Systematic Zoology* is still more emphatic:

> Evolutionary biologists have a choice to make: either we agree with Mayr that narrative explanations are the name of the game, and continue drifting away from the rest of biology into an area ruled only by authority and consensus, or we insist that whenever possible our explanations be testable

and potentially falsifiable and that evolutionary biology rejoin the scientific community at large.

The concept of creation does not appear to meet the criterion of falsifiability any better than evolution. Science is not at its best when dealing with unique past events, whether these be considered as evolution or creation. Therefore it is surprising to find a statement signed by more than 120 scientists stating that creationism is "a purely religious view" while evolution is labeled as "strictly scientific."

The controversy over whether or not evolution is a scientific principle has reached beyond the scientific community. In his article entitled "Darwin's Mistake," published in *Harper's Magazine*, Bethell (1976) states his belief that Darwin's theory "is on the verge of collapse." The jurist Macbeth (1971) in his book *Darwin Retired* presents a long list of illogical arguments employed in support of evolution. He does not defend creation, yet states that "Darwinism itself has become a religion" (p. 126).

The statement in the *Humanist* affirming evolution as a principle of science has the support of many influential scientists; yet a review of the literature of both science and the philosophy of science reveals significant doubt regarding its validity. In view of this, it is sobering to think that so many scientists should affirm, in a public statement to be sent to public schools, that evolution is a principle of science that meets "exceptionally well" the criteria of science which are based on "rigorous evidence." Apparently this is not the case at all. Evolutionists need to re-examine their thinking and re-evaluate their claims.

REFERENCES

Ball, Ian R., "Nature and Formulation of Biogeographical Hypotheses", *Systematic Zoology*, 24:407-430, 1975.

Barker, A. D., "An Approach to the Theory of Natural Selection," *Philosophy*, 44:271-290, 1969.

Beckner, Morton, *The Biological Way of Thought* (New York: Columbia University Press, 1959).

Bethell, Tom, "Darwin's Mistake", *Harper's Magazine*, 252:70-75, 1976.

Birch, L. C., and P. R. Ehrlich, "Evolutionary History and Population Biology", *Nature*, 214:349-352, 1967.

Bock, Walter J., "Philosophical Foundations of Classical Evolutionary Classification", *Systematic Zoology*, 22:375-400, 1973.

Chambers, Bette, et al., "A Statement Affirming Evolution as a Principle of Science", *The Humanist*, 37(1):4-6, 1977.

Eden, Murray, "Inadequacies of Neo-Darwinian Evolution as a Scientific Theory" (in) (Paul S. Moorhead and Martin M. Kaplan, eds. *Mathematical Challenges to the Neo-Darwinian Interpretation of Evolution*, The Wistar Institute Symposium Monograph Number 5, 1967).

Ferguson, Anthony, "Can Evolutionary Theory Predict?", *American Naturalist*, 110:1101-1104, 1976.

Flew, Antony, " 'The Concept of Evolution': A Comment", *Philosophy*, 41:70-75, 1976.

Grene, Margorie, "The Faith of Darwinism", *Encounter*, 13(5): 48-56, 1959.

Hull, David L., "Certainty and Circularity in Evolutionary Taxonomy", *Evolution*, 21:174-189, 1967.

Kerkut, G. A., *Implications of Evolution* (New York: Pergamon Press, 1960).

Lee, K. K., "Popper's Falsifiability and Darwin's Natural Selection", *Philosophy*, 44:291-302, 1969.

Macbeth, Norman, *Darwin Retried: An Appeal to Reason* (Boston: Gambit Incorporated, 1971).

Manser, A. R., "The Concept of Evolution", *Philosophy*, 40:18-34, 1965.

Mayr, Ernst, *Evolution and the Diversity of Life* (Cambridge: Harvard University Press, Belknap Press, 1976).

Orians, G. H., Book review of *Growth by Intussusception, Limnology and Oceanography*, 18:347-348, 1973.

Peters, R. H., "Tautology in Evolution and Ecology", *American Naturalist*, 110:1-12, 1976.

Platnick, N. I., "Review of Evolution and the Diversity of Life", *Systematic Zoology*, 26:224-228, 1977.

Popper, Karl R., "Science: Problems, Aims, Responsibilities", *Federation Proceedings*, 22:961-972, 1963.

Popper, Karl R., *The Logic of Scientific Discovery* (New York: Harper and Row, 1968).

Reichenbach, Hans, *The Rise of Scientific Philosophy* (Berkeley: University of California Press, 1951).

Ruse, Michael, *The Philosophy of Biology* (London: Hutchinson University Library, 1973).

Scriven, Michael, "Explanation and Prediction in Evolutionary Theory", *Science* 130:477-482, 1959.

Slobodkin, L. B., "Toward a Predictive Theory of Evolution" (in) (Richard C. Lewontin, ed., *Population Biology and Evolution*, New York: Syracuse University Press, 1968), pp. 187-205.

Smart, J. J. C., *Philosophy and Scientific Realism* (New York: The Humanities Press, 1963).

Waddington, C. H., *The Strategy of the Genes* (London: Ruskin House, George Allen and Unwin, 1957).

Waddington, C. H., "Evolutionary Adaptation" (in) *Evolution After Darwin, Vol. 1*, (Sol Tax, ed., Chicago: University of Chicago Press, 1960), pp. 381-402.

Wiley, E. O., and Karl R. Popper, "Systematics, and Classification: A Reply to Walter Bock and Other Evolutionary Taxonomists", *Systematic Zoology*, 24:233-243, 1975.

Williams, M. B., "Deducing the Consequences of Evolution: A Mathematical Model", *Journal of Theoretical Biology*, 29: 343-385, 1970.

Williams, M. B., "Falsifiable Predictions of Evolutionary Theory", *Philosophy of Science*, 40:518-537, 1973.

Science teachers should be comfortable using the evolution/creation confrontation approach to teaching first origins.

Chapter 2 is written expressly to afford the science teacher a condensed treatment of the evolutionary ideas about first origin of the *universe* which are held by the majority of scientific peers. Then "how to" methods are made explicit for handling the minority opposition ideas generated by creationist scientists, who offer their specific interpretations of the facts commonly known to all scientists.

Chapter 3 is written specifically to provide the science teacher with a condensed treatment of the evolutionary ideas about first origin of *life* on the earth which are held by the majority of scientific peers. Then "how to" methods are particularly itemized for handling the minority opposition ideas offered by creationist scientists, who are specialists in the biological sciences.

Chapter 4 is specifically organized to help science teachers grasp a condensed treatment of the evolutionary ideas about first origin of humankind which are held by the majority of the scientific peers. Then "how to" methods are provided for handling the minority opposition ideas offered by creationist scientists who are confronting the concepts of the animal origin of humankind with genuinely intriguing, alternative interpretations of the *same facts* utilized by evolutionists.

A final extra note to the science teacher involves mention of the most desirable method of employing the Classroom Teaching Aids with students as completed units. I suggest that the science teacher "build" particular ones as they are used with students. For instance, comparison of megaevolution and revelation (Classroom Teaching Aid 7) has generated much more impact and has much more instructional value if built by means of four successive steps, with an overlay for each step, before reaching the rather complicated final form. Thus, the main dual listing of the two column entries would be used as the first overhead projector overlay. Then the next overlay would show broken lines connecting the stellar and planet entries. The third overlay would show broken lines connecting only plant terms in the dual listing. And a fourth overlay is presented in which broken lines only connect animal terms in the dual listing. When the final composite of all lines shown separately in previous overlays is shown, the full impact is most impressive.

In similar fashion it is effective to build the triangulation or pyramid representation of total evolution before presenting Classroom Teaching Aid 4.

Figure 2 — USE OF CLASSROOM TEACHING MODEL

STEP ONE

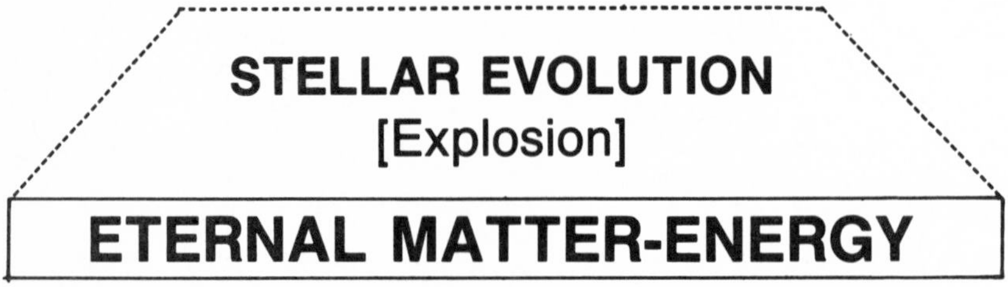

STELLAR EVOLUTION
[Explosion]

ETERNAL MATTER-ENERGY

STEP TWO

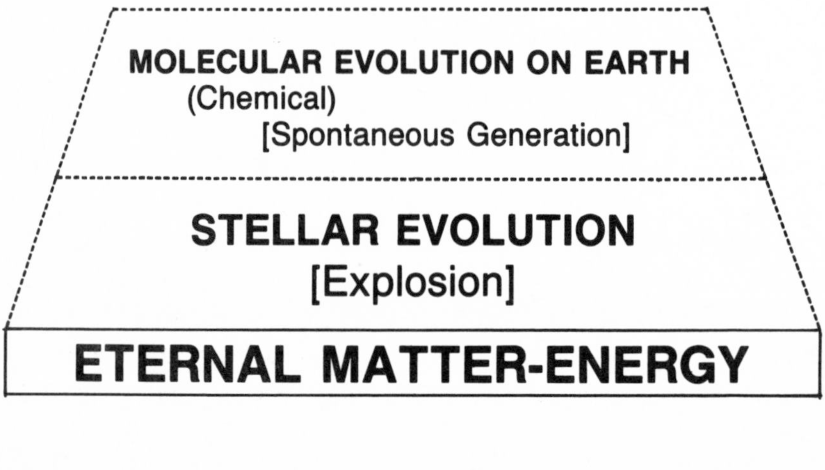

MOLECULAR EVOLUTION ON EARTH
(Chemical)
[Spontaneous Generation]

STELLAR EVOLUTION
[Explosion]

ETERNAL MATTER-ENERGY

STEP THREE

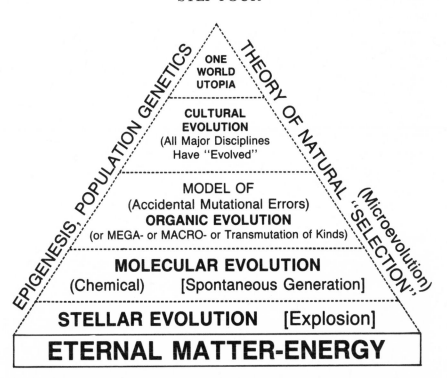

MODEL OF
[Accidental Mutational Errors]
ORGANIC EVOLUTION
(or MEGA- or MACRO-
or Transmutation of Kinds)

MOLECULAR EVOLUTION ON EARTH
(Chemical)
[Spontaneous Generation]

STELLAR EVOLUTION
[Explosion]

ETERNAL MATTER-ENERGY

STEP FOUR

EPIGENESIS, POPULATION GENETICS

THEORY OF NATURAL "SELECTION" (Microevolution)

**ONE
WORLD
UTOPIA**

**CULTURAL
EVOLUTION**
(All Major Disciplines
Have "Evolved"

MODEL OF
(Accidental Mutational Errors)
ORGANIC EVOLUTION
(or MEGA- or MACRO- or Transmutation of Kinds)

MOLECULAR EVOLUTION
(Chemical)   [Spontaneous Generation]

STELLAR EVOLUTION   [Explosion]

ETERNAL MATTER-ENERGY

When separate parts of compound charts or diagrams are utilized as building blocks or components of the whole unit, then individual parts can be discussed appropriately. Quite often when a teaching aid is presented as a completed construct, the result is too overwhelming. By using a building technique, the common problems of teaching inductively and/or deductively are involved in the use of these Classroom Teaching Aids.

Many suggestions for other illustrative materials and a wide variety of supplementary reading materials have been produced by the Institute for Creation Research, the Bible-Science Association, Creation-Life Publishers, the Creation-Science Research Center, and the Creation Research Society. Addresses and more specific details are provided in the Appendix.

FOOTNOTES

[1]The following points are drawn from Dr. Henry M. Morris, "Introducing Scientific Creationism into the Public Schools" (San Diego: Institute for Creation Research, 1975) and used here by permission.

[2]David B. Kitts, "Paleontology and Evolutionary Theory", *Evolution* , Vol. 28, Sept. 1974, p. 466. Dr. Kitts is Professor of Geology at Oklahoma University.

[3]Ernest Mayr, "The Nature of the Darwinian Revolution", *Science*, Vol. 176, June 2, 1972, p. 981. Dr. Mayr is Professor of Zoology at Harvard and one of the leading evolutionists of the world.

[4]Sir Julian Huxley (in) *Issues in Evolution* (Sol Tax, Editor. University of Chicago Press, 1960), p. 45. These words are from Huxley's keynote speech at the Darwin Centennial. The late Julian Huxley was probably the leading evolutionist of the present generation, more responsible than any other one person for the so-called modern evolutionary synthesis. He was selected as the first Director-General of the United Nations Educational, Scientific, and Cultural Organization, and also as the keynote speaker of the Darwinian Centennial Convocation at the University of Chicago in 1959.

[5]C. D. Darlington, "Origin of Darwinism", *Scientific American*, May 1959, p. 60. Darlington is an internationally-famous evolutionist at Oxford University.

[6]Francisco J. Ayala, "Biology as an Autonomous Science", *American Scientist*, Vol. 56, Autumn 1968, p. 213.

[7]Promotional brochure about the American Humanist Association, distributed by the Humanist Society of San Jose, California.

[8]Sir Julian Huxley, *Issues in Evolution.*

[9]John Dewey, "Evolution and Ethics", *Scientific Monthly*, February 1954, p. 66. Dewey was one of the founders of the American Humanist Association and was a strong evolutionary pantheist. He is best known as the chief architect of the present system of public education in America, especially the methodology of so-called "progressive education", later known as "life adjustment curriculum".

[10]H. J. Muller, "Human Values in Relation to Environment", *Science*, Vol. 127, March 21, 1958, p. 629. Dr. Muller of Indiana University was a leading evolutionary geneticist.

[11]A. G. Motulsky, "Brave New World?", *Science*, Vol. 185, Aug. 23, 1974, p. 654.

[12]Motulsky, "Brave New World?", p. 653.

[13]Muller, "Human Values", p. 629.

[14]The following material is reprinted here by special permission from the Editors of *Origin*, a publication of the Geoscience Research Institute, Berrien Springs, MI. It appeared in the first issue of Volume 4, 1977, pp. 4-10.

1 | What Is Science?

When you complete this chapter you should understand how to:

1. Specify that science is an application of certain process skills to obtain knowledge about naturally occurring object and/or events.

2. Explain rigorously the specifically different aspects of scientific activity.

3. State explicitly the limitations of scientists according to certain limiting principles.

4. State specific criteria for recognizing a good scientific theory.

What is science? The answer to this question is *the real* crux of any discussion of evolution/creation concepts on first origins. Today, it is assumed that scientists can investigate *any* area in inquiry. Yet, is it possible to study *scientifically* the ultimate origin of the universe, or origin of life on the earth, or origin of humankind? The answer is negative to each question.

First we will discuss important background information, then particular limitations of scientists and scientific methodology. Following such foundational material careful elucidation of the question, What is science?, is presented through consideration and exemplification of 17 pertinent aspects of scientific activity. The chapter closes with a discussion of ''The Heart of the Matter.''

Historical Background

Some pertinent background information is paramountly important to gain a historical perspective. The rise of modern science is often dated by

---

"Cover Word"
(Beware Semantic Confusion)

Historical, history: Proper use of such terms involves activities of human beings; so misleading use by megaevolutionists with respect to imagined geologic events conveys the connotation that real objects and events were involved in presumed past eras of time. Most properly all imaginative narratives of geologists are pre-historical.

---

the work of Copernicus, an astronomer, and Versalius, an anatomist. Prior to the work of these men, medieval science had been based extensively upon the authority of one man—Aristotle, rather than upon observation. Departure from Aristotlian science came when scholars at Oxford challenged the authority of Aristotle by showing that he had made certain mistakes about natural phenomena.

Contrary to what has often been taught in twentieth century science classrooms, the rise of modern science did not conflict with what biblical authors taught. This assertion can be supported most pointedly by reference to the thoroughly documented work of physicist Stanley L. Jaki[1], and others who have separately argued most accurately that modern science was "born" out of the Judeo-Christian world view.

It is certainly true that various beginnings of science as a discipline might be found in the cultures of the Greeks with their attention to logic and rules of reason, of the Arabs with their attention to algebra and geometry, and of the Chinese, Babylonians and Egyptains. But Jaki has established fully that science, as a discipline, was "stillborn" in each of these cultures. Not until "The Beacon of the Covenant"—as Jaki titled his chapter on the basic Hebrew world view—was taken seriously by Roger Bacon, Robert Grosseteste, Francis Bacon, Copernicus, Galileo, Versalius, Tycho Brahe, Linne Linneaus, Johy Ray, Robert Nuttall, Johannes Kepler and Isaac Newton did modern science truly begin. Admittedly, not all of these scientists held to the covenant at the same level or degree of commitment. Galileo, and even Kepler, often expressed himself more in consonance with the Greek emphasis on reason.

These early scientists believed that the universe, including the earth, was created by a reasonable God. Insisting upon the rationality of God as intelligible, early scientists believed that they could look for the explanation of any event in terms of earlier events, that is, cause and effect. They also believed that God created an orderly universe with uniformity of natural events. The existence of the orderly universe was contingent upon the very creative acts of God, who did all things in good order. The universe was not random; there was a uniformity of the natural environment. And the universe was "open" because God had intervened in the activities of human beings.

Further aspects drawn from the Christian world view by early scientists were (1) belief in the certainty that objective reality existed—there was something "there" that could be studied successfully; and also, (2) belief that the natural environment was worth studying—for to do so was to investigate God's creation.

This was possible further, because they believed that human beings were created in the image of God, that human beings could find out about natural things because they had been given dominion as God's creation over all things. In the Christian basis of science there was no separation, or need for conflict, between the Bible message and science.[2]

To summarize, modern science was started by those who accepted the beacon of the Covenant of God. They believed that heaven and earth were created by God; and, as biblical authors had written, they believed that God was reasonable. The stimulus to study God's creation came from realization of the uniqueness of the human being as made in God's image—hence able to reason after God; or as Kepler expressed the thought—to think God's thoughts after Him. They believed in an "open" universe in which God had intervened over the course of human history. Such was the base of belief from which modern science grew.

Continued impetus for implementation of that basic belief was given by Robert Boyle, Michael Faraday, James Clerk Maxwell, Gregory Mendel, and Louis Pasteur[3], as they did their scientific work within the thought forms derived from Christianity. In particular, these first modern scientists believed that God as the Creator established lawful relationships in His creation which could be discovered. Not only was God the giver of laws of human conduct, but He was the Lawgiver of laws of nature as well. The idea of laws in the universe and special methods of inquiry that could be used to discover such laws (God's laws, not Nature's laws) was another important part of the Christian base that made modern science possible. To a great extent all scientists, since the time of the early greats of the scientific revolution to present naturalistically oriented, non-believing scientists, must rely on the principles first drawn from the Christian base by Galileo, Newton, Kepler, and Linnaeus.

"Cover Word"
(Beware Semantic Confusion)

Science: often used propagandistically as anything done by scientists without clear attention to connotative aspects including methods, procedures, and practices involving specialized equipment and techniques.

These early greats of the scientific discipline built a tradition and momentum that was most helpful and directive for succeeding scientists. Traditional methods of scientists and the pragmatic necessity of technology, which accompanied expansion of science, carried scientific discovery along for many decades. Then the Christian base of science was lost (or at least became ignored). The Covenant belief of Copernicus, Galileo, Kepler, Newton, Linnaeus and others was lost (or ignored) as a tradition, as a momentum for further generations of scientists.

In the mind-set of leading thinkers, God became separated and remote to the universe. By the time of Spinoza and Kant, the universe was considered "closed". According to Kant, God was no longer thought to intervene. The providential function of God was separated into different realms. According to Kant, science and religion were to exist and function separately. Religion was separated from scientific accounts and religious beliefs were not to be extended into scientific explanation.

Limitations of Scientific Methodology

It is imperative to *establish* a clear understanding regarding *necessary limitations* of scientists and the discipline of science. In the present millieu a certain aura seems to exist about scientists: that scientists have practically unlimited capabilities to attack and, presumably, solve any problem turned over to them. However, it is important to know and communicate the limitations of science.

As shown in the previous brief discussion of historical considerations, modern science was begun by great physical and biological scientists, such as Galileo, Kepler, Newton, Linneaus, Ray, Maxwell, Faraday, Kelvin, Pasteur, Mendel and Virchow. All of these were theists and many were Christians—full adherents to the articles of biblical faith. They believed that the universe and the earth were created by God. Furthermore, they believed that since they were created in the image of God they had abilities for observation, search, and reason. They could "think God's thoughts after him" (an idea expressed by Kepler). These scientists also realized that they had limited abilities; therefore, they limited themselves to studies that were empirical, quantitative, mechanical, and correctable. A comment on each of these limitations is needed:

Empirical

Science is based upon events that can be observed. Early scientists studied things in the natural environment and used tools and measurements to extend their ability to observe. The empirical principle of science was a means for defining the nature of scientific beliefs; that is, beliefs were not regarded as scientific unless they could be tested by scientific methods.

Quantitative

Science is based upon measurements of changes of objects in their natural environment. The founders of modern science were concerned with physical reality and restricted their investigations to the kind of reality that is measurable. They deliberately altered or moved natural objects to measure changes or aspects of relationships of those objects. Physical scientists especially set the style in seeking to gain quantitative measurements in terms such as length, weight, volume and density. Just because values, morals and spiritual aspects of human beings were intangible and immeasurable did not mean that they were unreal, but that they were outside the scope of scientific investigation.

Mechanical

These scientists sought to represent the order and pattern of things they found around them. They took the view that natural phenomena can and should be studied, described and explained by reference to matter and motion and identified scientific laws. Science, then, was restricted to the direct or indirect study of the behavior of natural objects and/or events which were involved in natural cause and effect series. In some cases they set up physical models of what they were studying; in other instances they were able only to prepare lists and stated divisions and subdivisions of classification of objects and events.

Correctable

Under repeated examination and re-examination errors could be detected, and the same results under similar conditions could be gained and compared time after time. Through such steps they were able to arrive at certain lawful relationships of natural objects and/or events. No scientific concepts were regarded as final but were regarded as being open to revision and even rejection according to experience with natural objects and/or events.

Careful, orderly scientific work is centered on direct or indirect study of natural events and phenomena occuring during the lifetime of given researchers. Because Francis Bacon took the Bible seriously, he saw the science of his day as a way whereby human beings could strive to restore dominion over all things that had been lost due to Adam's fall when he sinned in disobedience to God. Bacon urged that deductive reasoning of scholastics be deemphasized for the greater attention to direct observation, and development of conclusions by induction. Newton repeatedly warned against careless speculation and hasty formulation of hypotheses without specific grounding in quantitative measurement.

A graphic illustration that the venue of scientists is the study of natural things in the present (bound by the limiting principles just enumerated, regardless of which decade or century in which they live) is presented in Classroom Teaching Aid 9. Two dimensions, size and time, can be used to represent the sources of all scientific knowledge and understanding regarding structures and phenomena. As is evident by the vertical lined portion

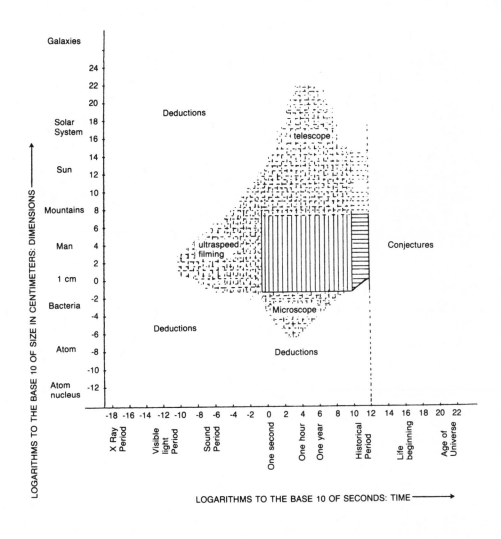

Classroom Teaching Aid 9
LIMITATIONS OF SCIENTISTS

—Adapted from Garrido

in the diagram, the *first* zone (that is, the most tangible zone) corresponds to acquisition of sensory knowledge, which includes sizes easily detected by the unaided eye, and time intervals ranging from one second to specific hours, days and years during the lifetime of an observer.

Within the *second* zone the sensory capacity or capability of human beings can be increased by use of special instruments and tools for observations, such as microscopes, telescopes, ultraspeed filming, spectroscopes, betatrons, etc. Of course, limits of this zone are changeable depending upon advancement and specific improvement of technological implementation of observing scientists, such as when telescopes have been improved; though light may traverse great distances, any one observation through a telescope is in the "present" for the astronomer involved.

Extending beyond the area of instrumental observation is a *third* zone which can be approached or studied under present technological restrictions only by deductive methods. Reliability of such deductive methods must always be placed in question as part of the correctableness of careful, orderly scientific work.

Of course, consideration of phenomena beyond the duration of any one observer is often the center of interest of scientists. Wherein it is possible, recourse can be made to the testimony of earlier, trustworthy observers of the natural environment. Thus a *fourth* zone can be defined and identified as a historical period, a time when there were careful observations— quantifications—made by some previously living human beings. Quite understandably then, the term "historical" most commonly connotes the actions and involvements of human beings.[4]

A *final* zone of knowledge and understanding with respect to structures and phenomena may be identified when men try to think of time and supposed natural objects and/or events prior to any possible historical period or written history. With respect to this zone the human being acting as a careful, orderly scientist can only *guess* about the way phenomena occurred. This is the "zone of conjecture" wherein ideas about the origin of life or the origin and age of the universe must be placed. By definition the concept "origin" refers to the coming into existence or use; that is, the beginning of something. Paramountly important, then, is careful acknowledgment that this fifth zone, involving first origins, is fully beyond the limits of careful, orderly scientific work, which is properly limited to study of natural objects and/or events of the present.

Definitional Formulations

On the basis of the two previous sections, "Historical Background" and "Limitations of Scientific Methodology", certain foundational assumptions can be drawn from the thinking of the originators of modern science. Most integral to understanding the work of any discipline of human knowledge is attention to the beginning premises upon which the discipline is based. A special list of the basic assumptions, which all scientists employ, would include:

Basic Assumptions of Science

1. Objectivity of study is possible;
2. Natural objects and/or events exist outside of (independent of) the observer;
3. Cause and effect relationships may be identified;
4. Scientific ideas are testable; that is, falsifiable;
5. There is uniformity in the natural environment.

These are the basic "givens" that are foundational to inductive thinking, which Bacon urged would be added to deductive thinking of the scholastics. These are the uncontestable grounds for development of generalizations from which deductive reasoning can be derived. The untestable notions, beliefs, faith-statements identified by David Hume in his rigorous study of human thought patterns are represented in these statements.

All scientific work is grounded in faith; faith in the basic assumptions stated above. The assumptive statements are each taken for granted as the bedrock for thinking human beings in scientific work, and are primal beliefs in all other fields of academic and intellectual pursuit. (At this point I would remind that the scientific discipline came from a non-science basis. "It must be pointed out that science itself has its roots and origins outside its own realm of thinking.")[5]

A belief commonly held today is that scientists can investigate *any* area of inquiry. A tangible consensus about the question, What is science?, is very important because so many scientists, and non-scientists as well, do not comprehend that areas of inquiry are different. Many scientists only speculate, or write scenarios when they are talking or writing about first origins. Many times scientists indiscriminately use such words as "could", "would", "should", "seem", "appear", "might", or "suppose" in their assertions about first origins.

Now I quite readily admit that these words are regularly used to formulate hypotheses about naturally occurring objects and/or events. It is quite proper for scientists to use the words "could", "would", "should", "seem", "appear", "might", or "suppose" when they hypothesize about naturally occurring objects and/or events. However, the science teacher should be fully cognizant of the fact that scientists are *not* hypothesizing about first origin problems in the same manner as when they successfully hypothesize about atoms, molecules and genes. The type of inquiry entered into about first origins is significantly different than the type or degree of inquiry involved when scientists hypothesize about imagined particles in naturally occurring objects, whether in plants or animals.

To clarify the different types of inquiry, then is the purpose of this section on "Definitional Formulations". As stated, a tangible consensus about the question, What is science?, is of paramount importance in drawing attention to the fact that areas of inquiry are different. This can be accomplished by (1) considering two general characteristics of science; and (2) reviewing 17 subdivisions of scientific methodology.

"Cover Word"
(Beware Semantic Confusion)

Hypothesis: In careful, proper, orderly scientific practice this term should be applied only to concepts that are testable by empirical procedures. Megaevolutionists make indiscriminate use of this term and hence give the impression that many of their ideas are in the same status as actually testable generalized statements formulated by empirical scientists.

Important clarification of two general characteristics of the discipline of science is explicated rapidly if different definitions of science are enumerated as Fig. 3. One general characteristic of science involves the accumulation of knowledge, the mere additive increase of facts and classes of data. In recent decades, however, the increase has been geometric. Often the accumulation of observational data has been utilized as an exclusive means of recognizing when science is being practiced; yet, such activity

Figure 3

WHAT IS SCIENCE?   WHAT IS SCIENTIFIC?

1. Science can be described as consisting of two forms: (a) science is a body of useful and practical knowledge and a method of obtaining it; (b) science is pure intellectual activity. N. Campbell, 1952.
2. Science is knowledge of the natural world obtained by sense interaction with that world. R. N. Bube, 1967.
3. Science is all knowledge collected by means of the scientific method, where scientific method is the cycle of induction, deduction, verification and eternal search for improvement of theories which are only tentatively held. J. G. Kemany, 1959.
4. Science is that mode of inquiry which attempts to arrive at knowledge of the world by the method of observation and by the method of confirmed hypothesis on what is given in observation. A. C. Benjamin, 1965.
5. Science is the ordered knowledge of natural phenomena and the rational study of the relations between the concepts in which these phenomena are expressed. W. C. Dampier, 1961.
6. Science is the body of knowledge obtained by methods based upon the authority of observation. Robert B. Fischer, 1975.
7. Science is a branch of study which is concerned either with a connected body of demonstrated truths or with observed facts systematically classified and more or less colligated by being brought under general laws, and which includes trustworthy methods for the discovery of raw truth within its own domain. Oxford Dictionary.
8. Science is an interconnected series of concepts and conceptual schemes that have developed as a result of experimentation and observation and are fruitful of further experimentation and observations. J. B. Conant, 1951.
9. The important distinction between science and those other systematizations is that science is self-testing and self-correcting. The testing and correcting are done by means of observations that can be repeated with essentially the same results by normal persons operating by the same methods and with the same approach. G. G. Simpson, 1961.

Therefore, the heart of scientific method is the problem-hypothesis-test process and, necessarily, the scientific method involves prediction. Predictions, to be useful in scientific methodology, must be subject to test empirically. This is the pertinent question to ask, then, "Is this the case with the origin of the universe, the origin of life, the origin of humankind, or any particular area of study whether in the natural sciences, or humanities, or so-called social sciences?"

is hardly the exclusive role of scientists. According to some of the mentioned definitions, science also entails process skills and specific methods by which facts and classes of data are acquired. Necessarily, then, there is a second general characteristic of science, which has been identified as the dynamic component of science. These *two* general components, static and dynamic aspects of scientific endeavor, must be understood fully before any really profitable discourse on evolution/creation ideas about origins can be entertained.

A more complete appreciation of science can be gained when the process skills and different aspects of scientific methodology are defined discretely and separately as sub-units of the more general static and dynamic components of science. The process skills and 17 aspects of scientific activity described below should be studied carefully and thoroughly *before* discussion of "how to" methods of teaching about first origins is undertaken in Chapters 2-4.

Process Skills of Science

At least 12 process skills may be expressed in succinct fashion, as is shown in Fig. 4. This is a minimum enumeration of what scientists do. Most basic is the process skill of observation. As stated in the definition by Fischer (1975), "Science is the body of knowledge obtained by methods based upon *the authority* of observation." Thus, the static and dynamic thrusts of the scientific discipline are brought together in one sentence. The prime importance of observation is especially keynoted as the authority upon which scientific endeavor is properly based. Importance of this fact will be made evident during the discussion of limitations of ideas of scientists on the size of the universe (Chapter 2).

Aspects of Scientific Activity

Although the activities or varieties of methods employed by scientists are many and often quite complex, all activities of scientists may be grouped under two headings: *empirical* (a special inclusive term for methods of observation) and *theoretical* (a special inclusive term for explanation and scientific theories by which scientists unify and correlate observations). Classroom Teaching Aid 10 contains a list of various methods used by scientists in

Figure 4
PROCESS SKILLS OF SCIENCE

1. **Observing:** skillful direct or indirect use of the senses of sight, sound, touch, smell, or taste

2. **Making operational definitions:** descriptions of physical features and/or processes or activities

3. **Classifying:** ordering, arranging information in convenient categories according to similar or contrasting characteristics

4. **Forming questions and hypotheses:** statement of conceivable perplexities and tentative answers that are testable

6. **Predicting:** stating expected conditions based upon already known data

7. **Measuring:** gaining numerical dimensions

8. **Experimenting:** careful examination of constant and variable conditions

9. **Interpreting data:** summarizing data from use of other process skills of classifying, inferring, communicating, etc.

10. **Communicating:** charts, graphs, oral or written reports to present significant facts

11. **Formulating models:** conceptual organizations designed to relate ideas and classes of data

12. **Re-examining:** further evaluation of interpretations, communications and models for the purpose of correction and improvement

their observational (empirical) work, and the main parts of their explanatory work (theoretical formulations).

In order to emphasize clear delineation of meaning, proper operational definitions with minimal examples will now be given for the 17 different aspects listed. (A summary collection of definitions is provided as a glossary for quick referral.) The *meaning* of all 17 subdivisions must be fully grasped. Otherwise, any discussion, dispute, or confrontation about first origins will be without proper points of reference.

I trust the science teacher will realize the importance for clear and concise communication of the following definitions which are finely worded with several close nuances of meaning. When vigorous effort is applied

Classroom Teaching Aid 10
ASPECTS OF SCIENTIFIC ACTIVITY

1. Observations (including initial observations)—recorded awarenesses (prior)

2. Descriptions

   3. Calculations—numerical manipulations

   4. Classification—grouping, ordering

   5. Generalizations (may become scientific laws)

6. Inductive reasoning

   7. Analogy

   8. Problems—questions (?)

   9. Hypotheses—testable (tentative answer)

   10. Predictions—testable (if . . . then)

11. Deductive reasoning

12. Controlled experimentation (testing) { trial and error

13. Experimental assumption

14. Scientific law . . . . 15. Explanation

----

16. Scientific theory (theoretical model) (conceptual scheme)

   —Theoretical assumptions—imaginary aspect, (list of postulates)   object or event   { atom molecule gene

17. Theorems—predictions (deductive reasoning)

EMPIRICAL

THEORETICAL

FOUNDATIONAL, BASIC ASSUMPTIONS (OR PRESUPPOSITIONS)
a. Objectivity of study
b. Cause and effect
c. Testability of ideas
d. Objects/events independent (outside) of observers
e. Uniformity of natural environment

to gain *mastery* over the meaning entailed in these operational definitions, then success in clear communication (a basic skill of scientists) with students, science colleagues, and others is possible. Without the use of such carefully worded operational definitions, conversations on the evolution/creation ideas of first origins never reach a conclusion. When careful definitions such as these are employed, clear direction is gained toward *understanding* the disparate positions of the evolution point of view and the creation point of view on first origins.

When the foundational assumptions of science are recognized and properly accepted as givens, proper and orderly scientific work can begin with the act(s) of observation.

1. Observation

A written or spoken record (as communication to self or another) of an awareness (perception) of a natural object and/or event.

All scientific work begins with and is based upon the authority of observation. Scientists specialize in analysis of natural objects and/or events in their environment. The awarenesses that men and women have of their natural environment are the initial awarenesses and prior perceptions that have stimulated the curiosity of scientific investigators.

Scientists become aware of some aspect(s) of the natural environment and sense a desire to pursue questions of "how", "when", "where", "what" or "who", and "how much". However, scientists cannot ask "why" questions. Such questions are part of metaphysical areas of study of ontology that, by the very nature of scientific work, are excluded from consideration by scientists.

2. Description

A statement about some natural object and/or event in space-time.

Because of the awareness of scientists of aspects of their environment, descriptions of natural objects and/or events are recorded at great length. Descriptions are recorded in the form of observations that scientists have noted about their natural environment. Color, size, shape, and multiple facets of objects and/or events that occur in a time-continuum are quantified by scientists in their zeal to objectively study their natural environment (as they seek dominion over their environment in the tradition of the founders of the scientific discipline).

Although natural objects and/or events in space-time cannot be considered true or false, statements made about natural objects and/or events may be considered as true or false. A statement about an object and/or event may be deemed true or false by comparing any such statement to the object and/or event. This involves the correspondence theory of truth. Although no scientist seeks absolute truth, certainly no scientist deliberately seeks falsehood. Thus each scientist actually operates to gain an approximation of absolute truth.

3. Calculation

Some arithmetic and/or mathematical manipulation of abstract and numerical symbols.

Because one of the limiting principles of proper, orderly science is that of quantitative measurement of changes of objects in the natural environment, scientists commonly strive to express many of their ideas in numerical form. There is a repeated need, then, for calculations in scientific work. Quantification is a definite hallmark of scientific work. When variables are identified, then scientists regularly work to measure those variables with regard to weight, linear or volumetric measure, or change of position with respect to other aspects of the study or experiment. Physical scientists have been most successful in representing interrelationships of variables in equations. In turn, these equations have been used for a wide range of mathematical calculations. Biological scientists in recent decades have become more and more successful in doing likewise with regard to structures and processes characteristic of living things.

But descriptions and calculations of natural objects and/or events must be ordered and classified to aid in detection of relationships.

4. Classification

The process of ordering natural objects and/or events according to stated criteria.

Classification, of course, is both the *process* of grouping similar objects and events, and also the very *end product* of ordering objects and events according to stated criteria. In short, scientists do not record observations and descriptions of their natural environment in any haphazard manner. They are orderly and as precise as possible so that they may properly detect similarities and differences in what they observe.

For it is the detection of similarities and differences that ignites curiosity in the minds of scientists about interrelationships in their natural environment. The detection of similarities and differences is basic to detection of patterns and regularities. All scientists alertly seek detection of patterns and regular repetition of observations. This is so important because the recording of detected patterns becomes the ideational means for expressing generalizations.

5. Generalization

A statement of common aspects of similar natural objects and/or events. (Or, assertion that something is true about all members of a certain class of natural objects and/or events.)

Here is an early crystallization of the effort to explain that is especially developed by scientists. Scientists abhor the unique, singular situation or event. They constantly seek to fit aspects of their natural environment into some generalized whole. Thus scientists formulate generalizations. These generalizations are found in the form of definitions, in the form of rules, in any broad statements offered as representative of common aspects of some similar natural objects and/or events. Particular assistance in the formulation of descriptions and, in turn, generalizations is gained when the scientist realizes the importance of inductive reasoning.

6. Inductive Reasoning

That phase of human thought whereby detected similarities and/or differences of the natural environment can be summarized under broad headings or generalized statements.

Formulation of inductions, which are statements derived from inductive reasoning, is basic to human thought patterns. Major premises of arguments are formulated by inductive reasoning. Often scientists find their inductive reasoning significantly aided by the use of analogy.

7. Analogy

An expression of the comparison of unfamiliar objects and/or events to like or similar aspects of known natural objects and/or events, or known ideas, concepts.

By means of analogy scientists try to gain some understanding of the unknown in terms of the known. They usually compare some individual aspects of the unknown to known natural objects and/or events. For instance, scientists have gained some understanding of life activities by comparison with the motion of a flame or with the growth of a crystal. In the same way, the human body can be compared to an internal combustion machine. In the latter case, food is taken and wastes are produced in life activities of the human being. Some degree of similarity can be noted to the fuel intake and waste by-products of an internal combustion engine. However, caution must always prevail wherein scientists regularly make clear that analogy in no way leads to identity. Thus the human body is *not* a machine, though admittedly the human body has machine-like features.

An excellent form of operational definition is accomplished in pointing at an object when the accepted name for that object is then recited. A working list of analogies used by scientists is included in Fig. 5. The list has been organized according to the tripartite sequence of consideration of ideas about first origins used in this book. You may want to add other analogies used by physical scientists and biological scientists.

After formulation of inductive generalizations based upon detection of similarities and differences, a particular genius of the scientist becomes manifest as he frames the problem in question form.

8. Problem

An interrogation or stated perplexity for which an answer is sought. (When properly expressed a problem will be framed in question form.)

Scientists are particularly interested in asking *scientific* questions which the scientist calls problems. No scientist begins serious study in the

Figure 5
WORKING LIST
FOR STRESSING IMPORTANCE OF ANALOGIES
TO NATURAL SCIENTISTS

UNIVERSE, MATTER
 Circle, ellipse—planetary orbits
 Solar system—atomic organization
 Doppler effect of sound—special shift (red) of light
 Ping pong balls—molecules
  (Billiard balls)
 Solid balls—atoms
 Liquid flow—electricity

LIFE
 Candle, crystal—life
 Honey comb—cell
 Executive, industrial plant functions—cellular organelles
 In vitro chemical reactions—"primitive" earth atmospheric reactions
 Internal combustion machine—human body
 Beads—genes
 Spiral stairway—DNA helix

HUMANKIND
 Artificial selection—"natural selection"
 Familial relationships—classificatory "relationships"
 Tree branching—megaevolution "tree"
 Animal behavior—human behavior

laboratory or in the field without some realized problem or question to which an answer is sought. The scientific questions that are asked are very important to the success of scientists in meeting their curiosity about their natural environment. Successful scientists must ask answerable questions. Of course, it must be admitted that unanswerable questions of one decade or generation may become answerable in another decade or generation of scientific investigation. This is paramountly true and dependent upon technological advances and availability of tools and equipment for investigation. For example, problems involving motion of celestial objects and terrestrial objects posed by early physical scientists became solvable as the discipline of science grew and developed. Biological scientists have striven to develop similar objective techniques for their studies of complicated living activities, large and small.

9. Hypothesis

A tentative answer to a problem. (When properly expressed the hypothesis will be expressed as an assertive statement in form suitable for testing.)

The scientist trying to solve a problem formulates a hypothesis, as an answer to the problem of the moment. The wording of a problem and the accompanying hypothesis goes a long way toward providing direction to scientific investigation. The hypothesis is restricted in scope. If the problem has been worded carefully, then the hypothesis provides a focus of attention for further observation and testing. But the hypothesis is also basic to formulation of predictions as to what might be expected if the conditions hypothesized are obtained.

10. Prediction

The expected or projected state of affairs or relationship of natural objects and/or events based upon known or understood conditions.

Predictions are commonly found as portions of "if . . . then" statements. If a certain set of conditions is known to exist, then predicted conditions should be found associated with the known conditions. This pattern of thought is characteristic of deductive reasoning.

11. Deductive Reasoning

That phase of human thought whereby conclusions can be detached from broad generalizations.

Quite often deductive reasoning has been considered the opposite of inductive reasoning. Rather than being opposable, however, inductive and deductive reasoning are most properly recognized as two phases of the total reasoning process of human beings. From broad inductive premises, more specific conclusions can be derived by deductive reasoning. Deductive logic can be constructed in the multiple forms of syllogisms. In the quantitatively more precise physical sciences, deductive formulations are often found. The formulations usually are made highly symbolic by means of elegant mathematical symbolization. A more loose and general deductive reasoning must be practiced by the biological scientists because of the less quantitative nature of biological objects and/or events.

Both physical and biological scientists must test inductive generalizations. Also they must test predictions deduced from conclusions. This test relationship is the very heart of scientific methodology: the problem—hypothesis—test relationship. The problem is stated, a tentative hypothesis is offered, and testing of the hypothesis begins. If possible, scientists test their ideas by way of experiment.

12. Experiment

A specifically designed use of equipment, tools of measurements, and controlled variable components to gain observations and descriptions usually otherwise unobtainable.

Great strides were made by early scientists when they applied the method of controlled experimentation in the study of their natural environment. They gained answers to problems that would have been unsolvable by ordinary direct and unaided observation. Initially thought out by Galileo, controlled experiments were worked into recognizable design by biological scientists such as Francisco Redi and Louis Pasteur. Usually all significant aspects of an experiment are the same except for one particular aspect which is allowed to vary. Then changes are recorded as differences and can be attributed most reliably to the varying aspect. Nevertheless, experimental assumptions are always involved.

13. Experimental Assumption

A statement about that aspect(s) of experimentation (controlled, or of trial-and-error category) that is taken for granted as "noncritical" and not measured in any way.

There are always some aspects of the experimental design not considered of crucial importance to the main question being studied and therefore can

Figure 6
SOME HYPOTHESES ARE DENIED

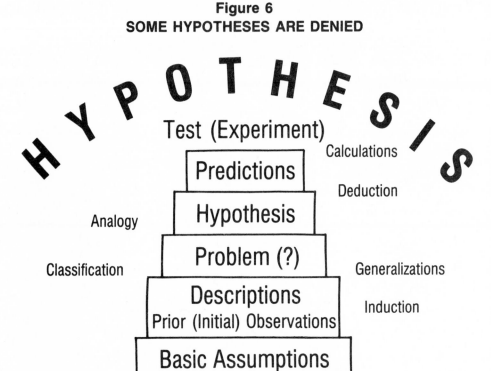

be reliably ignored. Often humidity is not measured or atmospheric pressure, or some other aspect of the immediate environment of the controlled experiment may be ignored. Some aspect of the very equipment being used is frequently disregarded. Based on experience and careful elimination of variables, the aspects that are ignored may be recognized as experimental assumptions. Therefore no experiment is ever completely controlled. There are always unmeasured aspects.

The accompaying diagrams (Fig. 6 and Fig. 7), depicting relationships of hypothesis and explanation and other scientific activities, are good examples of instructional material that the science teacher could build in stepwise manner.

Realistic candor requires that mention be made of the fact that many times denial of hypotheses of scientists results from their careful testing procedures. This condition can be represented diagrammatically by showing

Figure 7

EXPLANATION; SCIENTIFIC LAW

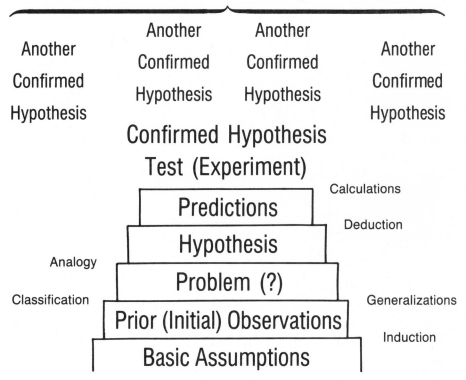

that the hypothesis explodes (Fig. 6). The hypothesis is not confirmed and must be changed and/or replaced in some way. But much of scientific research does entail successful confirmation of the hypothetical ideas of scientists. This positive condition can be shown diagrammatically also (Fig. 7). When positive results are gained from the testing of a hypothesis and subsequent predictions, then confirmation of the answers to problems (scientific questions) are gained by scientists. It is through such repeated observational and experimental testing that known scientific laws have been developed.

14. Scientific Law

A repeatedly tested and well supported or substantiated generalization of seemingly universal application regarding a certain set of facts.

Scientific laws are typically exemplified by the laws of motion of Newton, or planetary laws of Kepler, or inheritance laws of Mendel. Of course, scientific laws are essentially descriptions by scientists of repeatedly identified relationships of aspects of their natural environment. In general, relationships of natural objects and/or events are *not* set up by scientists but are only *detected* by scientists. Hence scientific laws are human approximations of the contingencies of the natural environment which have been identified by scientists over the centuries.

It is important to realize that scientific laws do not control the environment or the universe. The laws of nature are *descriptive* statements. Hence natural laws are distinct from civil or juridical laws, which are *prescriptive*. A scientific law is a statement that describes regularities found in the natural environment. However, natural objects *do not obey* natural laws or the laws of nature. Scientific laws *only describe the behavior* of natural objects. In contrast, the laws of human government are prescriptive as indications of how human beings should behave. Civil laws are types of controls over how human beings should behave. But civil laws are not necessarily descriptive of how human beings do behave. This is a basic distinction that science teachers should be very careful to make clear to students.

Science teachers should point out that scientists must be most cautious in framing broad conceptualizations until full attention has been given to the empirical basis of ideational formulations. In short, emphasis should be given to the fact that the crowning achievement of scientists is the *careful* promulation of broad conceptualizations or explanations.

15. Explanation

A particular frame of reference used to provide meaning for particular facts relevant to natural objects and/or events.

As has been stated by Kant and Einstein, and mentioned also by Darwin, isolated facts are nearly useless. They have meaning and value primarily when related to other facts and placed into some coherent ideational framework: an explanation. Something can be said to be explained when the statement, ''I understand'', can be uttered in response to the explanation offered. In other words, the hearer or reader comprehends relationships and relational aspects of individual facts in such a manner as to see the overall picture, to see where particulars fit into some universal formulations by which widely diverse and apparently isolated facts are organized into meaningful relationship. Such a universal formulation is a scientific theory.

16. Scientific Theory

A list of postulates or assumptions (theoretical) usually specifying existence, relationships, and events concerning an imaginary entity (such as an atom, molecule, or gene) whereby a meaningful explanatory system for a range of rather diverse facts is available.

Excellent examples of scientific theories are kinetic-molecular theory, modern atomic theory, nuclear theory, and gene theory. Each one of these broad conceptualizations entail a list of postulates (or theoretical assumptions) regarding existence of some imagined entity such as a molecule, an atom, an electron, or a gene. Further aspects are detailed in theoretical assumptions or postulates regarding supposed movement and interrelationship of molecules, atoms, electrons, or genes. Typical expressions of postulational formulations entailed in representative scientific theories are listed in Fig. 8. In turn, it is most advantageous when theorems can be deduced from a scientific theory.

17. Theorem

A statement derived from assumptions of a scientific theory more or less in the form of testable predictions or expectations.

Theorems are deduced from the list of postulates of a scientific theory in such a manner as to explicate unknown aspects of behavior or organization of the postulated imaginary entities, which can be tested in turn by experience. Although the scientist does not usually utilize formal logic, he is able to derive theorems from existing generalizations in somewhat the same manner that a conclusion is derived from a formal syllogism. Theorems are essential predictions that should be testable by empirical means if a scientific theory is to be given at least indirect evaluation.

Because of the logical consistency of the postulates involving the gene concept and the deductive reasoning applied to the gene theory, geneticists

Figure 8
EXAMPLES OF SCIENTIFIC THEORIES

What are good examples of scientific theories? On this page postulates of four outstanding examples of sound scientific theories are listed. Though some imaginary aspect is involved in each of these scientific theories, multiple tests by experience, though accomplished through indirect means, can be repeated over and over again with regard to atoms, molecules, and genes.

Postulates of Gene Theory
1. Genes exist in pairs per trait, usually, in zygotes, body cells, and gonadal generative cells.
2. Only one gene per trait, usually, exists in gametes.
3. Two genes exist per trait, usually, in a zygote after fertilization.
4. One gene may be dominant to another gene.
5. Gene pairs may combine randomly and independently during gamete formation and as a result of fertilization.
6. A series of genes may influence the same trait.
7. More than one gene are located on a single chromosome.
8. Exchange of genes is possible, as exchange of chromosome parts occurs.
9. More than one pair of genes may influence the same trait.

Postulates of Gas Kinetic Theory
1. All matter is composed of small particles.
2. Gas molecules are small compared with distance between them.
3. Particles are in motion.
4. When molecules collide with each other or walls of a container there is no loss of energy.

5. The average kinetic energy of all different gas molecules is the same at the same temperature.
6. The energy of molecular motion is heat energy, that is, the temperature of a gas is a measure of the average kinetic energy of the molecules.

Postulates of Dalton's Atomic Theory (Nineteenth Century)
1. All matter is composed of ultimate particles, called atoms, which are indivisible.
2. All the particles of a given element are alike in weight and in all other aspects. (But particles of different elements have different weights.)
3. Atoms are indestructible by chemical means and their identities are not changed in all chemical reactions.
4. Chemical combination occurs by the union of the atoms of the elements in simple numerical ratios.

Postulates of Nuclear-electron Theory
1. Atom is composed of nucleus surrounded by a cloud of electrons.
2. Nucleus is composed of protons and neutrons.
3. Proton is a positive charge.
4. Electron has a negative charge.
5. Number of protons equals number of electrons.
6. The number of positive charges on the nucleus is called the atomic number.
7. Neutrons are uncharged particles which still have mass.
8. Atomic weight of an element is the sum of the number of protons and neutrons in the nucleus.
9. Atoms of an element may have the same atomic number but different atomic weights (isotopes).

have successfully studied the mode of inheritance of physical traits and characteristics in plants and animals. Geneticists have used the gene theory to successfully deduce predictions (theorems) about expected generations of plants and animals. They now know a great deal more about genes and transmission of inheritable physical traits and characteristics than was possible with the early formulations of the theory by Gregory Mendel.

"Cover Word"
(Beware Semantic Confusion)

Theory: used commonly for almost any idea regardless of scope or inclusiveness; conveys status to some ideas similar to that accepted for proper *scientific* theory formulated according to rigorous criteria and in accordance with the limitations of scientists.

The Heart of the Matter

Emphasis should be given at this point to the fact that the postulates of a *scientific* theory are always based upon observations of relevant natural objects and/or events that scientists have noted *before* they stated theoretical postulates. No scientific theory has been formulated without some extensive grounding in accumulated empirical data. In turn, the postulates of a scientific theory are bases for theorems or predictions that can be tested by experience, either directly or indirectly. Fortunately, a representative set of criteria for recognizing a proper scientific theory can be offered such as the list given in Classroom Teaching Aid 11 paraphrased from Holton and Roller and their criteria might be expressed in question form as follows:

1. Are known observations explained by the theory?
2. Is the theory a basis for predicting what has not yet been observed?
3. Can the theory be modified as new data are collected?
4. Can the theory be evaluated indirectly by empirical test of predictions and/or theorems deduced from the theory?

No scientific theory can be tested directly because of integral involvement of some imaginary entity in the wording of the postulates. No one

Classroom Teaching Aid 11
CRITERIA FOR A PROPER SCIENTIFIC THEORY

Below, rigorous criteria for identification of a proper scientific theory are provided. These criteria are from an outstanding textbook for physical science.

Qualifications 1 and 3 are very important to any conceptualization of first origins. Very critical is the fact that no "prior observations" are possible, since no man observed first origins of the universe, life, or humankind; nor is it possible to "check with experience by test" in any manner when objective considerations are given to first origins.

Three qualifications have already been cited:
1. A fruitful theory *correlates many separate facts*, particularly the important *prior observations*, in a logical preferably easily grasped structure of thought.
2. In the course of continued use it *suggests new relations* and stimulates directed research.
3. The theory permits us to deduce predictions that *check with experience* by test, and it is useful for clearing up puzzling difficulties and solving practical problems.

The history of science has shown that a good theory frequently has, in addition to the three attributes above, one or more of the following three:
4. When the smoke of initial battle has lifted, the more successful of two rival theories often turns out to be the one that is simpler in the sense that it involves *fewer basic assumptions or hypotheses.*
5. A theory is more readily acceptable to contemporary scientists if its *postulates or assumptions are plausible.*
6. Successful theory is flexible enough to grow, and to *undergo modifications* where necessary.

—From Chapter 8, "On the Nature of Scientific Theory," In *Foundations of Modern Physical Science* by Gerald Holton and Duane H. D. Roller (Reading, Mass.: Addison-Wesley Publishing Company, Inc., 1958).

has photographed a gene completely as yet, and only possibly a limited number of atoms and molecules have been photographed. To a great extent, then, molecules, atoms and genes remain imagined entities. Yet there are extensive, excellent indirect tests and accumulated evidences for the existence of the imagined molecule, atom, electron, or gene.

Many examples could be given of the fruitfulness of scientific theories as generative of more knowledge about matter, energy and living things. Such fruitfulness is a reflection of the double-headed vertical arrow on the left-hand portion of Classroom Teaching Aid 10: Aspects of Scientific Activity. The science teacher must emphasize that all proper scientific theories are based upon empirical aspects of scientific activity associated with natural objects and/or events; and, in turn, scientific theories are fruitful of further scientific observation and experimentation with respect to natural objects and/or events.

Inspect Classroom Teaching Aid 9 (Limitations of Scientists) once again, and give particular attention to the area to the right of the historical period. That area of the diagram, of necessity, entails speculative statements and extrapolations. So, it is important for scientists and non-specialists in the twentieth century—the Scientific Age—to comprehend that areas of inquiry are different. When scientists use such words as "could", "seem", "appear", or "perhaps" in their assertions about first origins, which of necessity must be of the past, they are *not* truly hypothesizing. It is so very important that the science teacher be prepared to show the difference between ideas scientists have about naturally occurring events *in the present* and ideas scientists have about supposed events *in the past*.

Yet someone may urge that speculative statements and extrapolations *are* components of scientific work. This is true *when* speculations and extrapolations are confined within dimensions of size and time wherein test and possible corrections of ideas can be attempted and accomplished in the lifetime of a given set of investigators. But speculations about first origins are *forever* beyond any possible test or correction by empirical, quantitative, mechanical studies involving careful, orderly scientific work. Therefore, the ideas that some scientists have about the beginning of the universe, beginning of life on the earth and commencement of humankind—the only form of life known to be self-conscious—are ideas, which the founders of the scientific discipline would have fully recognized, that will forever remain speculations about imagined past structures and phenomena.

Biblical Christians are most seriously conscious of the linear concept of history.[6] They are particularly conscious of cosmic history: from "In the beginning" (when God created heaven and earth) to the bodily return of Jesus Christ (when heaven and earth will be made new again). Quite clearly because of the limiting principles of proper, orderly scientific work such extremes of cosmic history cannot be known apart from revelation. That is, revelation from the Creator who made all things in heaven and on earth as believed by Christian initiators of the discipline of science.

Thus science teachers in the tradition of the scientific discipline should be insistent on pointing out limitations of scientists, as scientists. Often naturalistically oriented scientists seem to overstep such limits when discussing first origins—especially when they urge the majority of non-specialists to accept speculative ideas (a) about the universe coming into existence due to an explosion of some dense particle (the origin of which is absolutely unknown), (b) about life on the earth coming into existence due to spontaneous generation of life at the sub-microscopic level (the origin of submolecular parts of which is absolutely unknown) and (c) about humankind coming into existence due to fortuitous accumulation of mutations—DNA replicative errors in animal forms until somehow present *Homo sapiens* emerged.

Some listeners at my public lectures ask, almost in a sense of desperation, "What *do you think* scientists *can do?*" I answer, in accordance with the previous operational definitions of scientific activities, that scientists observe, directly or indirectly, those facets of their *natural* environment about which they have become curious and about which they have formulated scientific questions for which they have sought answers. (Some of the salient factors of scientific methodology are highlighted again in Classroom Teaching Aid 12.) Hence, *scientists* produce orderly classifications of their observations and descriptions—which they have repeated and repeated. *Scientists* seek to test their ideas about *natural* objects and/or events by means of controlled experiment, if possible, or by trial and error testing, or certainly by tests of logical reasonableness and internal consistency.

The term "natural" definitely refers to things and processes that actually exist and really occur in the physical environment, and are directly or indirectly accessible to natural scientists. In point of fact, a "natural" thing

Classroom Teaching Aid 12
WHAT SCIENTISTS DO

SCIENCE: what scientists do
—so what do scientists do?
(See *Aspects of Scientific Activities* page)

1. Scientists observe; produce orderly classifications of observational descriptions which they have repeated and repeated

2. Scientists seek answers to problems, perplexities "generated" from observational work in form of *testable* hypothesis or hypotheses and predictions:
> by use of controlled experiment if possible;
> by trial and error testing;
> by tests of logical reasonableness, internal consistency

3. Scientists formulate broad conceptualizations to explain seemingly diverse, separate sets of observations

a. Scientific (Contemporary) Theories

Examples:
  Gene Theory
  Atomic Theory
  Nuclear Theory
  Kinetic-Molecular Theory

Function: to explain "present" phenomena involving events in life experience of human beings

Evaluation Criteria:

a. Identifiable *prior* Observations

b. Predictions,
    before the fact,
    that are testable by
    repeatable experiences,
    directly or indirectly

b. "Historical" (Imaginative Narratives)
   Theories (Arguments)

Examples:
  Big Bang "Theory"
  Geological reconstructs
  Macro- (mega-) evolution
  Continental Drift "Theory"
  Hominid macro- (mega-) evolution

Function: to explain unobservable *origins* of aspects of "present" environment

Evaluation criteria:

a. Identifiable observations of events in "present" life experience of human beings

b. Predictions, primarily *after the fact* that are testable *only* by logical reasonableness, internal consistency regarding past events

or event is different than a concept that is plausible or thinkable. Evidently many students and others who have adopted the "anything-is-possible attitude", consider that if an idea is at all thinkable, then it is somehow natural. Yet the thinkable idea may very well involve *no real*, naturally occurring object and/or event.

Commonly a person will say, "I have a theory". That individual expresses some idea that seems "thinkable". Often the non-specialist has no clear cognizance of the fact that a thinkable idea or theory is quite different from a scientific theory, according to rigorous scientific methodology. Thus, because of such a general, common use of the term theory by laymen and non-specialists, particular confusion abounds regarding scientific theories. Some would be satisfied to define scientific theories as any broad conceptualizations developed by scientists. However, to gain rigor of expression, to say what is meant with regard to past, present and future events, I urge adoption of two categories for those broad conceptualizations typically propounded by scientists. The two categories are: (1) contemporary scientific theories, and (2) historical theories, (Classroom Teaching Aid 12). When this two-way classification is employed, along with evaluation criteria, significant understanding is gained regarding scientific theories, which involve immediate activities of human beings.

Examples of contemporary scientific theories are the kinetic-molecular theory, atomic theory, and gene theory, because they are formulated in accordance with (1) identifiable prior observations (involving prior awarenesses of chemical reactions between elements or specific crossings of plants and animals), and (2) predictions (expectations) that can be developed from scientific theories *before the fact*; that is, predictions that are testable by *repeatable experience*, directly or indirectly. (Remember there is much indirect evidence for molecules, atoms, electrons and genes.) Scientific theories function to explain present phenomena involving events occurring in the lifetime of human beings.

In contrast, historical theories, proposed presumably within the naturalistic perspective, such as the big bang theory, geological reconstructions, megaevolution and continental drift theory, involve basically imaginative speculations because they are formulated with the primary function of explaining *unobservable origins* of aspects of the present natural environment. However first origins are not of the present; only past. Only unrepeatable events are involved in first origins. Hence careful, orderly science properly understood as limited to the present cannot be applied.

In attempts to explain *unobservable origins* of aspects of the present environment, scientists have formulated a very functional set of broad conceptualizations. Each of these broad conceptualizations involves identifiable observations or objects and/or events in the present life experiences of human beings, along with predictions primarily *after the fact* that are testable *only* by logical reasonableness or internal consistency regarding past events. True, credible and qualified scientists make observations, both direct and indirect, about objects and/or events in the natural environment. Let us look at some examples.

Astronomy

Astronomers observe stars, comets, planets, and galaxies which they describe, classify, and about which they predict in fully testable manner. These practices constitute the careful and proper scientific work known as cosmology. However, too often explanations about the *origin* of stars, comets, planets and galaxies involve objects and/or events totally outside life experiences of empirical scientists. Since *prior awareness* of some dense particle is impossible, limitations must be recognized; and the big bang theory is *different* than the atomic or gene theories, which are excellent examples of contemporary scientific theories.

Geology

Historical geologists observe rocks, rock formations with inclusions and impressions plus specific changes of the surface of the earth which they describe, classify, and about which they predict in fully testable manner. To that extent these scientists are empirically oriented. However, their attempted explanations about rock *origin* and relational aspects of rocks and presumably living organisms of the past involve objects and/or events totally outside life experiences of empirical scientists. Hence, limitations must be recognized. Since *no prior awareness* of mountain building or *prior awareness* of one land mass is possible, geological reconstruction and continental drift theories are *different* than contemporary scientific theories.

Biology

Evolutionist biologists observe plants and animals with respect to structure, function and continuity plus similarity of living and dead forms which they describe, classify, and about which they predict in fully testable manner. Again, to that extent these scientists are empirically oriented. However, the attempts of the evolutionist to explain about how structure, function, continuity and similarity *came into existence* in the first place involve objects and/or events totally outside life experience of empirical scientists. Since no *prior awareness* of an animal ancestor of human beings is possible, limitations must be recognized and megaevolution, including human evolution, are *different* than contemporary scientific theories.

Creationist scientists observe the *same* plants and animals with respect to structure, function and continuity, as do evolutionist scientists. Creationists also note differences of living and dead forms, as well as similarities, which they describe, classify, and about which they predict in fully testable manner. So, to that extent creationist scientists are also empirically oriented. But their attempts to explain the *origin* of diverse and discrete kinds of organisms from specially created forms involve objects and/or events totally outside life experiences of empirical scientists. Since *no prior awareness* of creative acts and *no prior awareness* of catastrophic events is possible, limitations must be recognized and creation models of origins, world-wide flood models and concepts about a world-encircling canopy are *different* than contemporary scientific theories.

Often the science teacher interested in the evolution/creation confrontation approach will be faced with the contention that historical theories are just as scientific as contemporary theories. That is, megaevolution or continental drift formulations are just as scientific as the atomic or gene theory. To provide a plausible means of meeting this assertion is the very reason for the two categories of broad conceptualizations generated by scientists. True, historical theories are formulated by scientists. But such theories perforce entail primarily *imagined events in the past* where no human beings were involved. Such events as movements of dry rock masses presumably resulting in block mountains, or tilted block mountains, or "new" mountain ranges like the Rocky Mountains are totally *imagined* and unknown by any practicing, empirical scientists. Such events as complete erosion of mountain ranges to sea level presumably resulting in peneplanes or extensive erosion surfaces that subsequently become buried due to further sedimentations, are totally *imagined* and unknown by any practicing, empirical scientists. These historical theories do *not* involve *natural* events.

Quite often the evolutionary-minded scientists declare that atoms and genes are unknown to practicing, empirical scientists. True, atoms and genes have not been directly observed, have not been seen directly by empirical scientists. But multiple *indirect* data, which are completely repeatable, have been accumulated within the life experiences of many, many scientists. Cloud chambers, betatrons, cyclotrons, and numerous other highly sophisticated instrumentations have been used extensively by physical scientists to detect *indirectly* the existence, behavior and interrelationships of many atoms. Furthermore, existence, behavior and interrelationships of many, sub-atomic entities have been well substantiated, *at least indirectly*, by careful and proper scientific work.

This is the very point of contrast which is gained by use of the two categories of contemporary scientific theories and historical theories. Contemporary scientific theories fully involve *natural* objects and/or events of the present (that are occurring during the life experience of some human beings), which are either directly or indirectly observable in a comprehendible fashion that can be repeated. This is true with regard to breeding practices involving presumed or imagined genes, studies of gases involving presumed or imagined molecules, or studies of physical structure of matter involving presumed or imagined atoms and sub-atomic entities.

In contrast historical theories *do not* fully involve objects and/or events of the present (that is, occurring during the life experiences of some human beings), which are either directly or indirectly observable in a comprehendible fashion that can be repeated and repeated. An explosion of some dense particle, dry rock mountain building or complete mountain range erosion, broad changes of plants and animals whether living or dead, or genetic lineage of human beings traceable to animal origin are not repeatable, if such events of such magnitude ever did occur.

Therefore, scientists interested in formulations of purportedly naturalistic historical theories violate the limiting principles of proper, orderly science. They really violate the whole commitment to working with *natural* objects and/or events in the *present*, and devote themselves to extensive speculations and involve multiple use of *supra*-natural concepts, which is tantamount to using the supernatural. In point of fact, proponents of historical theories regularly employ supernatural (in the sense of beyond the natural) concepts:

1. Historical theorists use the supernatural in their thinking about some "big bang" that supposedly started the universe.
2. Historical theorists use the supernatural in their thinking when they presume that spontaneous generation of the first life on the earth occurred at the sub-microscopic level of organization.
3. Historical theorists use the supernatural in their thinking when they imagine movement of great masses of dry rock that resulted supposedly in mountain building.
4. Historical theorists use the supernatural in their thinking when they propose some initial continental drift whereby the present land masses were derived from a single mass of dry land.
5. Historical theorists use the supernatural in their thinking as they imagine that accidental mutational changes (errors, mistakes) accumulated in some anthropoid form, which was then ancestral to present humankind.

Basically, proponents of historical theories only start with a major premise that has *not* even been developed inductively. Historical theorists use such major concepts as: (1) at one time there was a dense particle, (2) once one land mass existed on the surface of the earth, or (3) the present is the key to the past. Then imaginative supporters of historical theories examine the present natural environment to seek out conditions of the present that might be used *circumstantially* to support the major concept basic to a given historical theory.

For example, some astronomers use evidence about red shifts of stellar light, observed nova or supernovae, and background wave radiation and radio noise as circumstantial evidence to support their idea of a big bang origin of the universe. As *after the fact* thinkers, such supposedly naturalistically oriented scientists interested in historical theories derive ideas about possible natural-like events that they think might have happened if a dense particle once existed, or if one land mass once existed. However the following are noteworthy:

1. They cannot find any "key" in the present of some naturally occurring explosion of a dense particle comparable to the major concept of the big bang theory.

2. They cannot find a "key" in the present of some naturally occurring combination of sub-molecular parts of matter that form into living substance. (Remember synthesized amino acids that scientists have produced are not living.)
3. They cannot find any "key" in the present of naturally occurring events involving movement of dry rock masses that result in new mountains.
4. They cannot find any "key" in the present of any one land mass breaking into smaller land masses which move apart.
5. They cannot find any "key" in the present of mutational changes that give rise to any new physical traits.

Proper, orderly science is based upon the *authority of observation* experienced in the present with regard to natural objects and/or events. Proper, orderly science entails formulation of *scientific* questions that are answerable. What caused an explosion of a supposed dense particle that supposedly gave rise to the universe? What was the template that directed supposed spontaneous fusion of sub-molecular units? What mechanism was the cause of supposed movement of dry rock masses resulting in new mountains? What mechanism caused break up of some supposed single land mass? What was the possible cause of first appearance of feathers, or sexual reproduction, or of bipedal movement of any organism?

These are not scientific questions. Thus science teachers, who fully comprehend operational definitions of scientific activities, are qualified to proclaim to proponents of historical theories that there is a *significant difference* between broad, historical conceptualizations and proper scientific theories, such as the kinetic-molecular theory, atomic theory, or gene theory. All students should understand this difference.

Furthermore, if tested for logical reasonableness historical theories fall far short of credible acceptance. (Recall the criterion that postulates of a scientific theory must be *plausible*.) How credible is acceptance of the idea that all the observable cosmic order known to cosmologists came from the disorder that would follow logically from the supposed explosion of some dense particle? How credible is acceptance of the idea that all the complexity of life forms, even single-celled organisms, came into existence from non-living material without a Creator? How credible is acceptance of the idea that human consciousness and unique human conceptual thought came somehow from animal consciousness and animal perceptual thought? How rational is belief in the supernatural concepts inherent in historical theories?

Because of the clear-cut dichotomy delineated in this section, the science teacher is on sound logical grounds to refer to the two different categories of broad conceptualization by scientists; that is, (1) contemporary scientific theories, and (2) historical theories. Without this delineation confusion abounds in most evolution/creation discussions of first origins of the universe, life on the earth and humankind.

Actually, historical theories of naturalistically oriented men and women (who do not restrain themselves to naturally occurring objects and/or events, but think in terms of supernatural concepts) are offered either consciously or unconsciously as substitutes for "In the beginning" and the new heaven and new earth of bibical revelation. Historical theories have been developed at the expense of compliance with limiting principles of science. Fundamentally then, proponents of historical theories would turn the truth of God's Revelation into a lie. Interestingly enough they have presented *their* preferred ideas about *first* origins through mass communication media for over a century. Now is the time for science teachers to come to the aid of the understanding of their students regarding the different inquiries entered into by professional scientists.

FOOTNOTES

[1]Stanley L. Jaki, *The Road to Science and the Ways of God.* (Chicago: The University of Chicago Press, 1978), *The Origin of Science and the Science of Its Origin.* (South Bend: Regnery/Gateway, Inc., 1978), and *Science and Creation* (From Eternal Cycles to Oscillating Universe) (N. Y.: Science History Publications, 1974). See also H. Butterfield, *The Origins of Modern Science.* (N. Y. Bell, 1962); Robert R. E. D. Clark, *Science and Christianity — A Partnership.* (Mountain View, CA: Pacific Press Publishing Company, 1972); R. Hooykaas, *Religion and the Rise of Modern Science.* (Grand Rapids, MI: William B. Eerdmans Publishing Company); Eugene M. Klaaren, *Religious Origins of Modern Science.* (Grand Rapids, MI: William B. Eerdmans Publishing Company, 1977); Frank H. T. Rhodes, "Christianity in a Mechanistic Universe" (in) *Christianity in a Mechanistic Universe and Other Essays,* Edited by D. N. MacKay. (Chicago: Inter-Varsity Press, 1965); and Francis A. Schaeffer, *How Should We Then Live?* (The Rise and Decline of Western Thought and Culture) (Old Tappan, N. J.: Fleming H. Revell Company, 1976). Also Henry M. Morris, *Men of Science — Men of God* (Great Scientists Who Believed the Bible). (San Diego: Creation-Life Publishers, 1982).

Further corroboration of the fact that modern science is based on the Christian world view has been stressed by both Alfred North Whitehead, *Science and the Modern World* (N. Y.: Macmillan, 1926) and J. Robert Oppenheimer, "On Science and Culture", *Encounter,* October, 1962.

[2]See Francis A. Schaeffer, *No Final Conflict: The Bible Without Error in All That It Affirms* (Downers Grove, IL: Inter-Varsity Press, 1975).

[3]This listing could be extended greatly since Virchow, Cuvier, Agassiz, Morse, Hovey, Bartram, Steinmetz, Turner, White, Hales, Henslow, Sedgwick, Buckland, and Dalton could be mentioned. Two other founders of the Royal Society, Isaac Barrow and Seth Ward, were men of deep Christian persuasion.

⁴Attention must be called to an atypical use of the term "historical" when applied to portions of the sub-science geology. Actually, "historical" geologists are scientists operating within the traditional limits of proper, orderly science to the extent that they observe and study land features, rock strata, and inclusions found in them. However, when "historical" geologists begin interpretations and reconstructions of the past beyond limits of any possibility of human observation, then they essentially formulate narratives or scenarios about what they *believe* might have occurred in the past.

⁵Victor F. Weisskopf, "The Frontiers and Limits of Science", *American Scientist* 65 (4): 405-411 July-August, 1977. Page 411.

⁶John Warwick Montgomery, *The Shape of the Past.* (Ann Arbor, MI: Edwards Brothers, Inc., 1962). In his third chapter he contrasts the cyclical Classical View of history with the linear Old and New Testament View.

Chapter 1

General Discussion Questions

1. What are the stated goals of this chapter?
2. How would you explain to another person the fact that modern science was begun by those who believed in the creation of heaven and earth, and believed that Jesus Christ was the Creator of all life, including human beings?
3. What is meant by "limiting principles" of modern scientific endeavors?
4. Explain possible "zones of inquiry".
5. Contrast and compare the "static" component of science with the "dynamic" component.
6. Explain some possible criteria of a good theory in scientific work.
7. Discuss the study of "natural" objects and/or events and expression of "thinkable" ideas.
8. Discuss common meanings of the terms "history" and "historical" and "prehistory".
9. Compare and contrast: Contemporary Scientific Theories and "Historical" Theories.
10. Prepare a list of non-scientific questions.
11. Explain the meaning of the term "natural", and then compare and contrast "*super*natural" and "*supra*natural".

Class Projects or Individual Assignments

1. Prepare a topical outline of this chapter.
2. List "cover words" that could cause semantic confusion.
3. Prepare a chart containing the names and portraits of scientists who accepted theism and/or Christian theism, and who were founders of the physical sciences. Make a similar chart for founders of the biological sciences.
4. Prepare a chart of the limiting principles of proper, orderly scientific endeavor.
5. Make a large chart of main aspects of scientific activity.

6. Make a chart containing the basic assumptions (presuppositions) of modern science, and provide illustrations for each to explain the meaning involved.
7. Prepare a large chart with illustrations depicting the basic process skills of scientists.
8. Prepare a glossary of definitions of the 17 aspects of scientific activity discussed in this chapter.
9. Prepare a large chart with illustrations explaining the missing ''keys'' discussed in this chapter.
10. Work out a set of answers for the evaluation items provided at the close of this chapter. Now prepare a set of similar evaluation items for this general subject matter area.

Read: Henry M. Morris, Editor, *Scientific Creationism*. 1974. San Diego: Creation-Life Publishers.

On the Use of Scripture in Parochial Schools

1. Ask students to prepare a brief list of quotations from the Old Testament to show that God is the Creator of all things. Now ask students to prepare a brief list of similar quotations from the New Testament.
2. Direct student attention especially to Hebrews 11:3 and discuss the many implications that can be developed.
3. Give particular attention to Col. 2:8 with respect to the last paragraph of this chapter.

Evaluation Questions

Inquiries by scientists differ, since some center on the present and others have to do with the past. To test your understanding of such a differentiation, use the following key to evaluate each statement in items 1 through 10:

KEY: 1. Example of contemporary scientific theory, as associated with the present.
2. Example of historical theory, as associated with the past.
3. Neither of these stated here.

1. The Ptolemaic cosmological system of explanation of stars as he saw them. (1)

2. The kinetic-molecular theory for explaining phenomena of changes of state of matter. (1)
3. The big bang theory or evolutionary cosmogonical model about the universe. (2)
4. Fluid and particulate theories about electrical phenomena. (1)
5. The Copernican cosmological system of explanation of stars as he saw them. (1)
6. The Dalton and/or Modern Atomic Theory for explaining chemical reactions. (1)
7. The steady state theory or evolutionary cosmogonical model about the universe. (2)
8. The creation cosmogonical model about the universe. (2)
9. The Tychonian cosmological system of relating the sun and visible planets of the solar system. (1)
10. The Keplerian modification of the Copernican cosmological explanation of stars he saw. (1)

To gain some measure of your understanding of evidence and the concept of the term *natural*, select from the key the entry which is most closely associated with each item 11 through 24:

KEY: 1. Circumstantial evidence and unnatural cosmogonical events.
2. Conclusive evidence and natural.
3. Circumstantial evidence and natural cosmological events.
4. None of these entries provided here.

11. Big bang expansion from an infinitely large structure. (1)
12. Background radiation and background radio noise. (3)
13. Creation of whole universe as fully functioning. (1)
14. Detection of red shift of light spectra of radiation from stars and galaxies. (3)
15. Detection of a direct relationship wherein variables change such that both increase or decrease. (2)
16. Identification of orderly arrangements of stars in patterns called constellations. (3)
17. Detection of inverse proportionality wherein variables change such that the product of each pair is of constant value. (2)
18. Deduction of regular and orderly movement of planets (wondering stars). (3)

19. Reasoning that the universe is expanding from an explosion; matter will slow due to gravitational interaction; then all matter will contract to single concentration/explode. (1)
20. The rings of Saturn contain circling or eddying particles and also braided rings. (3)
21. Detection of inverse relationship such that variables change as one increases and the other decreases in value. (2)
22. Portions of the universe or cosmos have been seen to explode over the centuries as reported by Chinese, Babylonians, Europeans. (3)
23. Analysis and prediction of regular patterns of comet motion. (3)
24. Detection of a direct proportionality wherein variables change at uniform rates though the actual amount of change may be different for the two variables. (2)

By affording attention to differentiation between empirical and theoretical aspects of *scientific activity* a means was provided to contrast cosmogonical formulations and good scientific theories. For items 25 through 36 select from the key the entry that most appropriately fits the information in each item:

KEY: 1. Analogical reasoning, which involves detected similarities.
2. Empirical, as observational related.
3. Deductive-like reasoning, involving separation of conclusion from previous statements.
4. Theoretical, as involving some imagined entity.
5. Inductive-like reasoning, involving summary statement about common aspects of things or events.

25. Comparison of imagined structure of the atom to organization of the solar system. (1)
26. Explanation of change of state phenomena and also elemental isotopes. (4)
27. Derivation of the combined gas law from certain given definitions and equations. (3)
28. Use of cathode tubes with special slit arrangement, with paddle wheel or with portion of metal mounted inside to gain specifics about cathode rays. (2)
29. Comparison of shifts in spectra of light from stars to the Doppler effect of sound. (1)

30. Use of bar magnet and iron fillings to demonstrate lines of force around a magnet. (2)

31. Formulation of the pressure-volume gas law from raw data and calculated data gained from experiment. (5)

32. Development of the conclusion that an electric current in a wire is the movement of negatively charged particles. (3)

33. Relationship of pinpoints of light on planetarium dome to actual celestial objects. (1)

34. Representation of celestial motion by means of a plastic globe. (1)

35. Derivation of laws of attraction and replusion for static charges and also the magnetic poles. (5)

36. Use of a dry cell and a wire with current in it and iron fillings to demonstrate lines of force around the wire. (2)

37. Which of the following should now be recognized by you as specific limiting principles according to which proper and orderly scientific activities proceed? (1)
    1. Empirical, quantitative, mechanical, corrective
    2. Corrective, mechanical, empirical but not quantitative
    3. Quantitative, mechanical, empirical but not corrective
    4. Corrective, quantitative, empirical but not mechanical
    5. Mechanical, quantitative, corrective but not empirical

For items 38 through 53 select from the key the one entry which is your indication of the most closely related aspect of "what scientists do" for each item:

KEY: 1. Scientists observe, describe, and classify objects and/or events in their natural environment.
     2. Scientists seek testable answers to problems.
     3. Scientists formulate broad conceptualizations about events in their lifetime which are contemporary scientific theories.
     4. Scientists formulate broad conceptualizations about past events involving unobservable origins of the present environment which are historical models.

38. This aspect involves identifiable prior observations and also predictions before the fact. (3)

39. Is it possible to scientifically research or study the origin of the universe? (4)

40. Obsidian (volcanic glass) resulted from very rapid cooling of some molten mineral mix. (1)
41. This aspect involves identifiable objects or events in the life experience of human beings but essentially predictions after the fact. (4)
42. Different kinds of light sources were shown in the chart of the tree of light. (1)
43. Actual mineral composition and orientation of rocks were detected by use of microscopic slides. (1)
44. Movement of massive quantities of dry rock resulting in alterations of great magnitude such that new block (or tilted) mountains were formed. (4)
45. A chart of all populations or major kinds of plant life on the earth as presented by Volpe. (4)
46. Is it possible to scientifically research or study the origin of life on the earth? (4)
47. A chart of all populations of major kinds of animal life on the earth as presentated by Volpe. (4)
48. Ideas about the appearance of the first life on earth under a reducing atmosphere. (4)
49. Ideas about the appearance of true cells from beginning cells to explain how several of the special parts of complex cells came into being. (4)
50. Is it possible to scientifically research or study the origin of human beings? (4)
51. When rock fragments and particles of varying sizes become cememted and/or compacted then sedimentary conglomerate (often called pudding stone) was formed. (4)
52. What was the template for the formation of the first DNA molecule? (4)
53. What was the cause of the supposed explosion of some very dense substance to initiate the formation of the present universe? (4)

2 | Origin Of The Universe

When you complete this chapter you should understand how to:

1. Discuss questions concerning the origin of the universe.
2. Illustrate limitations of science and scientists.
3. Explain that different systems of cosmology were developed to explain motions of the *same* celestial bodies.
4. Explain an analogy between light and sound as basic to modern cosmogony.
5. State cardinal points of different modern cosomogonies.
6. Explain constrasting cosmogonical models (evolution vs. creation) of the origin of aspects of the universe (elements, stars, solar system).

Introduction

As has been stated, the science teacher should establish very early the fact that areas of inquiry are different. There is a discernable difference between inquires *in* the present, and inquiries *about* the past. The whole purpose of this chapter will be to show that limitations exist with regard to any study of the origin of the universe.

Ample support has already been given to the fact that scientists are specialists who do their work *in the present.* The special emphasis of natural scientists is upon accumulation of observations of *natural* objects and/or events, which then may be classified, generalized, and explained. The very beginning of the universe is a past event, and no observations of that presumably singular event are possible.[1] Once again consider the question, Is it possible to study scientifically the origin of the universe? The science teacher should be well prepared after this chapter to show why the answer to this question must be ''no''.

Of course, many scientists (astronomers, physicists, astrophysicists, engineers, and mathematicians) are studying *ideas* about the origin of the universe. But all of these are limited in putting forth their ideas about the origin of the universe. No scientist has ever studied any natural objects, events or conditions by which the universe might have come into existence. Modern scientist are still in the same position as Job when he was asked, ''Where wast thou when I (God) laid the foundations of the earth? (Job 38:4) Modern scientsts who ''hypothesize'' about supposed objects, events or conditions prior to the existence of the universe are *not* developing testable formulations, as scientists do with respect to the atomic theory, kinetic-molecular theory or gene theory.

Based upon a rigorous use of operational definitions as afforded already in chapter 1, a hypothesis in proper, orderly scientific work must be testable. Successful scientists develop properly testable hypothetical answers (though quite tentative) to the problems that they generate as a consequence of *prior awareness* of aspects of the natural environment.

However, leading astronomers have propounded, and the prevailing majority of scientists have accepted, at one time or another, certain basic thoughts relevant to the origination and generation of the universe which are associated with the big bang, steady state, or oscillating concepts. Ever since the early 1920's, following publication of ideas of Albert Einstein, the majority of scientists have accepted the view that the universe started with a big bang explosion of some dense particle and has been expanding ever since. The idea of the big bang hypothesis or theory is that many billion years ago (some hold to 10 billion, others to 20 billion, and some mention 30 billion) all the matter in the universe was concentrated in a single mass. Then that very dense mass exploded with a big bang with all of the parts of the universe expanding into space ever since the supposed explosion. Associated concepts include the proposal that, at some limit of gravitational interaction, all the expanding matter is to start contracting, ending in a final catastrophic collapse. Some scientists have even presented the idea that such collapsed matter could explode again; hence they have offered the oscillating universe hypothesis or theory.

In contrast to these ideas are certain concepts associated with the steady state hypothesis or theory. Proponents of this position hold that the density of matter in the universe is always the same because galaxies are continuously formed to fill of the space left by those expanding into space. Actually, this proposal is very much in disfavor because more and more evidence has been accumulated to support scientists' beliefs that the universe had a definite beginning, that the amount of matter has not always been steady. The steady state hypothesis has been discarded by the majority of scientists.

With regard to evolution/creation discussions about first origins, clarity of understanding is gained if we remember that a hypothesis must be testable. Thus, one can reliably refer only to a big bang *concept* as the most popular idea of scientists regarding the origin of the universe. No scientific hypothesis about origin is involved. Ideas of scientists about the origination and generation of the universe are *after the fact*, and no prior study of a big bang explosion has ever occurred, nor will ever be possible according to present technology. (Some might hope that a time machine will be invented).

Ideas of origination and generation of the universe must be recognized, necessarily, as part of cosmogony, and *not* directly involved with cosmology. True, it has become popularly accepted procedure to include cosmogony within cosmology. This practice is quite regrettable with respect to rigor of communication and meaning. A *careful delineation* of these two terms, cosmology and cosmogony, is singularly useful in certifying specific limitations of all scientists with regard to any study of the origin of the universe.

We must be significantly aware of the tendency of modern scientists, particularly some astronomers and astrophysicists, to ignore the previously itemized limiting principles of science. Today many astronomers and astrophysicists do not acknowledge the difference between cosmology and cosmogony. They do not abide by the fact that cosmogony cannot be properly or correctly subsummed under cosmology. Noteworthy is the fact that cosmology is the *science* of the cosmos.

"Cover Word"
(Beware Semantic Confusion)

Cosmology: often used in non-rigorous manner as if interchangeable with cosmogony; conveys connotations of seeming validity and reliability of *science* of cosmos when used indiscriminately to include ideas of scientists about the origination and generation of the universe, which are most accurately subsummed under the term "cosmogony".

Cosmology

The study of the nature of the universe; use of tools and technology to describe aspects of the observable and physical universe.

By the very definition of the term, cosmology entails those activities characteristic of scientists studying natural objects and/or events in space, as an extension of the natural environment of the surface of the earth. Cosmologists study the present brightness of stars, detect sequences of changes of stars and planets, and even deduce the arrangement of planets with respect to the sun.

In contrast, cosmogony involves ideas scientists have about the beginning of the universe.

Cosmogony

A list of ideas or formulations centered on origination and generation of the universe.

Much confusion has been generated in recent years because some astronomers and astrophysicists are unwilling to acknowledge that there is a difference between cosmology and cosmogony. The difference is significant because cosmologists study what is *now presently seen*; whereas, in contrast, the ideas of cosmogonists center around past events and the presumed or imagined events that might have occurred *before the present*. Even contentions about light coming from great distances (and hence related to some past events) do not significantly detract from the fact that the light is detected and observed in the present of the lifetime of some astronomer.

Thus, today, there are numerous sets of cosmogonical ideas about the beginning of the universe, and, in turn, certain cosmogonical ideas about the beginning of the solar system. But cosmogonical ideas about what might have occurred before the present are always beyond the scope of proper, orderly scientific work. Cosmogonical ideas about the first origin of the universe or the solar system, then, are part of the "zone of conjectures" (See Classroom Teaching Aid 9). Rigorously, cosmogonical ideas can only be checked as after-the-fact-ideas, subject to test with regard to logical coherency and rational consistency.

Part I: BOUNDARIES OF MEASUREMENT

With elucidation of the operational definitions of cosmology and cosmogony, we are ready to proceed to further consideration of the evolution/creation confrontation approach to teaching about first origins.

Astronomers have limitations. Like all other scientists, astronomers are restricted to studying aspects of the universe—especially the heavenly bodies—as they find them present during their lifetime.

Most commonly, scientists begin by stating a question or by formulating a problem. For instance, a scientist may ask, "What is the size of the universe?" With this question stated, a very valuable point can be made about *boundaries of measurement* within which astronomers must operate. Clarification about cosmological studies can be accomplished by reference to a distance-scale pyramid illustrated in Classroom Teaching Aid 13.*

"Cover Word"
(Beware Semantic Confusion)

Measurement: Too often this word is used when the term "estimate" would be more accurate. No scientist can measure the size of the universe. No scientist can measure the age of the universe. No scientist can measure the age of the earth. No scientist can measure the age of a rock. In each of these instances scientists are limited to stating *estimates.*

Valuable understanding will be gained by a careful explanation of the distance-scale pyramid. To measure distance in the solar system, some sort of distance scale near the earth is required. Within recent years radar methods (and laser beam techniques) have been used to gain most accurate results. A radar pulse is beamed toward the moon and a record is made of the time elapsed until receipt of a signal reflected from the moon. By knowing the velocity of the radar pulse (which is the velocity of light in outer space), the time elapsed between transmitting and receiving the radar signal (which can be measured very accurately) the distance of the moon

---

*(Students could be assigned an essay wherein they would describe the relationship of this teaching aid and Classroom Teaching Aid 9 also used to denote limitations of scientists.)

Classroom Teaching Aid 13
THE DISTANCE-SCALE PYRAMID

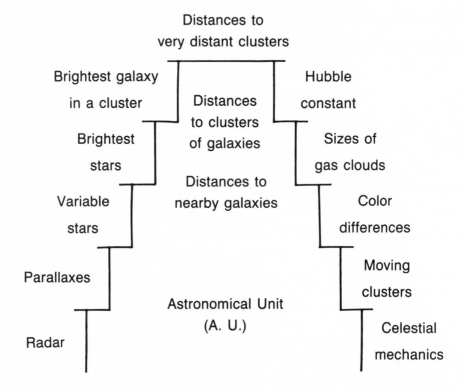

Distances to
very distant clusters

Brightest galaxy in a cluster   Hubble constant

Distances to clusters of galaxies

Brightest stars   Sizes of gas clouds

Distances to nearby galaxies

Variable stars   Color differences

Parallaxes   Moving clusters

Astronomical Unit (A. U.)

Radar   Celestial mechanics

from the earth can be calculated. By checking numerous other points about the velocity of light, orbits, size of planets and gravitation, an accurate comparison of the distance of Mercury, Venus, Earth and Mars from the Sun is possible. This is done by using the distance of the earth from the sun as one Astronomical Unit (AU) (See Classroom Teaching Aid 14). In this way celestial mechanics are used to gain approximations of comparative distance.

The next step in the distance-scale pyramid entails use of the parallax principle. The distance between the earth and a star can be calculated by noting comparative positions of that star against the background of stars as seen from the different positions of the earth during a given year. This is a parallax measurement. By means of trigonometry the triangle formed

Classroom Teaching Aid 14
DISTANCE IN THE SOLAR SYSTEM

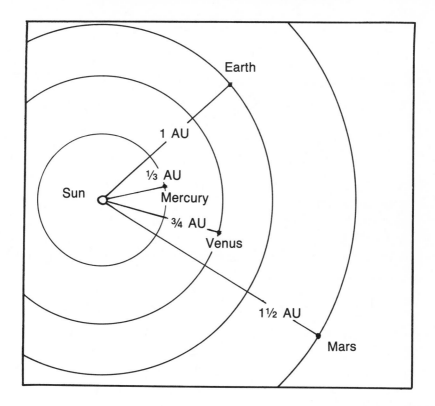

from the observer at two positions of the earth and some star can be measured to an accuracy of one percent out to a distance of 160 light years. (A light year is the distance light travels in one year at the speed of 186,000 miles per second.) Beyond that the accuracy becomes less and less and the parallax principle *cannot* be used with regard to further distances into space. What can be used?

The following is a most crucial point to emphasize in any evolution/creation discussion of first origins: Beyond 500 light years from the earth *only vague estimates* are possible as astronomers strive to gain information relevant to the problem stated earlier, "What is the size of the universe?" Initially, color differences of certain variable stars (the Cepheid variables) are noted to estimate distances to nearby galaxies. Then sizes of gas clouds of the brightest stars are used to estimate distances to clusters of galaxies, and finally comparisons of brightness of galaxies in different clusters are employed to estimate distances to very distant clusters.

It is true that lasar beams, radio telescopes and x-ray detection devices are used to derive further *estimates* of great distances in the universe. However, particularly important regarding limitations of astronomers is the fact that the distance-scale pyramid is mostly an array of vague estimates—involving *estimates of brightness.* Accuracy cannot be anything like that attained by radar measurements and parallax calculations. It is important for the science teacher to emphasize that measurements are *not* involved. Astronomers do not measure the size of the universe. They *only estimate* the size of the universe. One of the most outstanding problems for astronomers is the question of the geometry of the universe which is very relevant to the question of the size of the universe. Astronomers admit that no one knows the geometry of the universe.

It is important to realize that the initial exploratory grounds of the *earliest scientists* was in the area of cosmology, and not in pursuit of cosmogonical thinking.

Today cosmology is the science of the cosmos: the careful accumulation of observations, descriptions and scientific data of the present universe. As cosmologists, astronomers, use a wide range of tools to make observations about the universe in their present lifetime. These tools include the unaided eye, binoculars, prisms, many sizes of telescopes, radar, radio beams, lasar beams and even x-rays. Special observatories are centers for studying the universe: Palomar Observatory with its 200-inch reflecting telescope, Yerkes Observatory with its 40-inch refracting telescope, the National Radio Astronomical Observatory with its 300-foot radio antenna, and other similar observatories around the world.

But the early scientists did not possess such sophisticated tools. Therefore, they limited their studies to observable celestial motion. Early implementation of scientific methodology is found in written reports of their work. Babylonian and Greek observers recorded extensive data on the movements of celestial bodies. Evidently these first inquirers were most interested in the physical environment and particularly in celestial bodies. Because of their initial awarenesses of movements of celestial bodies and the steady accumulation of observational data, they formulated specific problems about celestial motion for which they sought particular answers by means of observation. These early scientists recognized certain patterns in their observations: seasonal changes, star zodiac constellations.

Important background to understanding the difference between cosmology and cosmogony, so very important to successful practice of the exolution/creation confrontation teaching approach, can be gained by having students engage in a data-gathering exercise. In the sense of doing *somewhat like* the earliest astronomers, modern students can experience the inadequacies of separate and individual findings about the natural environment; and, in turn, grasp the value of detected patterns or generalizations from accumulated data. Students realize more fully what is meant by cosmology through observations of celestial objects, organization of data in some classified manner, and development of generalizations by using Classroom Teaching Aid 15. This teaching aid is a means for emphasizing the fact that *scientists* are always looking for patterns as they study the *natural* environment, because they want to develop generalizations (all of which will help implement already mentioned operational definitions).

Classroom Data Gathering Exercise

Classroom Teaching Aid 15 can be used to draw attention to certain aspects of celestial motion and to illustrate implementation of scientific methodology. This page clarifies how scientists practice their specialty of recording data in orderly tabulated form so that such data can be examined for possible patterns or orderly, repeated relationships.

Three questions or problems are stated for which answers are sought. With specific attention to the sun, a somewhat narrow study can be made of its movements: (1) daily changes from morning until evening; (2) changes of position of the noonday sun from January through December; and (3) changes in the rising and setting positions of the sun, also, from January through December; each with respect to the northern hemisphere.

The science teacher must help students use their imagination regarding *apparent* motions of the sun. Also the teacher must explain two terms, azimuth and altitude, which have special meaning to astronomers. Azimuth and altitude are coordinates for locating a star with respect to an observer on the earth in somewhat the same manner as latitude and longitude are used to locate a position on the surface of the earth.

Classroom Teaching Aid 15
GATHERING DATA

Problem 1. What is the *apparent* daily motion of the sun?

Time	8 a.m.	10 a.m.	Noon	2 p.m.	4 p.m.
Azimuth	120°	155°	180°	205°	235°
Altitude	0°	18°	23°	18°	0°

Problem 2. What is the *apparent* annual motion of the noonday sun?

Date	Altitude	Azimuth	Date	Altitude	Azimuth
Dec. 20	35°	180°	June 20	67°	180°
Jan. 20	43°	180°	July 20	60°	180°
Feb. 20	45°	180°	Aug. 20	51°	180°
Mar. 20	48°	180°	Sept. 20	45°	180°
Apr. 20	52°	180°	Oct. 20	41°	180°
May 20	59°	180°	Nov. 20	38°	180°

Problem 3. What is the *apparent* annual motion of the rising sun and the setting sun?

Dates	Altitude	Azimuth	
		Rising	Setting
Dec. 20	0°	125°	225°
Jan. 20	0°	123°	233°
Feb. 20	0°	105°	250°
Mar. 20	0°	90°	266°
Apr. 20	0°	78°	288°
May 20	0°	58°	296°
June 20	0°	60°	300°
July 20	0°	61°	296°
Aug. 20	0°	74°	282°
Sept. 20	0°	90°	265°
Oct. 20	0°	119°	246°
Nov. 20	0°	123°	232°

NOW—Record possible generalizations for each problem.

Azimuth is the angular distance measured eastward along the observer's horizon from the point on the horizon below the North Celestial Pole to a point on the observer's horizon below the object in the sky. Thus any object below the North Celestial Pole has an azimuth of 0°. The position of an object described as due east of an observer in the northern hemisphere would be identified with an azimuth of 90°, and an object described as due west of an observer would have the azimuth of 270°. Also the azimuth under problem two of Classroom Teaching Aid 15 for the noonday sun could conveniently be considered 180° as the sun appears very close to due south each mid-day.

Altitude is the angular distance measured between the line of vision to an object in the sky and an imaginary line from the observer to a point on the observer's horizon beneath the object in the sky. An object on the horizon has an altitude of 0°. On the other hand, an object directly over head has an altitude of 90°. Thus, by definition the rising sun is at 0° altitude, as would be the case for the setting sun. The angular distance of the altitude is greatest at noonday than at any time between the moment of sunrise and the moment of sunset.

By use of Classroom Teaching Aid 15 the science teacher can illustrate very well how scientists gather specific observational data in certain numerical form. These are tangible data gained through use of the senses (though some instruments would be helpful in actual practice of gathering the data). As given here in completed form, the next step of formulating generalizations can be illustrated quite handily. By directing students to formulate generalizations, they gain limited practice in detecting common aspects of similar objects (or similar events as in these three problems), which is an explicit characteristic of the wording of generalizations. Typical generalizations that students might formulate on the basis of these data are:

1. The azimuth of the sun increases throughout the day from sunrise to sunset.
2. The altitude of the sun increases from sunrise until a maximum at noon and then decreases until sunset.
3. The altitude of sunrise is always zero.
4. The altitude of sunset is always zero.
5. During one year the azimuth of the noonday sun is always 180°.
6. During one year the altitude of the noonday sun increases from December to a maximum in June followed by a continual decrease until December.

7. The altitude of the noonday sun is essentially the same in March and
   September in the same year.
8. During one year the azimuth of the rising sun decreases from December
   to a minimum (in the northeast) in June and then increases to a
   maximum again (in the southeast).
9. During one year the azimuth of the setting sun increases from December
   to a maximum (in the northwest) in June and then decreases to a
   minimum again (in the southwest) in December.

Graphic representations of these orderly relationships could be required
as further means of illustrating possible generalization. (See Fig. 9)

Figure 9
AZIMUTH, ALTITUDE AND GENERALIZATIONS

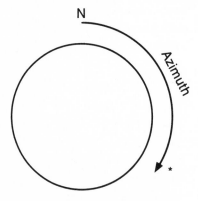

Azimuth, angular distance
measured eastward along
observer's horizon.

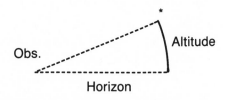

Altitude, angular distance
measured between line of
vision and observer's horizon.

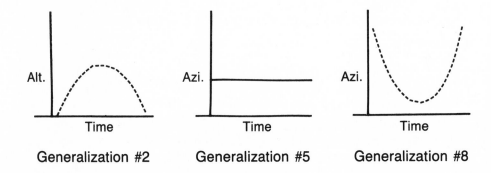

Generalization #2   Generalization #5   Generalization #8

Handling Contradictions

The ideas of scientists change constantly. Ideas in the field of science are especially open to test and retest, consideration and reconsideration. Cursory examination of broad systems of generalizations by early cosmologists is most helpful in strengthening the function of the evolution/creation confrontation. Fully developed systems of cosmological descriptions and explanations of planetary motion were propounded by Ptolemy, Copernicus, Tycho Brahe, and Kepler. By giving some attention to the cosmological system of each of these early scientists, students grasp more fully that ideas of scientists do change over the centuries; hence any current idea held by modern scientists should likewise be understood as open to change and reexamination. A functional way of approaching the changeableness of ideas of scientists is effected through careful consideration of *how scientists handle contradictions*, as presented in Fig. 10. This entails an emphasis on what scientists do when they are faced with contradictions between observational facts and cherished explanatory conceptualizations.

Figure 10
HOW SCIENTISTS HANDLE CONTRADICTIONS

The following list contains several of the common methods scientists employ to reconcile contradictions between their research findings and their scientific theories:

1. Usually the first step is to *ignore* the contradiction, since any specific research result will involve only a part of the theory in question. Also the contradiction may be of limited importance and further research may resolve the difficulty.
2. Secondly, a *claim of error* in research method or error of interpretation of findings is often made. Proponents of a favored scientific theory will often charge the author of the report of contradictory evidence with carelessness or inadequacy.
3. If real and vital contradictions are corroborated by repeated research reports, then the relevant part of the scientific theory may be *modified*. A change of this type in a scientific theory is taken only after repeated analyses whereby the same information prevails and an acceptable alteration of the existing theory can be developed.

4. Another possible approach to contradictions is to derive an *alternative theory*. Then research implications and ramifications would be developed for both theories which would more or less be considered coexistent scientific theories. For example, the wave and the particle theories of light have been coexistent in modern physics for some time (although the difference has been resolved mathematically in recent years).
5. And there are many examples in the history of science where a new theory *completely replaced* another theory. For instance, Mendelian genetics completely replaced the blending theory of inheritance, and the particulate theory of electricity completely replaced several fluid theories of electricity.

Actually, scientists are most reluctant to alter their basic theories. They have great affection for their paradigms, scientific theories and other broad conceptual frameworks. When isolated results of experiments are reported that are different than expected, or facts are reported that do not fit existing patterns of thought, most scientists continue to support the explanatory ideas held by the majority of scientists. The science teacher could use Fig. 10 to illustrate typical steps taken by scientists when faced with contradictions between research results and accepted theories. A pointed way of illustrating the handling of contradictions, which is most appropriate to the subject of this chapter, is found in a brief glance at the cosmological thinking of Ptolemy, Copernicus, Tycho Brahe, and Kepler. Each scientist handled contradictions in a different way.

Ptolemy. Ptolemy was an early codifier of many ancient observations of movements of heavenly bodies gained from Babylonian, Greek and other sources. The initial observations of Ptolemy are listed in Fig. 11.

Figure 11
MAJOR OBSERVATIONS OF THE ANCIENT SCHOLARS:
1. The stars move westward from day to day, but the sun moves eastward with respect to the stars on a day by day basis.
2. Daily the visible stars in the northern hemisphere move on circles around a point close to Polaris.
3. Mercury and Venus are always seen close to the sun.
4. The planets demonstrate retrograde motion periodically.
5. Most of the planets vary in brightness in a regular fashion.
6. No planet ever wanders far from the ecliptic.

Utilizing these observations and those collected by his contemporaries and himself, Ptolemy organized a common sense cosmological system. He deemed that the earth was the center of the universe. He took that position because of the commonly recorded major observations, (initial or prior awarenesses, it should be noted) (Fig. 11). The postulates of his system of cosmology are given in Fig. 12. His system may be described as geocentric and geostatic.

Figure 12
POSTULATES OF THE PTOLEMAIC
COSMOLOGICAL SYSTEM

1. The heaven is spherical and moves spherically.
2. The earth is spherical.
3. The earth is the middle (center) of the heaven.
4. The size of the earth is insignificant when compared to the sphere of the fixed stars.
5. The earth does not move in any way.

Early cosmologists were dependent upon the idea, accepted from Plato, that the circle is the perfect geometric figure. Further, early cosmologists believed that planetary motion was along perfect circles around the earth. Much understanding of the interrelationship of ideas and observations in the development of cosmologies can be gained if science teachers will research the fact that Ptolemy and his followers accepted the philosophically important idea of uniform motion of heavenly bodies along perfect circles around the earth. Conceivably this viewpoint is rooted in the ancient Hebrew concept of perfection of the world at one time immediately following the creative acts of God.

What is important further for the purpose of illustrating scientific methodology is the fact that accumulation of more and more data resulted in necessary modifications of the Ptolemaic system. This meant that the system was extended to include eccentrics (motion around a supposed point that was not the center of a circle), epicycles (circular motion on circular motion), and equants (having to do with angular motion on an orbit). (See Fig. 13.) By bringing out these points the science teacher can exemplify the third method by which scientists handle contradictions: they *modify* their conceptualizations.

Figure 13
PTOLEMY'S METHODS OF INTRODUCING
VARIATION INTO PLANETARY SPEED.

The eccentric.
One way to make a planet
appear to regularly *speed up* and
slow down, as well as move to
and away from the earth.

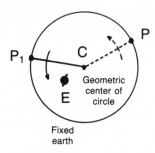

The epicycle.
Point C moves with constant
distance and with uniform
motion about E, the fixed earth.
By uniform motion is meant that
the line EC sweeps equal angles
(T_1, T_2, T_3, T_4) in equal times.
From the earth, the point C is
seen to move along the deferent
circle at uniform speed.

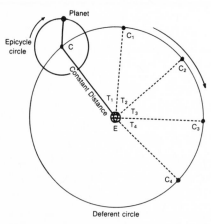

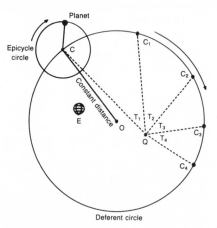

The equant.
Earth E has been displaced from
center of deferent circle. Point
C now moves in a circle around
O as center. C moves with uniform motion not about O,
however, but point Q, called the
equant. Although the line QC
sweeps equal angles (T_1, T_2, T_3,
T_4) in equal times, the point C
no longer moves along the
deferent circle at a uniform
speed.

Copernicus. Because of continued acceptance of the philosophical viewpoint that all motion in space occurred along perfect circles and because of repeated modification upon modification of the Ptolemaic system, in later centuries as astronomers studied the sun and associated planets in *their* present day, they felt that different cosmological systems would better represent the solar system.

Thus, after great popularity of the Ptolemaic system for about 2,000 years, Copernicus decided that a different cosmological system would be more in keeping with his concept of an orderly thinking Creator whom he believed created the heaven and the earth and all that is therein. Hence, the fifth method of meeting contradiction can be illustrated when students see that Copernicus *completely replaced* the geocentric cosmological system of Ptolemy and his followers with a new heliocentric cosmological system. (It was not really new since Aristarchus of ancient Greece had also thought of the sun as the center. However such a conceptualization was so completely contrary to unaided empirical study that the heliocentric idea was never given serious consideration by the ancient Greeks and other peoples.)

Ptolemy and Copernicus looked at the very *same physical objects.* Yet their respective explanations of motions of the heavenly bodies were significantly different because they employed different postulational beginning points: Ptolemy had the earth at the center, whereas Copernicus had the sun at the center of planetary motion. This phenomenon of scholars formulating distinctly different explanatory systems *for the same physical objects* could be itemized again and again by science teachers. Other examples include explanations for electricity, inheritance patterns, and similarities among living and fossilized organisms.

Because Copernicus felt that a heliocentric cosmological system would be less complicated (and more God honoring), he was able to discard the equant imagined by proponents of the Ptolemaic system. The postulates of the Copernican system of cosmology are listed in Fig. 14. His system may be described as heliocentric and heliostatic.

Figure 14
POSTULATES OF THE COPERNICAN COSMOLOGICAL SYSTEM

1. There is no center of all the celestial circles or spheres.
2. The center of the earth is not the center of the universe.

3. The sun is the center of the universe.
4. The earth performs a daily rotation on its fixed poles. Other motion is apparent.
5. The earth, like any other planet, revolves around the sun.
6. Retrograde motion is an apparent motion resulting from the motion of the earth as it passes or is passed by another planet.
7. The distance from the earth to the sun is small compared to the height of the firmament.

See Fig. 15 for comparisons and contrasts with the Ptolemaic and Copernican systems. Of particular note is the fact that Copernicus continued to adhere to the idea of uniform motion along perfect circles, and he continued to use eccentrics and epicycles. His cosmological system was really not a great deal more simplified from that of Ptolemy. However, more accurate predictions were possible according to the heliocentric cosmological scheme.

Figure 15
PTOLEMAIC SYSTEM COMPARED WITH
THAT CONCEIVED BY COPERNICUS.

Note that Copernicus' system is not less cumbersome than Ptolemy's.

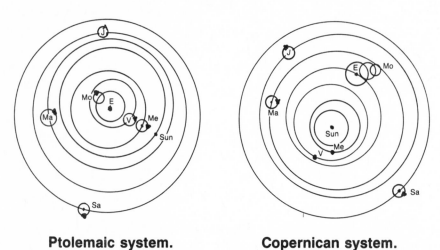

Ptolemaic system.   **Copernican system.**

Me - Mercury; V - Venus; Mo - Moon; E - Earth; Ma - Mars; J - Jupiter; Sa - Saturn.

Brahe. But neither Tycho Brahe nor Johannes Kepler were satisfied with the Copernican system. An increasing amount of accurate data was accumulated by Brahe and others. Contradictions between facts and cosmological expectations became abundant. Hence Brahe imagined a hybrid cosmological system; that the earth could still be at the center of the universe with the moon moving around the earth. Then he incorporated a heliocentric aspect by imagining that the remaining planets of the solar system moved around the sun, which in turn moved around the earth.

The cosmological system of Brahe was basically geocentric with heliocentric variations, and thus seemed too complicated when compared to the straight forward heliocentric cosmological system of Copernicus. The proposal of Brahe illustrates the fourth method of handling contradictions. His composite cosmological system involved some degree of *coexistence* of two contrasting systems.

Kepler. On the other hand Kepler determined through repeated calculations, particularly concerning the orbits of Mars, that the motion of planets could *not* be explained according to circular paths. Rather, he found that planetary motions in the solar system were more accurately described by means of elliptical paths or orbits. After extensive mathematical calculations Kepler devised three laws[2] for planetary motion. (See Fig. 16.)

Figure 16
KEPLER'S LAWS OF PLANETARY MOTION

1. Planetary orbits are ellipses with the sun at a focus of the ellipse.
2. Planets move faster when nearer the sun, and more slowly when farther from the sun.
3. The farther a planet is from the sun, the more time it takes to complete a revolution.

Kepler's modifications of the Copernican cosmological system have been adopted completely, though not without problems as Herbert Dingle, L. Essen and other contemporary scientists are pointing out.

So both Brahe and Kepler are examples of thinkers who *modified a part of a broad conceptual scheme* in different ways. Brahe kept the perfect circular motion along with part of the geocentric and part of the heliocentric cosmological ideas. Kepler kept the sun at the center but modified planetary motion to be along elliptical orbits.

Galileo. Galileo supported the Copernican system without reservations.[3] In fact by employing a new device for extending visual perception, the telescope, Galileo made very important observations that had great bearing upon the world view of his contemporaries and all who have followed him. A list of the main telescopic observations of Galileo is contained in (Fig. 17).

Figure 17
MAIN TELESCOPIC OBSERVATIONS OF GALILEO

1. There are irregular patterns of light and dark blotches on the moon.
2. The moon is not a perfect sphere.
3. There are innumerable stars.
4. There are four bright discs that move from side to side of Jupiter.
5. Saturn is oblate and not round.
6. The supposedly most perfect celestial body, the sun, has dark spots on it.
7. Venus goes through phases just like the moon.

Because of these observations Galileo stimulated release from the restraints of cosmological and idealogical patterns of pre-Christian and Christian thought. He contributed counteraction to the concept of past perfection of the universe. When Galileo showed that the moon and Saturn were not perfect spheres, he presented a fact that did not fit with the proposal of Plato that the circle was the perfect geometric figure. When Galileo showed that there were light and dark spots on the moon, and dark spots on the sun, he presented further facts that besmirched the perfection of God's creation. Such facts, and the detected phases of Venus, were resisted by scholars of Galileo's time. Such facts were contradictory to the world view that had been built up over centuries before Galileo looked through his telescope.

The first method for handling contradictions between observational data and theoretical expectations was practiced when the facts of Galileo were *ignored* for a long, long time. The work of Kepler, Newton, Huygens and the illustration of stellar parallax in the nineteenth century were all needed before the Keplerian modified heliocentric cosmological system was broadly adopted and understood by scholars and nonspecialists. Also, not until many centuries later has the fact been pointed out that Galileo's observations were contradictions of *ideas of men* and not specifically objections to any proper biblical textual material. Yet, for centuries the common interpretation has been accepted that Galileo presented denials of portions of the Bible, when most rigorous analysis brings out that he truly opposed only ideas of men more or less attributed to the Bible.

Part II: Cosmogony versus Cosmology

At this point a brief review might be in order to stress again the important *difference* between cosmology and cosmogony for any discussion of evolution/creation ideas on the origin of the universe.

Cosmology is a careful, formal science of the cosmos. Cosmology is based upon observations accumulated over the ages as human beings have been attentive to movements of celestial bodies. An outstanding part of the science of the cosmos has been the development by scientists of generalizations to represent their observations. These generalizations have been variously expressed in the cosmological system of Ptolemy, Copernicus and Tycho Brahe. (Of course the Copernican cosmological system was modified through use of the specifically important tool for extending visual sensory perception—the telescope.) This tool was well used by Galileo whose observations confirmed the data collected by Brahe. It was Brahe's data that were basic to mathematical formulations of planetary laws of motion by Kepler.

Thus those cosmologists were excellent scientists. They laid the basis for practices that are readily identifiable in the work of many physical scientists and biological scientists who followed them. Both physical scientists and biological scientists have repeatedly, carefully, and objectively *observed* multiple aspects of the natural environment—on the earth and with respect to ongoing study of the movement of celestial bodies. These cosmologists set the pattern of rigorous empirical scientific work in accordance with proper limiting principles of science.

But it is imperative to highlight the difference between studies accomplished in accordance with proper limiting principles of science, and the tendency of some thinkers after Galileo's time to move away from adherence to such limiting principles. The tendency to move from careful cosmological *study* into cosmogonical *thinking* is fully characteristic of writers since Descartes and Kant to modern astronomers and astrophysicists who discuss freely and openly their ideas on the origination and generation of the universe. To help make explicit the important contrast between cosmologies (discussed in Part I) and cosmogonies (the center of attention in Part II), I have developed the Classroom Teaching Aid 16. Actually the ideas summarized in this teaching aid are representative thoughts from Descartes, Swendenborg, Buffon, Lemaitre, Gamow, Hoyle, Bondi, and Gold.

These men formulated a variety of cosmogonical schemes as they continued the "free thinking" approach set in motion by Copernicus and Galileo. In contrast to the position held for centuries that God was the Creator of heaven and earth and all therein, these men have gone far beyond observationally grounded science of the cosmos (cosmology); and, as cosmogonists, have relied heavily upon their imagination about very *un*natural events of origination and generation of the universe. Lemaitre imagined a primeval atom that came into existence *ex nihilo*, appearing suddenly out of nothing; that is, from no previously existing matter. Gamow imagined that an infinitely large structure of eternal existence evidently was the source of the universe. These concepts *do not* involve naturally occurring objects and/or events of any magnitude known to scientists.

It is noteworthy that most cosmogonists displace God as the First Cause and begin with a generous supply of undifferentiated matter with infinite extent of time. Then, supposedly by means of what is known about natural laws—generalizations promulgated by *empirical* scientists, who have accurately formulated generalizations about *natural* objects and/or events— cosmogonists imagine a number of *un*natural beginnings of the universe. As pointed out already, cosmogonists have no "key" in the present of any explosion of a dense particle of the magnitude that would give rise to the universe.

No initial awareness of naturally occurring objects and/or events, no list of limited postulates, and full dependence on analogical thinking is involved in the work of cosmogonists (in contrast to the work of cosmologists).

The long standing cosmogonical frame of reference found in the tradition of the Hebrew people (and expressed conceivably in reference to the past, present and future by Peter in Chapter 3 of his second epistle) was accepted by the founders of the scientific discipline. But it was no longer accepted by "free thinkers" from the time of Descartes and Kant. Thus

Classroom Teaching Aid 16   ON COSMOGONIES

Making plausible guesses as to the origin of the universe is evidently a challenging pastime. Given: (1) a generous supply of matter in a simple "undifferentiated" form, (2) the known laws of nature, and (3) infinite time, the object is to derive the present state of the physical world.

Primeval Atom "Hypothesis"
(Lemaitre, 1927)

1. Superatom of radius equal to earth's orbit.
2. Explosive radioactive disintegration followed by:
   1. rapid expansion.
   2. deceleration by gravitation.
3. renewed expansion evidenced by red shift of distant galaxies.
4. During first and second stages, aggregations formed into planets and stars.
5. Cosmic rays are really "fossil rays" of expansion.
6. Primeval atom came into being *ex nihilo*; that is, appearing suddenly from no previously existing matter.

Big-Bang "Hypothesis"
(Gamow, 1947)

1. More sophisticated than one by Belgian Jesuit Lemaitre.
2. Began with infinitely large structure that expanded to present state. (How did explosion propagate over infinite distance?)
3. Primordial matter called "ylem" (i-lem) of 10^{14} g/cc density.
4. First contraction phase yielded pre-ylem stage of density, then violent elastic rebound of catastrophic episode.
5. Known atoms were synthesized from atoms in less than an hour in intense heat of explosion.
6. Evidently expansion will continue indefinitely.

Steady-State "Hypothesis"
(Hoyle, 1948)

1. That is, continuous creation.
2. Infinitely old, infinitely large universe is constantly expanding.
3. New matter appears to replenish lost matter in space.
4. Self-creating matter is hydrogen which condenses into galaxies within which evolve stars, planets, satellites, comets, plants, animals and people. (Mankind is condensation out of nothingness.)
5. Hoyle said question about source of new matter is "meaningless and unprofitable" (or Hoyle does not know)
6. After 17 years Hoyle abandoned his idea. (See *Nature* 208: 113, Oct. 9, 1965.)

the science teacher utilizing the evolution/creation confrontation approach to first origins should very candidly point out that some modern cosmogonists invent their cosmogonies apparently because they will not accept or seriously consider the long standing Hebrew tradition. By and large, unbelieving scientists, either consciously or unconsciously, entice their followers toward *their* way after the tradition of men, and away from God (Col. 2:28). Yet, the way of the cosmogonists is *not* really naturalistic, but substitutionally *supra*-naturalistic. Cosmogonists of the nineteenth century to the present repeatedly utilize unnatural or supranatural ideas about objects and/or events regarding their imagined origin of the universe. But careful natural scientists deal with *naturally* occurring objects and/or events *in the present*. Whereas cosmogonists, with their emphasis on origination and generation of the universe, are *never* able to do so.

Cosmogonists misuse the term "hypothesis". It is important to remember that on the basis of a rigorous analysis, a hypothesis is a statement of a testable answer to a scientific problem. A hypothesis is generated because of some perplexity that arises *after* accumulation of significant empirical findings. But scientists have never studied or been aware of any objects, events, or conditions prior to some supposed big bang explosion whereby the present universe might have come into existence.[4] Furthermore cosmogonists do not formulate their ideas in clear lists of postulates based on any *prior observations* by some investigators of specific features of the natural environment, which was one of the specified criteria for contemporary scientific theories provided in chapter 1.

Cosmogonists must depend upon a very crucial analogy that they set up between aspects of sound transmission and light transmission, presumably over great stretches of space from distant stars to the earth. At the beginning of any serious discussion of evolution/creation ideas on the origin of the universe a careful analysis of the astronomer's analogy between known, *measureable* sound transmission and interpolated, *deduced* light transmission over expanse of space should be made quite evident by the science teacher. This important analogy between sound and light is basic to the concept of red shift of light, which in turn is one of the basic arguments raised regarding the expansion of the universe.

Some careful study of the Doppler effect with regard to sound will be most instructive in building understanding of the Doppler shift in light upon which astronomers base so much of their thinking about the big bang, expanding universe cosmogony. It is paramountly important that the science teacher make very explicit that this analogical reasoning is at the heart of modern cosmogonical thinking. Remove this analogy between sound transmission and light transmission from their thinking and modern cosmogonists would be without some most crucial *circumstantial* support for their expanding universe idea.

In brief review, the Doppler effect as it applies to sound is noted when a train whistle, for example, seems higher as the train is approaching a listener and lower as the train passes on in the distance. A simple explanation of this observational phenomenon is that the wavelength of sound heard is affected by the velocity of the object from which the sound is emitted. Thus the approaching train seems to have a higher pitch because the wavelength of the sound is shorter, whereas a departing train seems to have a lower pitch because the wavelength of the sound is longer.

Similarly for light, the wavelength that is measured is also dependent upon the velocity of the object emitting the light. (Of course, astronomers still accept Einstein's idea that the velocity of light is absolute, and is not affected by the velocity of the source of light.) By means of a prism that separates light into a complete spectrum of wavelength, it is possible to analyze the light emitted by stars, galaxies and nebulae. From such data astronomers have calculated the velocity of stars, which seem to move only a few miles per second. However, many galaxies seem to be moving at very high velocities as detected through analysis of those light sources. Characteristic of Doppler shifts of light of many galaxies is a shift in the spectrum lines that move systematically further and further to the red end of the spectrum of light. This is called the red shift. Since red has a long wavelength in contrast to blue which has a short wavelength, astronomers *interpret*, analogously to sound transmission interpretations, that distant galaxies are moving away from the observer and the earth.

But the red shift is difficult to detect. There is significant controversy between astronomers, such as Arp and Bacall, regarding various anomalies in red shifts. Results are not consistent for light from certain stellar objects considered to be at the same distance or any varying distances from the earth. Of course, for nearby objects, the brightest stars must be used for estimating distances of such light sources from the earth. (For review see Classroom Teaching Aid 13.) Even farther out the brightest galaxies in a given cluster must be used as a basis for *estimating* distances of larger and

larger galaxies from the earth. Once again the science teacher should emphasize the fact that astronomers only make *estimates* of distances of very
distant stellar objects, and *not* measurements.

Since the velocity-distance relationship of galaxies involving the Hubble
constant really involves certain approximations,[5] there are limitations to
application of it to very fast velocities. Also the geometry of the universe
enters into the calculations; and, since that characteristic of the universe
is unknown, much uncertainty surrounds all attempts to calculate the size
of the universe and to determine whether the universe is expanding or not
expanding.

Cosmogonies: Historical Theories

How, then, shall the cosmogonical ideas of origination and generation
of the universe be classified? Cosmogonists deal with historical theories.
Yet it is not history involving human beings, but rather historical in the
sense of *past* imagined, conjectured, speculated events presumed to have
been antecedent to the present universe. Basically the tests that cosmogonists
employ are tests of the internal consistency and reasonableness of their ideas.
Is it reasonable that the present order of planetary orbits, star constellations, cycles of elements and cycles of seasons came out of the chaos that
would logically follow explosion of some presumed dense particle? The
order, patterns and regularity of the present universe are consistent with
the design argument for the existence of the Creator, the Ultimate Cause
of all things in the heaven and the earth.

Historical theories are most properly labeled *models* of origin and then
clearer separation from contemporary scientific theories is possible. Now
the majority of scientists resist making such a separation or distinction between models of ideas of origin and contemporary scientific theories. No
doubt resistance to such a delineation centers in the conscious or unconscious
realization by cosmogonists that they do not want their scientific specialist
colleagues, or nonspecialist citizens, to appreciate the difference.
Cosmogonists would like their ideas on origination and generation of the
universe to *appear* as scientific as the broad conceptualizations identified
previously as good scientific theories.

However removal of confusion between historical theories and good scientific theories as clearly *different* types of broad conceptualizations (though

developed by scientists) would go a long way toward helping nonspecialists evaluate space investigations. To the degree that space investigations have bearing on questions of *origin* of the earth, of the moon, or of the universe, federal expenditures are completely useless and doomed to generation of huge fiscal expenses *without* any real potential of tangible outcome. Again, no scientist can study scientifically the *origin* of the earth, the moon, the planet, star, comet or galaxy.

Of some significance regarding public reporting of cosmogonical ideas is the fact that cosmogonists write of their ideas of the origination and generation of the universe or parts thereof in terms of scenarios! To make cosmogonical ideas attractive to even the least scientifically trained person, authors of such ideas, even in prestigious scientific publications, draw up scenarios of moon origin or the origin of Mars. Of course scenarios are mere imagined dramas when completed by playwrights or novelists who write with the hope and anticipation that their work may be some form of *entertainment*, as in a play, or a feature film. These scenarios are a significant contrast to the contemporary scientific theories regarding the nature and structure of matter generated by physicists and chemists.

Thus, when the ideas of cosmogonists are viewed as models whereby they try to imagine, speculate, or conjecture about the origination and generation of the universe, a profitable operational definition is employed as an addition to those given separately in Chapter 1, and collected in the Appendix. Of course a model may be a physical object designed to show some analogical representation in reduced size of object and/or events. But in the current context, a model may be *operationally defined*:

Model

A conceptual pattern involving listed statements about imaginary objects and/or events and supposed relationships especially associated with concepts of origination and generation.

Actually, cosmogonists concentrate on preparation of various complex formulations about what they deem were phases of the origination and generation of the universe, including elements, stars, planets, comets, galaxies—that is, everything—from the popularly advanced big bang beginning.

After close to a quarter of a century study of facets of the evolution/creation controversy, I find that only *two basic* world views or points of view are involved. *All* thought systems are essentially reducible to variations of atheism or theism. Careful study of different postulates of different world views is basic to this conclusion.

A concise means of handling cosmogonical ideas on the origin of the universe is gained and represented in Classroom Teaching Aid 17. There are *two basic models* of origin of the universe. These are the evolution model and the creation model.

Evolution Model

An explanatory belief system based upon eternal existence of matter from which have come an ascending series of elements by nucleogenesis, changed by stellar evolution of young stars into old stars, galaxies, planets (especially the earth with life that appeared spontaneously through molecular evolution followed by organic evolution, including human evolution).

Necessarily, ideas of the evolution model have to do with *origination* of order out of disorder and *integration* of more complex patterns out of less complex patterns.

Creation Model

An explanatory belief system based upon existence of an Eternal Creator who established a completed, finished and functional universe in all aspects regarding elements, stars, galaxies, planets (especially the earth with mutually exclusive groups of animals and plants).

Necessarily, ideas of the creation model have to do with *conservation* of known conditions; yet, changes of *decay* and *degeneration* are evident and easily documented.

"Cover Word"
(Beware Semantic Confusion)

Evolution: When used without any prefix, confusion is generated and ambiguity prevails because of no indication of degree of change involved (i.e., prefix mega- or micro- should be used so that readers clearly know the degree of change intended by writer).

Classroom Teaching Aid 17
ON THE ORIGIN OF THE UNIVERSE

Because the primeval origins are completely beyond the limitations of scientific method, which is based upon initial observations, experimentation and repeatability, no one will ever be able to say, within present technology, (a) "Scientists have proved that all things have evolved from a primeval common origin," or (b) "Scientists have now proved the special creation of all things in the beginning."

Therefore the question as to which *model* of origins is ultimately the better model of origins can never be fully resolved scientifically, and one of the two models of ultimate origins is accepted by an individual, eventually, as a belief, not by any scientific proof or historic proof.

In the chart below, certain features of origins are related to the two possible models of origins:

EVOLUTION MODEL	CREATION MODEL
(a) Origin of the universe:	
Eternal existence of some form of matter (no cause).	Universe created essentially in present form (cause: Eternal Creator).
1. Big-bang concept: explosively expanding from primaeval state of extremely high density.	1. Light sources established.
2. Steady state concept: continual appearance of matter with simultaneous decay of matter, resulting in constancy.	2. Light rays, with electromagnetic fields, created directly and light sources seen instantly.
(Above violate law of conservation of matter and second law of thermodynamics and cause and effect assumption.)	3. Whole universe created full grown and functioning perfectly with unique fitness of earth for life quite evident. (No observed facts of scientists can be used to contradict above ideas.)
(b) Origin of elements:	
Nucleogenesis of subnuclear and subatomic particles involving hydrogen initially leading to ascending series of elements. (No mention of initiating energy source.)	Creator was source of cosmic nucleosynthesis which He empowered.

(c) Origin of stars, galaxies:

Stellar and galactic evolution in some kind of evolutionary series based on assumption of what "must have happened": "young" to "old".	Essentially stable, completed (finished) creation with concurrent principle of disintegration consistent with all astronomic measurements since man began to make such observations.

(d) Origin of solar system:

Nebular, tidal, dust cloud, collision, and close encounter concepts have been proposed but no evolutionary theory can be used to explain these peculiarities: anomalous distribution of moons, differing chemical compositions, geometrical placement, and the unique atmosphere and hydrosphere of the earth.	Primeval perfect, complete, functioning earth, moon, and planets created simultaneously; followed by imposed principle of disintegration with great catastrophes (asteroids, comets, bombardments of moon and Mars, etc.)
—Processes of cosmos supposedly processes of origination and integration	—Processes of cosmos observed to be processes of conservation and degeneration or decay

The question as to which model of origins is ultimately the better model of origins can never be fully resolved scientifically. Fundamentally, one of the two models of ultimate origins is accepted by an individual, eventually—as a *belief*—but not because of any scientific or historic proof. (Parenthetically, it might be pointed out that scientists *never* prove anything, as they must admit that they never are able to study all conditions relevant to objects and/or events in the natural environment. Hence scientists really specialize in denying or falsifying ideas, hypotheses, theorems, formulations or conceptualizations.)

Cosmogonies: Circumstantial Evidence

Is cosmogony only speculation, imagination and conjecture? No! Cosmogonists *do* use certain empirical findings accumulated by cosmologists, *after the fact* of the beginning of the universe, which can be employed to support circumstantially the big bang expanding universe cosmogony.

Cosmogonists do utilize certain conditions of the present as a basis for extrapolations backward into time. But cosmogonists are limited to beginning with *circumstances of the present*, and they are totally unable to test scientifically, through any repeatable observations, how these circumstances came into existence. Specifically, the *circumstantial* evidence utilized by cosmogonists are listed in Fig. 18.

Figure 18
CIRCUMSTANTIAL EVIDENCE FOR
BIG BANG ORIGIN OF THE UNIVERSE

1. Red shift of light spectra.
2. Nova and supernovae.
3. Background radio "noise" and background wave radiation.

"Cover Word"
(Beware Semantic Confusion)

Creation: Too often used by scientists to convey coming into existence of something new *as if* by some natural means; conveys connotation most accurately reserved for supernatural acts of Supreme God.

Cosmogonists do have *circumstantial* evidence in support of their commonly adopted ideas. But the evidence is *only* circumstantial. Yes, the red shift of light spectra might be a basis for maintaining that aspects of the universe are expanding from some point of beginning. But no one can identify that point. Astronomers do admit that they do not know from what point the universe is expanding, if in fact it is expanding. Yes, exploding stars might be a basis for maintaining that if some parts of the universe explode, then maybe the entire universe resulted from an explosion from some beginning point. Yes, background radio noise and background wave radiation might be a basis for maintaining that remnants of some supposed initial explosion have been detected.

However, no one knows or can describe the initial conditions of the universe. Each one of the points of circumstantial evidence may be used to support the contention that some *beginning* of the universe is required. Students can easily grasp that a-theistic cosmogonists begin the universe with the big bang concept, which is most popular today. Conversely, theistic cosmogonists maintain that in the beginning the universe was created essentially in present form. No evident cause is given by a-theistic cosmogonists. Apparently proponents of evolutionary cosmogonies consider that some inherent propensity for organization into a dense particle preliminary to explosion was characteristic of eternal matter. What caused the formation of the dense particle? A-theistic cosmogonists ignore the cause and effect assumption basic to all scientific thought (explained in Chapter 1). And a-theistic cosmogonists ignore excellent *circumstantial* evidence in support of the creation model. (See Fig. 19.)

Figure 19
CIRCUMSTANTIAL EVIDENCE FOR
CREATOR ORIGIN OF THE UNIVERSE

1. Orderly patterns of constellations.
2. Orderly patterns of planetary motions.
3. Orderly patterns of comet motions.

The science teacher utilizing the evolution/creation confrontation approach to teach first origins cannot avoid presenting such circumstantial evidence. Students should realize that creationist scientists *also* are reasoning *after the fact*, but specific points of order, pattern and symmetry may be employed to support the concept of a Designer for detected order and design.

The theistic cosmogonist accepts Eternal God, who has existed outside of time and space, as the ultimate cause of the heaven and the earth, and all that is therein. Thus the theistic cosmogonist goes one step beyond the a-theistic cosmogonist as far as cause and effect is concerned. Yet even the theistic cosmogonist must have a given: the Creator, —the original cause of it all. Belief in the Eternal Creator was commonly characteristic of those early scientists who began the discipline of modern science. Modern theistic cosmogonists stand with those same early scientists in contrast to the majority of a-theistic, evolutionary cosmogonists.

No scientific facts can be gathered to contradict the first postulational points of the creation model. However, such is not the case with the evolution model. The a-theistic cosmogonist's ideas of a big bang beginning is contradictory to a most important scientific law: the law of conservation of matter and energy, which entails the concept that matter/energy can neither be created nor destroyed. Modern cosmogonists presume that all atoms known were formed after the imagined big bang explosion.

Furthermore the second law of thermodynamics is violated by big bang cosmogonists when they suppose that components of the universe today are essentially extensive condensations of hydrogen. No known natually occurring accretions or integrations of matter are known *in the dimensions imagined by modern cosmogonists.* On the contrary, degeneration or decay and conservation of present conditions are the naturally occurring events known to scientists. These conditions are plainly subsumed in the first and second laws of thermodynamics. To claim, as the a-theistic cosmogonist does, that the present universe is the result of processess of origination, integration, and generation is to accept ideas that are contradictory to sound scientific laws, the first and second laws of thermodynamics (which supposedly the cosmogonists utilize in generating their explanations of the origin of the universe). Cosmogonists have no way of handling the above contradictions except to ignore them.[6]

Logically the science teacher will want to explicate further aspects of cosmogonical thinking that need careful attention. Questions such as: What is the universe expanding from? Where is the center of the universe? What caused the proposed expansion after the supposed big bang explosion should be raised. These questions, of course, cannot be answered scientifically within the present technology. No one can answer what caused the deduced expansion. Furthermore, astronomers do not know of any center of the universe. Here again the basic problem of what is the geometry of the universe is paramountly important. Yet no one knows the geometry of the universe. Of course discussion of such interrogations will help students comprehend more fully the distinction possible between *scientific* questions and what are essentially *metaphysical* questions about first origins which fundamentally are outside the purview of orderly, properly organized scientific work.

The evolution/creation confrontation approach to science teaching entails a confident attempt to clarify aspects of scientific methodology. The science teacher who makes a consistent application of the analysis and operational definitions provided in Chapter 1, will need to be prepared to contrast the ideas of cosmogonists and research work of cosmologists, physicists and chemists, who describe objects and/or events in the *natural* environment.

These scientists always work in the present. They have been and continue to be *the* scientists gaining more and more information of the nature and structure of matter—as they work toward increasing their dominion over the things around them.

Therefore much should be made of the contrast between speculative, conjectural thinking of cosmogonists and precise, careful scientific work of cosmologists, physicists and chemists. Research that is completed by cosmogonists regarding the present is always *after the fact* of the formation of the universe. Evolution/creation confrontation teachers should not hesitate to point out that cosmogonists must of necessity *extrapolate* from circumstances. Yet cosmogonists are not at all able to offer any *empirical* explanation for the existence of present circumstances. Evolutionary cosmogonists cannot give any naturally occurring conclusive evidence that the present universe came from a big bang explosion of some dense particle.

The science teacher, then, should give rigorous attention to the successful work of physicists and chemists who have analyzed more or less sequentially the atomic structure of matter. Of course imaginative ideas have been involved. However, Dalton's early drawings of atoms were indirectly the result of his empirical work and the work of others who were early initiators of the modern science of chemistry. Close study of Classroom Teaching Aid 18 will be basic to appreciation of the interaction of experiment and theory as physicists and chemists sought solution to the question, What is the nature and structure of matter?

As atomic physics and chemistry developed, there was interplay and interaction between experiment and theory (i. e., contemporary scientific theory). In Teaching Aid 18 some relationships of experiments and theoretical constructs with regard to light and the atom are presented. Particular attention is given to the development of theories of atomic structure. After the early work of Dalton, who initially thought of the atom as a solid ball for each element, a succession of models of the atom can be traced: (1) the raisin pudding concept of Thomson, (2) the solar system model of Rutherford, and (3) the models of Bohr, deBroglie and Chadwick plus ideas of Dirac. Yet highly significant for clearly understanding the *contrast* of the work of these scientists with the work of cosmogonists is the fact that the models of the atom were always subjected to test and re-test, at least indirectly. Physicists have employed bombardment of gold foil, cloud chambers, cyclotrons, betatrons and many recently invented,

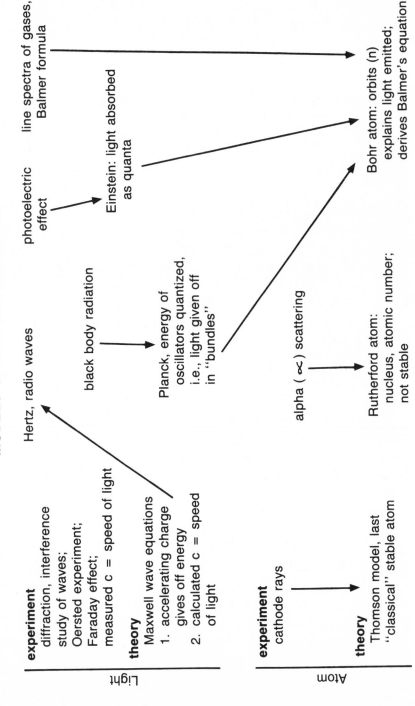

Classroom Teaching Aid 18
MODELS OF ATOMIC STRUCTURE

"Cover Word"
(Beware Semantic Confusion)

Historical, history: Proper use of such terms involves activities of human beings; so misleading use by megaevolutionists with respect to imagined geologic events conveys the connotation that real objects and events were involved in presumed past eras of time. Most properly all imaginative narratives of geologists are pre-historical.

"Cover Word"
(Beware Semantic Confusion)

Natural, Nature: Megaevolutionists grossly misuse this term, as if they have knowledge of or have studied natural objects and/or events of the past. Too often megaevolutionists consider that if some event or process can be thought of; that is, if an idea is thinkable, then, the event or process involved is natural. Such is not the case, for example, for tectonic or orogeny concepts regarding mountain building, since such concepts are supra-natural in the degree or magnitude imagined by megaevolutionists.

When the term nature is capitalized, as Nature, then reification and deification of all or part of the natural environment ensues. Such anthropomorphic usage is inappropriate for scientists who claim to be operating from a naturalistic position.

---

highly sophisticated tools and equipment, always within the limiting principles of orthodox scientific methodology. Because of rigorous methods of investigation, refinement followed upon refinement (much like refinement of cosmological systems) leading to the present complicated, highly abstract formulations about atomic and subatomic structure. Today, whole families of particles are associated with the electron, proton, neutron and quarks.

As a consequence of specific empirical work on the nature and structure of matter, many important generalizations have been derived which now have been so corroborated that they are considered laws of nature, or natural laws. Of course, laws are only well substantiated, approximate representations of interactions of natural objects and/or events as studied and analyzed by scientists. Again the science teacher should make clear that natural laws *do not control* matter or the universe. Natural laws are only descriptive. Natural laws are not prescriptive. Natural laws only contain descriptions of behavior of natural objects.

"Cover Word"
(Beware Semantic Confusion)

Mechanism: Essentially a cover word for observable conditions with no real explanation about how such conditions came into existence; use of this word gives connotative support to the mechanistic world-view that centers on the idea that causal factors are known and a more or less deterministic situation prevails.

"Cover Word"
(Beware Semantic Confusion)

Natural laws (*laws of nature*): Statements of seemingly universally applicable generalizations that are really only descriptive, and not at all prescriptive, like civil laws, as is often the implication of the context in which these words are used. Natural laws do *not* control or govern the universe, or any part thereof. Natural laws only *describe* regularities that scientists have detected with regard to objects and/or events in the natural environment.

Classroom Teaching Aid 19 contains a representative list of laws. These formulations are fully the result of careful, proper scientific endeavor. They are quite in contrast to the wide ranging formulations about totally *unrepeatable* events inherent in cosmogonical thinking. Science teachers should take full advantage of the nature of these laws (and the manner in which they have been derived, if classroom time is available) to help students understand what cosmogony really is: seemingly unlimited application of speculative thinking by non-theistic scientists toward the formulation of scenarios about the cosmic past; the explanation of ideas about conditions of the origination of the universe which are fully outside the limits of proper, orderly science and present technology.

Classroom Teaching Aid 19
NATURAL LAWS

Gas Laws

The volume of a confined gas is inversely proportional to the pressure of the confined gas, when temperature is held constant.

The pressure of a confined gas is directly proportional to the temperature of the gas, when volume is held constant.

The volume of a confined gas is directly proportional to the temperature of the gas, when pressure is held constant.

Electrostatic Laws

Like static electric charges repel. Unlike static electric charges attract.

Magnetic Polar Laws

Like poles of magnets repel. Unlike poles of magnets attract.

Laws of Chemistry

The weights of elements making up a compound are directly proportional to each other.

When two elements can unite to form more than one compound, weights of one element combining with fixed weight of other elements are in ratio of small whole numbers.

In gas reactions, the volumes of two gases that combine are in relation to each other as ratio of small whole numbers.

Thermodynamic Laws

Matter and energy can neither be created nor destroyed.

A physical system will tend toward increased disorder (increase entropy) without an outside ordering agent to prevent it.

FOOTNOTES

[1] "But now science comes to a great event—the birth of the Universe—and it asks: What Cause Produced this Effect? Who, or what, put the matter and energy into the Universe? Was the world created out of nothing or was it gathered together out of pre-existing materials? And: What force or forces created the outward momentum of the initial explosion? But that is just what science cannot find out." Dr. Robert Jastrow in talk on "God and the Astronomers", Phi Beta Kappa Lecture AAAS meeting, Washington, D.C., February 14, 1978.

[2] Kepler's laws are excellent examples of well substantiated descriptive generalizations but they are *not* laws which control planetary motion. In accordance with the explanation of the operational definition of scientific laws (Chapter 1), the Keplerian natural laws are descriptive, and not prescriptive, as is characteristic of civil laws in human society. This significant distinction should be made clear by the science teacher in this context of laws related to cosmological thinking. Similar opportunities will present themselves with regard to laws in electricity, chemistry and genetics.

[3]Discussion of his supposed recantation is beyond the scope of this book. However, "The Greatest Scandal in Christendom" by Arthur Koestler (*The Observer Weekend Review*, London, February 2, 1964, pp. 21, 29) sets the record straight.

[4]In a copyrighted article published in many metropolitan newspapers in late 1978, Dr. Robert Jastrow, director of NASA's Goddard Institute for Space Studies and professor of astronomy at Columbia University, and adapted from his book, *God and the Astronomers* (New York: W. W. Norton Co., Inc., 1978) raised these questions about the universe coming into existence at a certain moment from an explosion, "What cause produced this effect? Who or what put the matter and enery into the universe? Was the universe created out of nothing, or was it gathered together out of pre-existing materials? And science cannot answer these questions . . . "

[5]The velocity-distance relationship, called Hubble's Law, is described simply as: the velocity is equal to the distance multiplied by a constant (v = dH where v is the velocity, d is the distance, and H is a constant.) By measuring distance and red shift of nearby galaxies, the value of H can be calculated, which in turn can be used to derive estimates of distances of other galaxies.

[6]In the late 1970's considerable effort has been expended by evolutionary-minded scientists to explain away such contradictions between their supposed explanations and sound orderly, proper scientific findings and laws. The Nobel Prize in chemistry was given to a Belgian scientist, Ilya Prigogine, for his suggestions for explaining away entropy with regard to living tissue. Specific critiques of Prigogine's speculations were written by Henry M. Morris, "Thermodynamics and the Origin of Life," Impact Series No. 57, March 1978, and Duane T. Gish, "Thermodynamics and the Origin of Life: Part II", Impact Series No. 58, April 1978, both published by the Institute for Creation Research, San Diego, Ca.

Chapter 2

General Discussion Questions

1. What are the stated goals of this chapter?
2. Discuss each of the following: "big bang", "steady state", and "oscillating" concepts with regard to the universe.
3. Discuss what is meant by "boundaries of measurement".
4. How are the terms "cosmology" and "cosmogony" differentiated in a rigorous manner?
5. Explain the reason that Ptolemy and Copernicus and Galileo and Brahe believed that planetary objects moved along perfect circles.
6. Explain the analogy between sound transmission on the earth and light transmission through space presently accepted by modern astronomers and cosmogonists.
7. Because of his reliance upon careful quantitative analysis, what conceptual change was Kepler forced to make to develop his cosmological system?
8. Explain what is meant by circumstantial evidence.
9. How do "natural laws" differ from "societal laws"?

Class Projects or Individual Assignments

1. Prepare a topical outline of this chapter.
2. List "cover words" that could cause semantic confusion.
3. Prepare a large chart of the Distance-Scale Pyramid.
4. Prepare large drawings to illustrate the concepts of azimuth and altitude.
5. Work out a chart to illustrate each of the common steps scientists take to handle contradictions.
6. Prepare a chart of comparison of the postulates of Ptolemy and the postulates of Copernicus.
7. Prepare large drawings of each of the cosmological systems of Ptolomy, Copernicus, Brahe, and Kepler.
8. Prepare a diagram of the Doppler Effect of sound transmission.

9. Prepare a large wall chart of the Evolution Model and the Creation Model on the origin of the universe, elements, stars, galaxies, and the solar system.

10. Prepare a two-column chart of the circumstantial evidence for a Creator origin of the universe and for a "Big Bang" origin of the universe.

11. Prepare a two-column chart to itemize points of comparison and contrast of "natural laws" and "societal laws".

12. Work out a set of answers for the evaluation items provided at the close of this chapter. Now prepare a set of similar evaluation items for this general subject matter area.

Read: Thomas G. Barnes, *Origin and Destiny of the Earth's Magnetic Field.* 1973. Technical Monograph No. 4. San. Diego: Institute for Creation Research.

         Harold S. Slusher, *The Origin of the Universe.* 1978 Technical Monograph No. 8; *Age of the Cosmos.* 1980. Technical Monograph No. 9; *The Age of the Earth* (with Thomas P. Gamwell). 1978. Technical Monograph No. 7; and *The Age of the Solar System* (with Stephen J. Duursma). 1978. Technical Monograph No. 6. All are available from San Diego: Institute for Creation Research.

On the Use of Scripture in Parochial Schools

1. Ask students to read 1 Peter 3, with special attention to verses 4 thru 7. Now ask students to discuss how these verses contain a possible three-part cosmogony.

2. As time is available contrasts could be made with ideas from the Hindus, Egyptians, and other ancient peoples, more or less contemporary with Moses and the Hebrews.

Evaluation Questions

Select from the key the appropriate entry most closely associated with each statement in items 1 through 12:

KEY: 1. Circumstantial evidence for the big bang cosmogony
2. Feature of evolution model of cosmic origin.
3. Circumstantial evidence for Creator origin of the universe.
4. Feature of creation model of cosmic origin.
5. Argument against nontheistic origin of universe.

1. What started supposed pre-established harmony of recession of nebulae into unobservability and the creation of isolated particles near at hand? (5)
2. Order and pattern of zodiac and other stellar constellations. (3)
3. Detected background radio noise and background wave radiation. (1)
4. Nova and supernovae or stellar explosions detected over the centuries. (1)
5. Red shift of light from different stars toward red part of light spectrum. (1)
6. What caused the explosion of some cosmic egg? (5)
7. Order and pattern of reasoned orbits of comets. (3)
8. Order and pattern of reasoned planetary motion. (3)
9. The entire universe came into existence in essentially the present functional relationships. (4)
10. Expansion of material is contradictory to condensation of material to form galaxies and stars. (5)
11. An ascending series of elements came from nucleogenesis of sub-nuclear and subatomic particles involving hydrogen. (2)
12. It is predicated upon a Doppler shift interpretation of the red shift of light from galaxies. (1)

Select entries in the key to show your understanding of aspects of possible cosmogonies for items 13 through 22.
KEY: 1. Most closely related to evolutionary cosmogony (model)
2. Most closely associated with creational cosmogony (model)
3. Unrelated to either origin model.
13. Red shift of light from different stars toward red part of the spectrum. (1)
14. The entire universe came into existence in essentially the present functional relationships. (2)
15. Order and pattern of zodiac and other star constellations. (2)

16. The universe is continually changing through decay of matter and replacement of matter. (1)
17. The entire universe resulted from an explosion of some quantity of extremely dense matter. (1)
18. Order and pattern of reasoned planetary motion. (2)
19. Nova and supernovae (star explosions). (1)
20. Stable and completed or finished arrangement of stars and galaxies exists and has existed since astronomical measurements were made by human beings. (2)
21. Order and pattern of reasoned orbits of comets. (2)
22. Detected background radio noise and background wave radiation. (1)

23. As scientists have imagined certain beginnings of the solar system other than in accordance with the creation model, they have offered which of the following? (d)
    a. Collision of two stars
    b. Near passing of two stars.
    c. Rotating gaseous or nebular matter
    d. All of the above as given
    e. Actually only #1 and #2 as given above.

24. Your attention was drawn to the fact that the big bang concept of cosmogonists is fully based upon analogical reasoning, such as: (b)
    a. Dust particles in space are like molecules in constant motion.
    b. Comparison of the change of sound tone with change of light spectra.
    c. Suggestions that atmospheric pressure around you is a type of sea of air.
    d. Any one of these as listed here.
    e. None of these listed here.

3 | Origin of Life on the Earth

When you complete this chapter you should understand how to:
1. Discuss questions about the origin of life on the earth.
2. Explain weaknesses in the majority position on the origin of life on the earth.
3. Explain a life—death continuum as a frame of reference for discussion of the origin of life on the earth.
4. Explain five main ideas of scientists regarding generation of life on the earth.
5. Contrast ideas about spontaneous generation of life with steps to synthesize actual components of living substance.
6. Identify and explain principle ideas of reductionist biologists such as Dr. Francis Crick.

Whereas changing concepts and descriptions of the universe can be collectively handled under the term cosmology, and ideas on the origination and generation of the universe can be subsumed under the term cosmogony, there are at least five main ideas of scientists about the origin of life on the earth, including the modern majority position. However, just as the origin of the universe is a question of ultimate origin, so the origin of life on the earth is a question of ultimate origin. Of course biological scientists can *talk about* and *write about* their ideas on the origin of life on the earth. They do so very much like cosmogonists expound on their various ideas about the origin of the universe. However, since scientific endeavor is focused on the present, the ultimate origin of life on the earth is beyond application of scientific methodology. Biologists will never actually be able to study the origin of life on the earth. In point of fact, J. D. Bernal has expressed that the principles of experimental science do not apply to discussions on the origin of life and ''indeed cannot apply to any problem of origin.''[1] Thus the science teacher can reiterate confidently that only a negative answer can be given for the question, Is it possible to study scientifically the origin of life on the earth?

Chemical Evolution

What *is* the present position of the *majority* of biologists? According to their mechanistic, materialistic view of the universe, all reality came into existence through evolution. Thus proponents of this view require that life arose on the earth (or somewhere in the universe) from inanimate matter through chemical and physical processes still operating today. I will now give a brief summary of chemical evolution.

Stage 1: Primitive Earth Scenario

Biologists who speculate on the origin of life on the earth require a primitive earth model that includes tolerant conditions in which postulated chemical reactions leading to the origin of life could occur. Today there is a general consensus among geologists that the oceans of the earth formed rapidly in such a manner that early in the existence of the earth the acidity (pH) and temperature of the oceans became approximately the same as the present time. However historical theorists interested in the origin of life on the earth are forced to postulate a primitive earth atmosphere very different from the present atmosphere, as mentioned in the itemization of five proposed stages of evolution of life on the earth. (See Fig. 20.)

Figure 20
EVOLUTION MODEL FOR THE ORIGIN OF LIFE ON THE EARTH

According to the evolution model, the story of life on the earth began some five billion years ago and gradually unfolded through a series of five stages:

Stage 1
In stage 1 evolutionists have imagined that the atmosphere of the early earth was quite different from the present atmosphere. In contrast to the present *oxidizing* atmosphere, which contains 21% free oxygen (O_2), 78% nitrogen (N_2), and 1% of other gases, supposedly the early earth was surrounded by a *reducing* atmosphere made up mostly of methane (CH_4), ammonia (NH_3), hydrogen (H_2), and water vapor (H_2O).

Stage 2

Because of ultraviolet light, electric discharge, and high-energy particle bombardment of molecules in a reducing atmosphere, stage 2 came about with the formation of small organic molecules such as sugars, amino acids, and nucleotides.

Stage 3

Presuming all of this happened billions of years ago in a reducing atmosphere, then stage 3 is imagined during which combinations of various small stage 2 molecules resulted in formation of large polymers such as starches, proteins, and nucleic acids (DNA).

Stage 4

During stage 4 these large molecules supposedly joined together into gel-like globs called coacervates or microspheres. Possibly these coacervates attracted smaller molecules so that new structures, called proto-cells, might have formed.

Stage 5

Evolutionists believe that, finally, at stage 5 at least one of these globs absorbed the right molecules so that complex molecules could be duplicated within new units called living cells. These first cells consumed molecules left over from earlier states, but eventually photosynthesis appeared in cells, in some way, and oxygen was released into the atmosphere. As the percentage of oxygen in the early earth atmosphere increased, most of the known forms of life on the earth today began to appear. Because of the presence of oxygen, these early life forms destroyed all the molecules from earlier stages, and no more chemical evolution was possible.

Evolutionists are forced to imagine, *a priori*, that the primitive earth atmosphere contained no oxygen; that is, it was not an *oxidizing* atmosphere. If the primitive earth atmosphere had contained a significant quantity of oxygen, then an evolutionary origin of life would not have been possible, since all substances would have been oxidized to water, carbon dioxide, nitrogen compounds, and other oxidized products. Therefore, most modern biologists have insisted that the primitive earth atmosphere was a *reducing* atmosphere. A reducing atmosphere would have been a chemical environment high in electron donors like hydrogen, such as found in methane (CH_4), ammonia (NH_3), water vapor (H_2O), and hydrogen (H_2).

Of course some evolutionists have found certain difficulties with the assumption of a primitive reducing atmosphere of the earth. There are those who insist that no evidence can be found for a primitive methane-ammonia atmosphere.[2] There is no geochemical evidence that the atmosphere of the earth ever contained methane. In addition, the rocks of the lowest layers do not contain unusually large amounts of carbon or organic chemicals as might be expected if some kind of reducing atmosphere of the earth ever existed.

Stage 2: Synthesis of Relatively Simple Organic Compounds

Although scientists are unable to agree upon an original reducing atmosphere, they do agree that a variety of biologically important molecules can be produced by energizing a mixture of methane, ammonia, and water.

An early investigator, Dr. Stanley Miller, successfully synthesized amino acids and a few other simple organic compounds under assumed primitive earth conditions. Miller and his research team circulated a mixture of methane, ammonia, hydrogen, and water vapor through a very special apparatus containing an electrical chamber. (See Classroom Teaching Aid 20.) After circulating the gases for about a week Miller analyzed the aqueous solution and found that it contained synthetic products that had collected in a cold trap. The aqueous solution contained glycine and alanine, the two least complex amino acids, plus small amounts of other amino acids (glutamic acid and aspartic acid), non-protein amino acids, and other substances. These results have been repeated by Dr. Ponnamperuma and others who have produced a variety of amino acids, sugars, purines, pyrimidines, and other compounds under a variety of conditions and using various gases.

A vital part of Miller's experimental apparatus was the cold trap where the synthesized products collected as they were formed from chemical reactions. Without that trap the chemical products would have been destroyed by the energy source (i.e., the electrical sparking). Significant also is the natural tendency for biological molecules to go from the complex and well ordered to the less complex and disordered state at temperatures at which life processes commonly occur. The success of all experimentors to synthesize amino acids and other substances was due to special conditions enumerated in Fig. 21.

Classroom Teaching Aid 20
THE MILLER "*ORIGIN OF LIFE*" APPARATUS

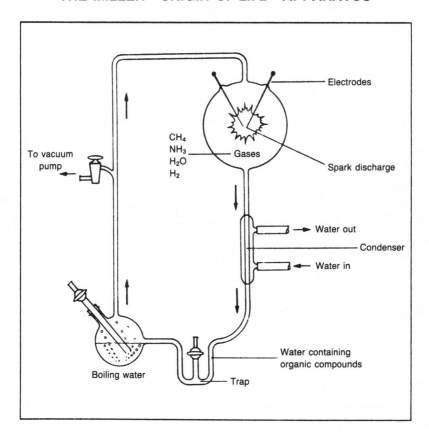

Stage 3: Origin of Large, Complex Molecules

It is noteworthy that the simple molecules produced by Miller and Ponnampuruma are *not living* substance. Synthesized organic compounds are not the same as the complex, large molecules, such as enzymes (chains of amino acids), so importantly characteristic of the *organization* and *coordination* that makes living systems different from nonliving matter. Enzymes are very special kinds of ordered proteins, and so far, modern biologists have only produced proteins more or less randomly.

Figure 21
SPECIAL CONDITIONS FOR ANY SYNTHESIS
OF SIMPLE ORGANIC COMPOUNDS

1. A special cold trap was used to isolate products synthesized from the source of energy (which would have caused destruction of simple organic compounds produced).
2. Any possible solar radiation available during primitive earth conditions would have been more efficient in destruction of biological products than in their formulation.
3. Time required would have been several years, and with no way to trap the products of synthesis in the natural environment, the rate of destruction would have far exceeded any production rate.
4. Because of the instability of organic compounds unless temperatures are below 25°C, and since the early ocean probably would not have been that cool, then the early oceans could not have been the site of synthesis of simple organic compounds.
5. Accumulation of significant quantities of simple organic compounds would have been precluded by the fact that rates of destruction would have far exceeded synthesis.
6. Only very small quantities of simple organic compounds could have accumulated since ultraviolet radiation penetrating sea water would have been destructive.
7. Amino acids and sugars react with mutual destruction.

The suggestion of Dr. Sidney Fox, called the thermal model for the origin of life, has received much attention. According to his thinking, large complex proteins formed on the earth in ponds of warm water near the edges of volcanos.

First, Dr. Fox produced in his laboratory protein-like molecules by heating pure, dry amino acids at 150°-180° for four to six hours. Next, Fox dissolved the product obtained in hot water. Upon cooling, he observed that small microspheres formed, which he called proteinoids, since they were globules that seemed to bud and grow. He even suggested that the first living cells were formed in this way. But other biological experts have disagreed with him. And, of course, no biologist has been successful in producing all 20 of the *specific* amino acids commonly found in living tissues. Fox's scheme would require a unique series of events and conditions with questionable probability, summarized in Fig. 22.

Figure 22
PROBABILITIES AGAINST THERMAL MODEL OF ORIGIN OF LIFE

1. Heating of the right materials at an appropriate temperature would be so limited, and the timing of rain as an agent of transport (just six hours plus or minus from the time heating began) so restrictive, that production rate would be less than destruction rate by hydrolysis.
2. Probability of a mixture of pure amino acids accumulating anywhere would be absolute zero.
3. The very special ratio of amino acids utilized by Fox would not occur under any naturally occurring conditions.
4. Since serine and threonine undergo severe destruction during heating, such as required in the thermal model, only minor amounts of these amino acids could occur in contrast to naturally occurring proteins.
5. There is no valid evidence in the product obtained by the Fox method for the presence of amino acids arranged in highly specific sequence, but rather an enormous number of polypeptides with random structures. Fox cannot demonstrate formation of *only* left-handed amino acids which is the form found exclusively in living things.
6. Catalytic, or enzymatic, properties claimed for the product are barely detectable and dissimilar to present enzymes.
7. The proteinoid microspheres are unstable and easily destroyed by dilution with water which would supposedly have been abundant on the early earth.
8. Division of microspheres is essentially similar to separation of soap bubbles and quite dissimilar to the incredably complex cell division processes.

Stage 4: Origin of Stable, Complex Biologically Active Systems

Evolutionary biologists believe that if large polymers, such as starches, proteins, and nucleic acids (DNA) could form on the primitive earth, then it would be possible for gel-like globs called coacervates, or microspheres, to form. The common experience of watching fat droplets form on the surface of a bowl of soup, and then seeing them come together and even divide, *seems* to be a logical analogue for primitive earth events imagined by evolutionists. Oparin has proposed that coacervates may have been intermediate forms between loose moleclues and living systems. Oparin believed that some coacervate globule might have absorbed just the right molecules to become a living cell (although he knew that coacervates were unstable and would also absorb harmful molecules). However, the association of macromolecules to form coacervates, and the absorption of molecules from the surrounding medium is the consequence of simple chemical and physical phenomena. Such processes are not selective, not stable, nor the basis of organization that would be duplicated.

"Cover Word"
(Beware Semantic Confusion)

Self-reproducing (*Self-replicative*): Use of "self" conveys connotation of "selfness" or "selfhood" as of human existence, as involving human volition—at base this practice involves anthropomorphism that is not appropriate for impersonal scientific work; no cell component reproduces in isolation.

Stage 5: Origin of Independent, Stable, Duplicating Units—The First Cells

As mentioned, the significant difference between living cells and coacervates is organization and coordination that makes living systems different from non-living matter. In all living systems the most fundamental example of coordination is the manner in which DNA codes for protein formation. DNA is *the* complex molecule of heredity and proteins are *the* macromolecules of structure (organization) and function (coordination).

Noteworthy is the fact that many specific enzymes, which are proteins, are necessary for proper functioning of the DNA code during protein synthesis. Also, formation and selection of each amino acid in proteins depends upon several DNA molecules. In fact, the whole process of protein synthesis is very complex. (See Fig. 23.)

Furthermore, living cells contain defense mechanisms against several injurious processes such as (1) dimerization of the thymine unit in DNA, (2) deamination (removal of an amine group) of cytosine, adenine, and guanine in DNA and RNA, (c) deamination of glutamic and asparagine in proteins, and (d) production of toxic peroxide.

Figure 23
WEAKNESSES OF ORIGIN OF STABLE METABOLIC SYSTEMS

1. Vast quantities of macromolecules would have to be present in primeval seas at some saturation point where complex coacervates or proteinoid microspheres would precipitate out of solution.
2. Such globular products are unstable and would easily disintegrate because there is not a natural tendency for more complex systems to form spontaneously from less complex systems.
3. Even if some catalytic ability did appear it would have been useless and plainly destructive.

According to the materialistic, mechanistic origin of life, enzymes are special kinds of proteins that resulted from time, chance and unknown, supposed natural chemical processes. According to the materialistic, mechanistic origin of life, the complex relationship between DNA and proteins found in living cells also resulted from time, chance and natural processes. Yet the dilemma of the appearance of the first cell according to this viewpoint has not been solved and seems to be the final insuperable barrier to the origin of life on the earth. Many notable scientists have wondered about this dilemma as shown by the given in Fig. 24. The statements are representative of many more in the scientific literature.

Figure 24
COMMENTS OF NOTABLE SCIENTISTS ON COMPLEX RELATIONSHIPS IN LIVING CELLS

1. Francis Crick, recipient of Nobel prize for the discovery of the structure of DNA, has said that the trick in life is to make the translation machinery, which will require an "elaborate bisoynthetic mechanism."
2. Leslie Orgel, who co-authored the book, *Origins of Life on the Earth*, with Stanley Miller, has said that the big problem is to tie DNA reproduction into the mechanism of protein production. He has wondered openly, "is the problem chemical or philosophical?"
3. Dr. O'Connor has written in his college chemistry textbook: "There is no reason for scientists to discard belief in God. Indeed, there are many who feel the need for a faith that suggests human life is more than a series of chemical changes. . . .If true, and many of us are convinced that it is, it is far more important than anything science, technology, or this world has to offer."

At this point the reader could very well wonder why I have given so much attention to these essential ideas of the majority position held by internationally famous biologists. I have done so because the science teacher must have some basic understanding of the majority position to be prepared to meet the tremendous promotion of the thermal model put forth by Fox, and the incredibly persuasive presentations of Oparin's ideas on the possible stages of formation of the first living cell on the earth.

Too often authors of high school and college science textbooks have uncritically accepted the ideas of evolutionary biologists. Textbook authors, of course, have been encouraged to write as they have because of the almost unilateral acceptance of the ideas of Fox and Oparin and the lack of critical analysis of Miller's experiment by leaders of scientific organizations and by editors of scientific journals and magazines. Such successful acceptance of the materialistic, mechanistic viewpoint of the origin of life on the earth confirms the bias and unscientific attitudes that dominate the educational and scientific establishments with regard to questions of origin of life on the earth. The science teacher should be prepared to show students that not all written material that incorporates the evolutionary outlook is necessarily acceptable as scientific when gauged against criteria of proper, orderly scientific endeavor. (See Fig. 25.) To help the science teacher develop teaching strategies and to provide a further objective analysis of ideas contained in the majority position, the substantive content of this chapter is presented in five distinct sections.

Figure 25   FOUR SPECIAL CONDITIONS REQUIRED BY COMPLEXITY OF LIFE

The complexity of life requires at least four special conditions:
1. An open system of chemical change (which is characteristic of a green plant).
2. An adequate energy supply (which basically is the sun in this solar system).
3. An energy conversion system.
4. A control system for the whole complexity of the life processes (even in the single-celled life forms, which can never properly be called simple since all life forms are complex).

The fact that living organisms require *all four* of these conditions is quite a sufficient basis for students to realize that the passage of time alone could never result in the appearance of independent, stable, duplicating cells, as structural and function units of the complexity of life.

Life—Death Continuum

For proper and complete consideration of the materialistic, mechanistic majority position just presented in brief resume, an objective frame of reference is needed. An excellent point of departure is the life—death continuum provided in Classroom Teaching Aid 21. (This teaching aid contains many elements and, therefore, it would be most advisable to build it piece by piece before presenting the completed whole to students.)

Consideration of this teaching aid provides an overall picture for orientation of discussion of the ultimate origin of life on the earth (which is of the past), as well as aspects of life in the present (to which the law of biogenesis can be applied), and even currently popularized writings about those who claim to have experienced life after death (which is of the future). Classroom Teaching Aid 21 is a fully useful means of relating and correlating many, many seemingly diverse concepts.

Please note that vertical dotted lines are boundary lines which enclose essentially those aspects, concepts and events of life and death that are in the present—hence amenable to *scientific* research. By using this teaching aid the science teacher can help students understand limitations of scientific methodology. By considering the questions, Which can be repeated?, and Which are naturally occurring events? (and therefore open to *scientific* study), we may more fully appreciate the limitations of science and scientists. (Chapter 1)

What is life? What is death? Although the terms life and death are admittedly very hard to define, at least these questions are of the present. They involve naturally occurring objects and/or events and can be studied scientifically during the lifetime of investigators. Of course, with regard to scientific studies of life to date, biologists have found *no* exceptions to the fact that all life, either plant or animal, has come from some living organism(s). Actually, life is known to come only from other life. This is essentially a statement of a most fundamental law of biology, the law of biogenesis. Flies are known to come only from previously existing flies; bacteria are known to come only from previously existing bacteria. The law of biogenesis is a very scientifically substantiated law of biology that resulted from the inductive work of many biologists, the most renowned of whom are Francisco Redi and Louis Pasteur. The work of these men

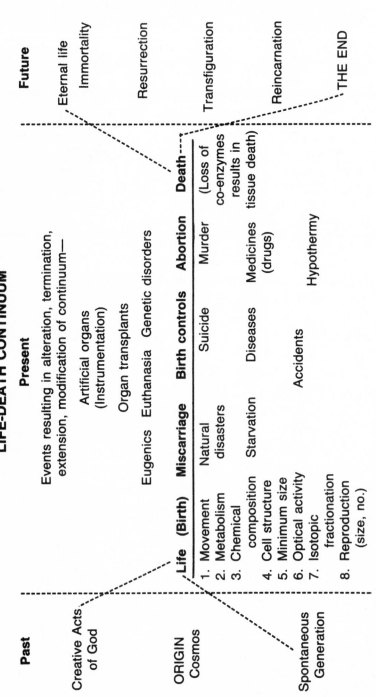

Classroom Teaching Aid 21
LIFE-DEATH CONTINUUM

Past	Present				Future

Past

Creative Acts
of God

ORIGIN
Cosmos

Spontaneous
Generation

Present

Events resulting in alteration, termination,
extension, modification of continuum—

Artificial organs
(Instrumentation)

Organ transplants

Eugenics Euthanasia Genetic disorders

Life (Birth) Miscarriage Birth controls Abortion Death---

1. Movement
2. Metabolism
3. Chemical
   composition
4. Cell structure
5. Minimum size
6. Optical activity
7. Isotopic
   fractionation
8. Reproduction
   (size, no.)

Natural
disasters   Suicide   Murder   (Loss of
                                                 co-enzymes
Starvation   Diseases   Medicines   results in
                                  (drugs)   tissue death)
        Accidents
                                  Hypothermy

Future

Eternal life
Immortality

Resurrection

Transfiguration

Reincarnation

THE END

Questions: Which can be repeated?

Which are naturally occurring events, and, therefore open to *scientific* study?

is most relevant to that part of Classroom Teaching Aid 21 that involves the past when the ultimate origin of life on the earth occurred.

The term *present* is placed over those parts of the chart which are mainly aside from the purpose of this book. Please note that commonly accepted properties or characteristics of life are enumerated, that a possible definition of biological death (in contrast to legal death) is given parenthetically, and that multiple events are given as possible causal factors which would result in alteration of the life—death continuum. Events of the present that are below the horizontal line *would be mentioned only*, and discussion and real attention is assumed to be part of the role of teachers in social studies, sociology, medicine or related courses.

The term *past* is placed over that part of the chart associated with origin of life, whereas the term *future* is placed over those concepts associated with after death. Clearly, careful and proper science *cannot* be used effectively to study what occurs after death. At least that seems to be widely accepted with regard to immortality, resurrection[3], transfiguration and reincarnation, which are believed by many people in different cultures. True, recent publications have appeared in which authors purport to reveal experiences recounted by those who have died and then come back to life. Comment on those materials is beyond the scope of this book. However much can be gained through a discussion of the question, What is death? In doing so, limitations of scientists are made manifest again. Realistically, any future moment is of the present in the life of any investigator, i.e., the moment when procedures of proper, orderly scientific endeavor can be employed.

If scientists do not find any means for careful and proper scientific study of the future, then the logical question follows, Can investigators scientifically study the past? An answer to this question requires clarification of what is meant by the term *past*. Any single moment that passes becomes a part of the past. What is meant by the past is very hard to delineate to the complete satisfaction of all. Right now it is sufficient to reiterate that cosmologist, physicists, and biologists always scientifically study aspects of the natural environment as they find them in the present.

But human beings still ask, Where did life come from? This *is* a most logical question to be faced in any discussion with scientific orientation because it involves a most natural utilization of the cause and effect presupposition of all scientists. Life exists on the earth. Whence cometh life?

Figure 26
ON "HISTORY"

The importance of the term "history" is relevant to any consideration of
the terms of "past", "present", or "future". In chapter 1, I established that
"history" most naturally and commonly involves activities of human beings.
Thus it follows that no scientist was present, as a scientist, when first life
appeared on the earth. Therefore there has been no scientific study of the
origin of first life on the earth—nor can there ever be any careful and proper
scientific study of first life on the earth (within present technology).

Ideas on the Origin of Life

As soon as the science teacher has established certain bounds of the
biological scientist, then students can realize fully that, over the centuries—
and even today, there are certain *choices* as to the origin of life on the earth.
Over the centuries there have been repeated outbursts of debate about the
origin of life on the earth. It is almost as if a debate question had been
formulated back in ancient times, and human beings had been taking pro
and con positions on a question such as, "Resolved: Life on the earth came
from some inorganic source." In brief, two main positions have been taken
from ancient times to the present: (1) some persons have supported
abiogenesis, the belief that living substance has arisen from nonliving
substance, whereas (2) others have maintained the position of *biogenesis*,
the belief that living substance has come only from other living substance.

An expansion of the two main positions is most advantageous in teaching
about the origin of life. Five categories of ideas about the origin of life on
the earth are condensed in a pro and con treatment provided in Classroom
Teaching Aid 22. This teaching aid can make a significant contribution
to clear thinking and comprehension for participants in any discussion of
evolution/creation ideas about the origin of life on the earth.[4]

Basically there are three variations of the concept of heterogenesis, which
is a synonym for the more commonly used term of spontaneous generation of life. Then there is a fourth concept that life on the earth came from
outer space, and a fifth concept that life was created on the earth by God.
The belief that God created life is very ancient and traceable to the Hebrew
traditions regarding first origins. In other words the position that God
created life on the earth was held by scientists through the centuries until

Classroom Teaching Aid 22
IDEAS ON THE ORIGIN OF LIFE
(No scientific theory or hypothesis is possible)

ABIOGENESIS

BIOGENESIS

PRO-Position	CON-Position
1. Macrozoic ideas: Ancient people *believed* in spontaneous generation of *whole* organisms, because they thought they saw mice come from mud and snakes from horses hair, etc. (Aristotle, others)	Conclusive controlled experimentation of Francisco Redi (1650) with covered and uncovered meat *established* that life came from life, at least flies from maggots which came from eggs laid by flies.
2. Microzoic ideas: Next, people *believed* in spontaneous generation of microbes or bacteria because Pouchet (1860) and others thought they saw such occur in nutrient broths.	Conclusive work by Appert and controlled experimentation by Louis Pasteur (1864) with swan-necked flasks *established* that bacteria may be dust-laden and a source of bacterial life from life.
3. Sub-microzoic ideas: Today many scientists *believe* in spontaneous generation of sub-vital units of matter that formed into coacervates or proteinoids. (Darwin believed in one or many beginnings; Oparin believed in one combination of sub-vital units; Miller, Fox, Ponnampurumma have used controlled experimentation to *synthesize* amino acids, which are not living.)	Instantaneous synthesis of amino acids requires human intervention, hence no man can study spontaneous generation, which by definition entails *no external* intervention. (Blum and Cook point out chance of life coming from no life; Coppedge indicates high improbability of *only left-handed* protein substances in living organisms.
4. Cosmozoic ideas: Over the decades and still today some scientists *believe* that life came to the earth from other planets or other parts of the universe by way of spores or meteorites.	These ideas "beg the question", side step problem of origin of life; no other planets known from space probes (Mercury, Venus, Mars, Jupiter, or Saturn) seem to have life as we know it. Heat of meteorites, x-rays, ultra-violet light would have real deleterious effects on life.
5. Theozoic ideas: Over the centuries some scientists *believe* life is result of supernatural creative acts of Creator God; life that has always been complex. (Note: *Beliefs* in #1 thru #4 all entail *supra*-natural events.)	No scientific study possible, but a Creator of life would not be in contradiction to concepts of cause and effect, or degradation or degeneration from complex organizational order.

popularization of the philosophy of naturalism. Essentially, the various spontaneous generation beliefs, and the belief that life came to the earth from space (cosmozoic),[5] are substitute concepts to the long held belief that God created all life (theozoic).

Because there is a widely accepted belief, in the present millieu, that the concept of spontaneous generation has been denied completely and is no longer in use by modern biologists, it is most important to comprehend an important sequence of ideas that has developed over the centuries. If the science teacher clearly sees that there has been a sequence of concepts of spontaneous generation of life from the macro- to the micro- to the submicro-level, then the majority position of modern biologists can be fully understood. Macrozoic ideas (whole organism spontaneous generation) were put forth initially by the ancient Greeks, but these were replaced in modified form in the nineteenth century, which have been replaced in the twentieth century by sub-microzoic ideas involving supposed spontaneous generation of life substance, resulting from chance combinations of submolecular parts of matter.

But the belief that the concept of spontaneous generation was denied completely by Louis Pasteur is common in the culture today. It is true that Pasteur, a theist who did not believe in spontaneous generation of life, conducted a very famous and crucial experiment relevant to the question of the origin of life. But his *controlled* experiment with swan-neck flasks was limited to the study of microbes. Characteristically, scientific experiments are designed so that as many aspects as possible are controlled and, ideally, only one aspect is allowed to vary. By means of his controlled experiment with the swan-neck flasks Pasteur showed that *microbes* do not appear spontaneously in a nutrient broth. But it is noteworthy that Pasteur's work was relevant *only* to the fact that microbes do not arise spontaneously.

With regard to further historical perspective the science teacher should stress the limited scope of the experiment of Francisco Redi on the origin of life. His experiment was designed to show that *whole* organisms do not come into existence spontaneously. Redi gained very adequate evidence from his crucial, *controlled* experiment that flies are not generated spontaneously from putrifying meat—one form of inanimate, non-living matter.

Now, after this clarification regarding Pasteur and Redi, let me emphasize that modern biologists *do believe* in spontaneous generation of life. Modern biologists, who will not take seriously the theistic creation model, regarding the origin of the universe and all therein, believe in spontaneous generation of life. I will demonstrate that this is very well documented in the writings of scientists of this century.

Beliefs of many modern-day biologists can be grouped under two headings: (a) a single spontaneous coming together of inorganic matter has occurred to form living substance from which *all* other forms and stages of life have come, and (b) multiple coming together of inorganic matter has occurred to form living substance from which *all* life forms have come along separate lines. These two positions are exemplified in the following two groups of statements:

One Spontaneous Generation of Life

All competent biologists today are biogenesists. They accept the view that on the earth today life comes only from life. But wait, have we answered all parts of the question? If life comes only from life, does this mean that there was *always* life on the earth? It must, yet we know that this cannot be so. We know that the world was once without life—that life appeared later. How? We think it was by spontaneous generation. But this was not the same as the events occurring in a flask of boiled hay infusion.[6]
George Wald, evolutionary biologist, has asserted that since the origin of life belongs in the category of at-least-once phenomena, time is on its side. He feels that time is the hero of the plot, and given so much time, the impossible becomes possible, the possible probable, and the probable virtually certain.[7]

Multiple Spontaneous Generations of Life

Multiple biopoeses have been proposed most boldly by R. L. Berg (1959). Similar is the proposal of repetitive neobiogenesis of Keosin (1960).[8]
The difficulty of placing viruses, bacteria, certain "algae", sponges, and so on, in a fitting scheme based on a monophyletic hypothesis may stem from the possibility that the discontinuities are real and represent existence of separate lines of descent from independent instances of neobiogenesis at different times in the history of the earth down to the present.[9] (Neobiogenesis is used to describe presumed repeated origination of life in nature.)

Science teachers in biology should make clear that many modern biologists have turned away from belief in God as the ultimate origin of life on the earth, which belief was held by Louis Pasteur and many other leading scientists who were founders of the biological sciences. It is a clear fact that many modern biologists have turned away from belief in God as the ultimate origin of life on the earth because of their frame of mind of wanting to accept only a presumed naturalistic origin of life on the earth.

Yet these men know of *no* naturalistic origin of first life on the earth. As stated, careful empirical findings have been basic to development of the law of biogenesis. No evidence contrary to that law of nature (or natural law) has ever been identified from scientific study of objects and/or events in the natural environment, which is the venue of careful, proper scientific endeavor. That many modern biologists do *not* stay within restrictions of their supposed naturalistic outlook or philosophy is manifest in their imagined belief that a *reducing* atmosphere surrounded the early earth. A reducing atmosphere is *not* a naturally occurring phenomenon. It is only imagined.

Actually, any belief in spontaneous generation of life is a direct contradiction of the law of biogenesis. It is a contradiction that Wald should turn from a belief in supernatural origin of life on the earth to acceptance of spontaneous generation (i.e., supra-natural) origin of life on the earth. Yet supernatural and supra-natural both entail a meaning beyond the natural. Both terms connote something over and above the natural.

It is necessary to make clear to students engaged in a confrontation about evolution/creation ideas that the cosmozoic concept regarding the origin of life of the earth is truly a "begging of the question" on the basis of rigorous and logical examination. No evidence of life, as biologists know of it today, has been identified at all by way of any experiments in space. Even if some strong positive indications of life, or life supporting conditions, were found on Mars or another planet in the solar system, no answer would really have been gained regarding the basic question of the ultimate origin of life. The question would follow most logically, Whence cometh any life on Mars, or elsewhere?

I am often asked the question, Do you believe there is extraterrestrial life? As was mentioned, no significant data are on hand from which any scientists could deduce that life, as biologists know it now, might exist anywhere in the solar system, except on the earth. Thus the whole idea of extraterrestrial life remains a speculation, a total figment of the imagination of some human beings.[10]

Thus the theozoic concept of the ultimate origin of life still remains, in this day of twentieth century science, as a viable, comprehenable, and fully rational belief. How rational is the belief that presently known complex life came into existence after some chance combination of sub-molecular units? To many scientists, a belief in the eternal Creator as the source of plant and animal life, including humankind, on the earth is wholly logical, rational and in keeping, in turn, with the cause and effect assumption so fundamental to careful, proper scientific thinking. Theistic belief about the ultimate origin of life on the earth is not in any way anti-scientific.

Scientists who desire a natural origin of life on the earth rather than a supernatural source of life, as according to the creation model, imagine some other causes. Yet the idea of living cells coming into existence after some spontaneous generation of the first living substance on the earth is totally *un*natural, or basically supranatural; that is, beyond the natural. So-called naturalistically oriented scientists really utilize supernatural ideas without any clear admission that is what they do.

Synthesis Versus Creation

It is important to reiterate that the majority of scientists are devoted to thinking about a non-theistic or what they believe to be naturalistic origin of life on the earth. Many biologists, chemists, biochemists, and biophysicists have attempted to implement the idea of submicroscopic (submicrozoic) spontaneous generation of life at some distant time in the past.

Such scientists have spent a great deal of effort attempting to *simulate* early conditions of the atmosphere of the earth and early conditions of the surface of the earth which they have imagined. As has been developed in the first section of this chapter, the majority of scientists have accepted a scenario of specific conditions of a so-called primitive earth. I have already given a briefly detailed summary of the *present position* regarding chemical evolution by means of a five-part scenario.

In short, most evolutionists believe that life arose on this planet from inanimate matter through chemical and physical processes still operating today. Chemical evolution is supposed to have followed stellar evolution, presumed to be consequential to the imagined big bang, and formation of the earth.

As was pointed out in discussion of chemical evolution (Stage 2: Synthesis of Relatively Simple Organic Compounds), several scientists have successfully synthesized amino acids and a few other simple organic compounds under assumed primitive earth conditions. We have briefly looked at a vital part of the experimental apparatus used by the scientists, that is, the cold trap, which is labeled on Classroom Teaching Aid 20. To help science teachers understand explicitly the nature of the work completed in the laboratory, which Fox, Miller, and Ponnampuruma present as *simulations* of primitive earth conditions, we must now give particular attention to the cold trap of their experimental apparatus.

The cold trap is a most significant feature of the apparatus used by Miller in his studies of conditions wherein amino acids can be synthesized. The reader may want to restudy the diagrammatic representation of the experimental apparatus provided in Classroom Teaching Aid 20. The science teacher should help students realize that in all such experiments whereby scientists try to simulate some imagined early earth conditions, a special trap has been used to *isolate* the product from the energy source used for the synthesis. In other words, successful production of amino acids in the laboratory was achieved as a consequence of very special conditions imposed by the research scientists; conditions not known to have existed on the primitive earth.

Research scientists have brought together a mixture of methane, ammonia, water, and hydrogen in their laboratory apparatus, and used a spark discharge as a source of energy. The gaseous mixture was circulated through the laboratory apparatus. Yet in all such origin of life experiments, as a result of the interaction of the gaseous mixture and the electric discharge, whatever amounts of amino acids and other products that were derived had to be *isolated* in a trap so that the products would not come into contact again with the source of energy. For instance, in Miller's experimental apparatus the amino acids and other products derived in the sparking chamber had to accumulate in the trap provided for isolating nongaseous materials. The gases were allowed continuous movement throughout the apparatus, but any nongaseous substances were immediately trapped out and isolated so that they would not be broken down again by the spark discharge.

Any source of energy is far more efficient in the destruction of the organic products involved than in the production of them. The necessary function of the trap was removal of the synthesized organic substances from the chemically active area of the apparatus. If such a means of removal, or trapping, had not been provided, then the synthetically formed amino acids would have broken down because of their thermodynamically unstable nature.

Now Dr. Miller and his fellow researchers presumably are proponents of the philosophy of naturalism. As scientists they are supposedly devoted to studying naturally occurring objects and/or events. But the cold trap to which I have just called such explicit attention has *no natural* analogue. There is nothing known in the present natural environment and nothing is known of any presumed primitive environment which could function as a trap. Thus, a plainly *un*natural feature is involved by these scientists in their apparatus which they purport simulates some imagined primitive atmosphere. No oxygen free atmosphere is known, and specific geologic evidence can be used to deny that there ever was an oxygen free atmosphere associated with this earth. Also, no conditions are known that could trap organic substances supposedly formed by lightning discharges or ultraviolet radiation. Dr. Miller and his associates have devised specifically *un*natural conditions in their laboratory apparatus. They have not been consistent with their philosophy of naturalism.

Another important aspect of Miller's work should be pointed out. The Miller and Fox experiments are *not* instances of creation of life, as claimed so often by headline writers. Have modern scientists created life? No, not at all. Miller and like-minded scientists, in their zeal to try to simulate what they *imagine* occurred under what *they* call primitive conditions on the early earth, have only *synthesized* components of living substance. But they have not created life because the amino acids that have been synthesized are really not living.

God alone created new matter. God created life. God brought into existence the elemental atoms from which he formulated living plants and living animals. These statements summarize what the people believed who inaugurated the profession of modern science. True, modern scientists utilize elemental materials at their disposal to prepare a certain mixture in their experimental apparatus. *But whence cometh the elemental materials?* Did Miller create life? No![11]

The science teacher should carefully note that the proper word used regarding these experiments to simulate early earth atmospheric conditions is *synthesis* or *synthesize*. The former term refers to a composition, the putting together of two or more things, or a process of making a compound by joining elements. Synthesize means to unite things into one whole, to form something by bringing together separate parts. The fact should be highlighted that scientists *synthesize*; whereas God *creates* that which did not ever have previous existence. Scientists synthesize amino acids that are the building blocks of living substance. Again, scientists have not created life.[12]

"Cover Word"
(Beware Sematic Confusion)

Spontaneous: since no scientist can avoid external intervention (of direct or indirect degree), no scientist is ever involved with spontaneous chemical reactions; rather the correct term is instantaneous, as all chemical processes occur at some instant of time. All experiments and basically all observations are the result of interventions of one type or another by scientists practicing the procedures and methodologies of the profession.

Students might ask the science teacher, What if scientists do *synthesize* living substance? Of course, if scientists are successful in synthesizing living substance, their work will be the result of careful planning and controlled execution—so that the whole process can be repeated. All careful, proper scientific work must be repeatable.

Living substance is complex. If scientists do successfully *synthesize* living substance, they will do so because of a planned recipe, a proper complex mixture of elements (of unknown origin which they have not produced). Thus biology teachers should make it clear to students that synthesis of living substance, if it ever occurs, will be a forthright attestation of the human intellect involved. Human intelligence will of necessity have been involved since scientists selected the ingredients. Human intelligence will of necessity have been involved since the process will not have been an accident and of necessity will be repeatable according to a definite formula.

By analogical reasoning, if human intelligence of necessity will be involved in any successful *synthesis* of living substance, then it follows logically that an intelligent Creator was involved in the *ultimate* origin of life on the earth.[13]

Of course, any synthesis in the laboratory is not spontaneous. The science teacher in biology should give attention to the fact that the phenomena that occurred in the Miller apparatus involved fully *instantaneous* chemical reaction. Emphasis is given to the term *instantaneous* in contrast to the improper reference by many scientists that chemical reactions in the Miller apparatus are spontaneous. Actually, no chemical reaction can be thought of as spontaneous if a scientist is involved with it. By definition the term spontaneous has the connotation of an object and/or event occurring *without any external intervention*. A so-called spontaneous act or event merely occurs— without any direction or alteration of conditions on the part of any causal agent.

But scientists must always be recognized as causal agents in their laboratories. They select the experimental apparatus; they select the ingredients of their experiments regarding *synthesis* of amino acids. Scientists must intervene in the selection and very execution of their experiments. Their intervention is required if the experiment is to occur at all. Their intervention and recording of aspects of the experiment is required if there is even the barest possibility that the experiment may be repeated and repeated again.

Thermodynamic specialists are prone to refer to spontaneous chemical reactions; that is, they say that a chemical process may proceed spontaneously in one direction or another direction. However, the chemical actions that do occur, must be recognized as *instantaneous* chemical reactions. Even slow chemical reactions occur at some instant. Chemical reactions that do occur are *at least indirectly* contingent upon the intervention of scientific investigators. Therefore such instantaneous chemical reactions are really *not* spontaneous.

But instantaneous actions are those that may properly be associated with the sustaining act of God. Hence the theistically oriented biologist may most rationally maintain that the instantaneous chemical reactions detectable in a scientific experiment regarding the *synthesis* of amino acids—or any scientific experiment—are conceivably the ongoing, sustaining actions of the Providential God in whom he believes. In short, the evidence for God—the Sustainer—is all around the theistic biologist. He is without excuse in pointing to possible evidences of the Creator in the chemical reactions that are not seen involving the ingredients that are seen. All things consist in His power. Or, as it has been written, God moves everything continually according to physical laws which are expressions of His fixed character. The scientist who describes regularities of naturally occurring objects and/or events in his expressions of scientific laws, natural laws or laws of nature may very well be describing the way God acts as He sustains and maintains His creation.

An Important Corollary

An important corollary to the cold trap aspect of the Miller apparatus is the fact that there is the potential for the formation of *two* forms of synthetic amino acids in the trap. Yet, with regard to amino acids and proteins in living organisms, a condition exists which has been called a mystery by biologists. But, first a word about amino acids.

Amino acids can exist in either a right-handed or a left-handed form. A useful analogy to this situation can be found in a person's right and left hands. Although the two hands have the some components, fingers and a thumb, the thumb of the one hand is on the left, and the thumb of the other hand on the right. The two hands are mirror images of each other. Amino acids molecules are like that.

The amino acid molecule is built on a simple plan: (Classroom Teaching Aid 23) The three atoms of nitrogen (N) and oxygen (O) form a backbone in the direct line of the protein chain formed when an amino acid is united with other amino acids. In the center is the alpha carbon atom, with a nitrogen atom on one end of the backbone and a carbon atom at the other end. From the perspective of the carbon end, it is possible to tell whether an amino acid is left-handed or right-handed.

Students must give particular attention to the central carbon atom of the backbone, which appears to be elevated with respect to the other two atoms of the main part. The carbon atoms are attached (bonded) to it. By considering the R group (or side group) as labeled in the teaching aid, the science teacher can help students realize that the R group is on either the left or the right of the main part of the amino acid. Thus, if the R group is on the left, the amino acid is left-handed (i.e., L or levo), whereas if it is attached on the right, then the molecule of the amino acid is right-handed (i.e., D. or dextro).

Classroom Teaching Aid 23
LEFT- AND RIGHT-HANDED AMINO ACID RESIDUES

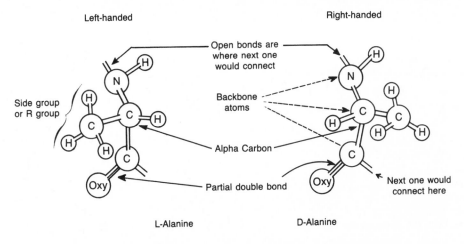

L-Alanine   D-Alanine

Left- and right-handed amino acid residues. The molecules shown are L-alanine and D-alanine (L = levo, or left handed; D = dextro, or right-handed). Alanine is the simplest of the amino acids which are isomeric or handed.

The bonds in the figure are not drawn to scale, but are lengthened so that the left- and right-handedness is more easily seen. In real molecules, the bonds are shorter so that the "surfaces" overlap, making the molecules more compact. The initials on the atoms indicate carbon, nitrogen, oxygen, and hydrogen. Note that the only difference between the two is the position of the side group, on either the left or right side.

Over one hundred years ago Louis Pasteur had identified this one-handedness of molecules. Dr. Francis Crick, co-discoverer of the DNA structure, has described this handedness of molecules with respect to living organisms in the following manner:

It has been well known for many years that for any particular molecule only one hand occurs in nature. For example the amino acid one finds in proteins are always what are called the L or levo amino acids, and never the D or dextra amino acids. Only one of the two mirror possibilities occurs in proteins.[14]

While there is a potential for the formation of *two* forms of synthetic amino acids in the cold trap, *only* left-handed amino acids comprise the proteins of living organisms. This is a real mystery to modern biologists. They cannot explain the absence of right-handed amino acids in proteins of living things. The science teacher should point out that this is a very special difficulty for those who believe that life originated from nonliving matter supposedly by natural processes. Leading proponents of the Miller-Fox-Ponnampuruma scenario on the origin of life have recognized this puzzling fact.[15]

If the processes involved in the laboratory apparatus of Miller really occurred on the primitive earth, then *both* right-handed and left-handed amino acids presumably would have been formed during the chance combinations of submolecular units of matter. Logically, therefore, one could have expected that both right-handed amino acids would have been included in living substance on the early earth. However, *only left-handed forms of amino acids are found in living organisms!*

The science teacher might want to share some of the following facts with their students on the immense improbabilities for the one-handedness of amino acids in living organisms:[16]

Some biologists have estimated that the smallest living entity might have about 239 individual protein molecules. Biologists have calculated further that the average protein molecule in the smallest living thing (strictly theoretical) would contain 445 amino acid units of the usual 20 kinds.

Of course one of the 20 types of amino acids, glycine, does not have the previously described asymmetrical structure. Since glycine amounts to about 8 per cent of the total amino acids in living things, one can estimate that the average protein in the smallest living thing would contain 35 glycine units. Therefore a balance of 410 of the total estimate of 445 could be either right- or left-handed.

If amino acids ever were formed in the primitive atmosphere, there would have been an equal chance statistically for either the right- or left-handed mirror image to be formed. By assuming the simplest formation of amino acid chains to produce proteins, if a protein chain ever formed at random, all 410 of the nonglycine amino acids could be either L or D type amino acids. The first would have been left-handed by a 1 out of 2 chance. The same would have been true for each of the remaining 409 presumed to be present in the smallest living thing. What would be the probability that all 410 non-glycine amino acids would have been left-handed?

This situation is like flipping a coin 410 times to try to see if only one side will appear every time. That chance of that happening is 2^{410}, which is the equivalent roughly of 10^{123}. So the probability that an average size protein molecule of the smallest imagined living thing would randomly contain *only* left-handed amino acids is, on the average, 1 in 10^{123}.

In his chapter "The Odds Against Proteins with Only Left-Handed Components", James Coppedge presents further statistical analyses. He argues without any further qualifications that the probability that a small living thing of 239 protein molecules would be composed *only* of left-handed amino acids is 1 in 10^{29345}. Then he adds particular conditions of preference and concludes that, on the average, the probability would be less than 1 in 10^{8373} that any given set of 239 protein molecules would be *all* left-handed. Before he closes his chapter Coppedge arrives at the astounding conclusion that there is, on the average, 1 chance in 10^{8318} that of all the proteins that ever existed on earth there would be a set of 239 which would be all left-handed.

It is interesting to note that in general, physicists do not consider a problem worth studying if the probability that particular conditions will occur is less than 10^{40}. Or some might use a criterion of 10^{50}. Either way the probabilities for exlusively left-handed proteins are much, much less!

Of crucial importance, then, to any evolution/creation discussion is the fact that *only* the left-handed form of any amino acid (except glycine) is ever found in living organisms. This strange characteristic of protein molecules of living organisms is a real mystery, and a very special difficulty for scientists who want to believe that chemical and physical processes operating today were the means whereby the first life on the earth came into existence. That natural amino acids contain *only* the left-handed forms of amino acids is the mystery referred to at the beginning of the section.

Obviously, the existence of the mirror image condition in amino acids and the presence of *only left-handed* amino acids in the proteins of living organisms are important aspects of the design argument for the existence of God. But many leading biologists will not accept the design argument for God. Rather, they insist on trying to reduce life to physics and chemistry.

Modern Biologists Are Reductionists

Whence cometh life? All those who would not accept God as the Creator of life have consistently sought to accept an inanimate or plainly physical-chemical process as source of animal and plant life on this earth. In short, so-called naturalistically oriented investigators have painly expressed their belief in spontaneous generation as a source of first life of the earth.

Authors of that quotation from Harcourt, Brace and World, Inc. textbook for high school biology (commonly referred to as the Yellow Version in a series of three books produced by the Biological Sciences Curriculum Study) indicated that they think it (the appearance of life) was by spontaneous generation.[17] Granted, the authors did not mean spontaneous generation of whole organisms, nor did they mean spontaneous generation of bacteria in some nutrient broth. But it is abundantly clear from this textbook that scientists *believe* in spontaneous generation of life from inanimate submolecular units of matter.

It is amazing that this Yellow Version textbook, along with the companion Green Version and Blue Version, comprise the most pointed thrust by majority leaders of the biological sciences to bring all of biology teaching in line with current evolutionary thought. The Blue Version, which has been subtitled "From Molecules to Man", is particularly influential because of full implementation of the definite point of view that life can be described in terms of modern physics and modern chemistry. This is the point of view of *reductionism*. Science teachers involved in the evolution/creation confrontation procedure must make abundantly clear to their students that leading biologists are *reductionists*, who claim that it is possible to reduce all life processes to the ordinary concepts of physics and chemistry. Reductionism is the favored theme of most popularly adopted biology textbooks. A very apt phrase that expresses this reductionist theme is "from hydrogen to human beings".

Basically, then, biologists who accept the reductionist point of view think of complex life forms as nothing but collections of molecules and/or hydrogen atoms. This approach involves the logical fallacy of considering complex things as nothing but collections of simple, component parts of which the complex whole of things is composed.

Francis Crick, one of the most famous leaders of the reductionist movement, has stated, "The ultimate aim of the modern movement in biology is in fact to explain *all* biology in terms of physics and chemistry."[18] (Emphasis in the original.) As a leader of this modern movement in biology, Crick has opted for one version of the world view of naturalism, but in the end Crick and all other so-called naturalistically, oriented scientists really opt for supra-naturalism: Spontaneous generation at the submicroscopic level, which in no wise can be termed natural.[19]

A complete review of the Crick book is beyond the scope of this chapter portion. However, since Crick's book is actually a collection of three public lectures presented at the University of Washington in February and March, 1966, under the title "Is Vitalism Dead?", it is well that the science teacher be prepared to clarify ideas contained in the book. As a frontispiece for his book Crick offered the statement, "Exact knowledge is the enemy of vitalism." The basic context of his use of that sentence is found in the last page of his book where he asked the question, "Will vitalism then be dead?", and answers by referring to a "lunatic fringe" that will always remain. In so writing, Crick involves himself in a pattern of thinking and writing that is often employed by evolutionist, naturalistic scientists. They use the logical fallacy of *argumentum and adhominem.*

The term *vitalism* has been used commonly by mechanists as a derogatory term. Without going into a review of the history of the use of the terms *vitalism* and *mechanism*, I will merely say that many scientists have candidly written about the complexity of life and life functions and have maintained that there is something more to life than what has been described in term of physics and chemistry. Men who have expressed this "something more than" theme have been and still are referred to as vitalists.

Crick touched on several arguments *for* the main aim of reductionists *against* vitalism. He properly explained that vitalism entails the ideas that there is some special force or component directing the growth or behavior of living systems which *cannot* be understood in terms of physics and chemistry. Crick has mentioned candidly that three modern scientists— Dr. Walter Elsasser, Dr. Peter Mora, and Dr. Eugene Wigner—have written critically to convey that present molecular biology is *not* sufficient to explain the difference between living substance and the non-living.

Science teachers will find this book by Crick very useful as a source of the kind of expressions reductionists use to push their point of view. Students should be helped to evaluate some of the following expressions and aided in the practice of applying criteria of scientific writing.[20] The middle section of Crick's book contains useful source material.

Classroom Teaching Aid 24
CRITERIA FOR SCIENTIFIC WRITING

The nonspecialist particularly asks for criteria in these days of both increased technological advancements and broadly disseminated reports of speculations and conjectures about extraterrestrial life, genetic human engineering and other high interest topics.

Commonly, the words used about topics such as these are a good means for noting the storytelling or scenario-play writing aspects of an author trying to communicate his ideas about what "could", "would", "supposedly", "possibly", "probably", or "might" come to pass. These terms are used heavily in speculative, conjectural writing that can be readily contrasted with careful scientific writing.

In scientifically written material, the reader can expect to find these main sections (not necessarily in this order):

1. Initial observations and statement of a problem for which an answer can reasonably be sought.
2. A review of scientific literature for summary of any similar research reports and a listing of relevant findings that might be useful in the current problem area of research.
3. Statement of a hypothesis, or tentative answer to the problem presented, and even some mention of possible alternative answers that could be checked out if the problem seems to have several facets or aspects that could be studied in separate but related parts.
4. Description of the methods, materials, and equipment used in the research on the primary hypothesis and any corollary answers to various related aspects of the problem.
5. Report of results.
6. Discussion of the results.
7. Summary and conclusions, and often mention of further problems that became evident as the research was completed.

Clearly there is a characteristic format of careful scientific writing. Absence of such a format with most, if not all, of the stated elements means the reader has a specific basis for considering such deficient writing as mostly speculative and conjectual, and not an example of good, careful scientific writing.

Speculations and scenarios about the origin of the universe, origin of first life on the earth, existence of extraterrestrial life, and origin of humankind are *not* examples of proper scientific writing.

In the middle section Crick tried to establish much exact knowledge about the processes of the simplest living things. He referred to DNA and RNA synthesis in bacteria, such as *Escherichia coli*, Crick does use exact knowledge about amino acids and interactive functions of enzymes. However, Crick repeatedly used such phrases as "partly understand", "we do not know", "only partly understood", and "in principle it should" or "in principle it is possible". Students should be helped to see that reductionists possess greatly limited "exact knowledge". They have not explained the amazing paradox that enzymes (which are proteins) *must* be present for proper synthesis of amino acids (which are organic building blocks of proteins) and synthesis of proteins. How did the proteins, and enzymes ever come into existence in the first place so as to be present in the natural environment to be functional in the formation of complex proteins? Dr. Crick and other reductionists *do not know.*

Interestingly enough, Crick even stated in the middle section of his book that "it is arranged" that the synthesizing of DNA is "exceptionally designed." Yet he did not explain to his readers exactly who arranged or who designed the known life processes of the simplest bacterial forms on which he reported. The absence of such an explanation and the willingness to interpose Nature in reductionists' discussions should be made notably explicit by science teachers. Twice Crick wrote about Nature in a manner that is clearly personification or reification.[21]

Crick is *not* using exact knowledge when he claims something is designed or arranged. Such terms require a "causer" which Crick cannot identify except to carelessly refer to Nature. Science teachers involved in the evolution/creation confrontation procedure must identify and explain that such a practice is common in the writing of many molecular biologists who hold to the reductionist point of view of trying to reduce life to processes of physics and chemistry.

The third section of the Crick book can be most instructive in evolution/creation confrontation teaching. In discussing "The Prospect Before Us", Crick made multiple use of typical qualifying words. In that one section of 30 pages Crick used the following words 67 times: "probably", "presumably", "could", "would". "hope", "seem", "possibility", "possible", "perhaps", "appear", "believe", "expect", "imagine", "think".

Science teachers will do well to review with their students that scientists *do* use such words in formulating proper hypotheses. However, students living in the scientific age should clearly recognize that when scientists use such qualifying terms in their hypotheses, scientists are also using proper, orderly scientific procedure to *test* their ideas. Hypotheses in proper, orderly scientific endeavor must be testable. Such is not presently the case regarding the highly qualified ideas discussed by Crick with respect to the "prospect before us".

Again I would urge the science teacher to help students realize how to apply criteria of evaluation of scientific writing, such as has already been provided in Classroom Teaching Aid 24. Students should have some specific means whereby they can evaluate fully the position of Crick and other reductionists. Students should see that reductionists essentially present imaginative scenarios *as if* they were writing something quite like properly testable scientific hypotheses.

To make further use of the representative reductionist writing of Crick, my students can examine the book (as could be done with all similar books) for answers to such questions as:

1. What exact knowledge does Crick use?
2. In one section (lecture) count the number of times Crick employed the terms, "seems", "appear", "might", "could", etc.
3. How many gaps does Crick acknowledge? How many does he omit?
4. Find examples by pages of Crick's use of "well designed" or "it is arranged".
5. Which problems does Crick cite?

Classroom Teaching Aid 25 presents a representative answer to the third question. As is so characteristic, the proponent of the evolutionary point of view talks or writes *as if* one could use fully naturalistic terminology when considering the origin of all life forms on the earth. But, as is shown in the Classroom Teaching Aid 25, much is left unstudied scientifically; and, thus many *un*natural concepts and/or events are incorporated into the thinking of total evolutionists.

Classroom Teaching Aid 25
PROBLEMS CITED BY CRICK

Borderlines Admitted by Crick

1. Understanding of control mechanisms in cells (p. 62)
2. Borderline between the living and the nonliving (origin of life, p. 63)
3. Origin and nature of higher nervous system (p. 71)

Borderlines Ignored by Crick

(Representative only, as more are itemized in
Classroom Teaching Aids 37 and 38

1. Border between noncellular and unicellular
2. Borderline between unicellular and multicellular
3. Borderline between vertebrate and nonvertebrate
4. Borderline between flowering and nonflowering
5. Borderline between human consciousness and animal consciousness

FOOTNOTES

[1] J. D. Bernal (in) *The Origin of Prebiological Systems and of Their Molecular Matrices.* (S. W. Fox, Ed., New York: Academic Press, 1965), p. 52.

[2] P.H. Abelson, Director of the Carnegie Institute of Washington, wrote: "The methane-ammonia hypothesis is in major trouble with respect to the ammonia component, for ammonia on the primitive earth would have quickly disappeared . . . ", *Proceedings of National Academy of Science,* 55:1365,1966.

[3] I should mention that my general education natural science students did hear the special lecture by a graduate student who had researched the pros and cons regarding the one reported resurrection of a human being, namely, the resurrection of Jesus Christ.

[4] For somewhat similar treatment in chart form see Josephine Marquand, "A summary of the different views on the origins of life by the end of the 19th century", in *Life: Its Nature, Origins and Distribution* (New York: W. W. Norton Company, Inc., 1968).

[5] By borrowing the suffix-zoic, meaning life form, from the historical geologists, I have coined the terms, *cosmozoic, theozoic, macrozoic, microzoic,* and *sub-microzoic* and utilized them in Classroom Teaching Aid 22.

[6] *Biological Science: An Inquiry Into Life* (New York: Harcourt, Brace, and World, Inc., 1973), p.51. Copyright 1973 by Biological Science Curriculum Study.

[7] George Wald. "The Origin of Life," in *Physics and Chemistry of Life* (New York, Simon and Schuster, 1955), p. 12. Also, in 1954, Dr. Wald admitted in a *Scientific American* article, October, 1954, on "The Origin of Life", that modern biologists have the choice of believing either in spontaneous generation of life, or in special creation of life. The author of a supplemental booklet for cassette recordings on the "The Origin of Life" released in 1972 by the American Association for the Advancement of Science (AAAS) used the special subheading, "The New Spontaneous Generation".

[8] J. R. Nursall, "On the Origins of the Major Groups of Animals", *Evolution* 16: 118, 1962.

[9]John Keosin, "On the Origin of Life", *Science* 131: 482, 1960 Copyright by the American Association for the Advancement of Science.
Reports of a new form of life have been published by microbiologist Carl R. Woese of University
of Illinois as a separate original form of life: methanogens. This microscopic organism resembles
bacteria except that it produces methane gas as it metabolizes hydrogen and carbon dioxide. The
researchers believe that the methanogens represent a line of evolution separate from the higher and
lower forms of life known. Of course only genetic lineage would afford a full scientific basis for
any relationship. These seem to be specially adapted organisms which are killed by even a trace of
oxygen. *National Academy of Science*, Oct./Nov., 1977.

[10]The evolution/creation confrontation teacher has ample opportunity (I would add responsibility) to
make clear the motivations of many modern biologists searching for the origin of life. Much gain
can be expected from careful explanation in this area. In particular, students will gain an objective
basis for evaluating projects proposed for federal government funding. For instance, the search for
life on Mars was one of the clearly announced goals or objectives of space probe expenditures. Yet
the search for life on Mars or on the moon, could never shed light on the *ultimate* origin of life on
the earth, or anywhere else. The origin of life is not of the present where proper, orderly scientific
endeavor occurs. Thus the ultimate origin of life anywhere is beyond the scope of proper scientific
study.
The following noteworthy quotation is provided from a recent publication of the National Aeronautics and Space Administration: "Recognizing that many scientific secrets still lie hidden
throughout the solar system, NASA has a program of solar system exploration aimed at answering
the following questions: (1) How did our solar system form and evolve? (2) How did life originate
and evolve? (3) What are the processes that shape our terrestrial environment?" W. R. Corliss,
The Viking Mission to Mars.   National Aeronautics and Space Administration, Washington, D.C.
(1974), p.2.

[11]Here the science teacher can help students appreciate a parallel to the situation mentioned in the
previous chapter regarding the reaction of Dr. Hoyle when asked about the source of the imagined
dense particle that he presumed exploded into the present universe. Hoyle did not know the origin
of such an imagined particle. Modern biologists do not know the origin of the elemental materials
they have utilized to *synthesize* amino acids.

[12]Scientists have successfully synthesized urea. They have successfully synthesized rubber. And now
they have successfully synthesized amino acids. But scientists do not say they have created urea
nor created rubber. Just as scientists have *only synthesized* (but not created) urea and rubber, they
have *only synthesized* (but not created) the building blocks, of living substance. Scientists have not
created amino acids. They have not created life.

[13]Even the most elementary student really has no difficulty in noting pattern and order, hence has an
appreciation of design. All school buildings, all machines, all play equipment are carefully assembled,
as is fully appreciated by all students. They *know* there was some blueprint for all of man's inven-
tions. So they can understand God was the Designer of all original life on the earth.

[14]Francis Crick, *Of Molecules and Men* (Seattle: University of Washington Press, 1966), p. 60.

[15]For example, Nobel laurate in chemistry Linus Pauling: "This is a very puzzling fact . . . All
the proteins that have been investigated, obtained from animals and from plants, from higher organisms and from very simple organisms—bacteria, molds, even viruses—are found to have been of
L-amino acids." Linus Pauling, *General Chemistry*, 3rd. Edition (San Francisco: W. H. Freeman
& Co., 1970) p. 774.

[16]My presentation at this point is based upon Chapter 4 of James Coppedge, *Evolution: Possible or
Impossible?* (Grand Rapids, MI: Zondervan Publishing House, 1973).

[17]*Biological Science: An Inquiry Into Life*, p. 51.

[18]Crick, *Of Molecules And Men*, p. 10.

[19]Ample enlargement of the Crick thesis of trying to reduce all life to physics and chemistry can
also be found in many other books, among which are *Chance and Necessity* by J. Monod (N. Y.:
Knopf, 1971) and *Chemical Evolution* by M. Calvin. (N. Y.: Oxford University Press, 1969).

[20]See Classroom Teaching Aid 24 for a presentation of "Criteria for Scientific Writing" which I have used most successfully in my classes to communicate *some* kind of specifics which the nonspecialists can readily expect to be followed when scientists are writing about their ideas.

[21]Crick, *Of Molecules And Men*: "Nature's own analogue computer—the system itself—works so fantastically fast. Also *she* knows the rules more precisely than we do. But we still hope, if not to beat *her* at *her* game, at least to understand *her*—to give a concrete example, to calculate how a particular protein molecule folds up." p. 12 (Emphases added)

"Nature is able to make them because nature has been at the job for so long, the process of natural selection having gone on for several thousand million years." p. 54.

Chapter 3

General Discussion Questions

1. What are the stated goals of this chapter?
2. Discuss the difference between an imagined "reducing" atmosphere that is *un*natural and the present oxidizing atmosphere that is fully empirical.
3. Define carefully the terms: "macrozoic", "microzoic", "sub-microzoic", "cosmozoic", and "theozoic".
4. Discuss the fact that modern biologists *do believe* in spontaneous generation of life.
5. Explain the difference in the meaning of the terms "synthesis" and "creation".
6. What is the significance of the trap in the apparatus of the Miller experiment?
7. Explain the difference in the meaning of the terms "spontaneous" and "instantaneous".
8. What is the "mystery" or "puzzle" of life admitted by Dr. Crick and Dr. Pauling?
9. What is a basic probability argument about the one-handedness of protein molecular structure?
10. Explain the criterion accepted by physicists for deciding whether a given problem is worth studying at all.
11. What is meant by "reductionism"?

Class Projects or Individual Assignments

1. Prepare a topical outline of this chapter.
2. List "cover words" that could cause semantic confusion.
3. Prepare a large wall chart of the "Life"—"Death" Continuum chart included in this chapter.
4. Prepare a large chart of the different ideas people have held over the centuries about the origin of life.

5. Prepare a chart of the five-stage evolutionary scenario of the origin of life on the earth.
6. Make a large wall chart to represent the left- and right-handedness in models of amino acid molecular structure.
7. Prepare a large chart of criteria of scientific writing.
8. Prepare a large chart of admitted and ignored borderlines given in this chapter. Add to the latter listing.
9. Work out a set of answers for the evaluation items provided at the close of this chapter. Now prepare a set of similar evaluation items for this general subject matter area.

Read: Richard B. Bliss and Gary E. Parker, *Origin of Life.* 1979. San Diego: Creation-Life Publishers.

Donald England, Chapter 4, "A Critique of the Three-Stage Mechanistic Hypothesis of the Origin of Life", (in) *A Christian View of Origins.* 1972. Grand Rapids, MI: Baker Book House.

Duane T. Gish, *Speculations and Experiments Related to Theories on the Origin of Life: A Critique.* 1972. Technical Monograph No. 1 San Diego: Institute for Creation Research.

On the Use of Scripture in Parochial Schools
1. Ask students to search for Biblical references of instantaneous, fiat acts of Jesus Christ which may logically be thought of as clues as to how He created the heaven and the earth and all that is therein. They should be reminded of Christ's changing of water to wine, of of His multiplication of the fish and the loaves of bread for the multitude, of His raising of Lazarus from his death bed, and of Christ's return to normal of the ear struck off by Peter.
2. Students should be asked to search for Scripture wherein clues are given that God spoke and it was so; and search for action that was very good, such as the coming into being of plant life and animal life before the breath of life was breathed into the dust of the earth to bring Adam into existence.

EVALUATION QUESTIONS

For items 1 through 9 select from the key the entry which is most closely illustrated by each item:

KEY: 1. No longer repeatable *past* events and hence outside of scientific study.

2. Unapproachable *future* and hence outside of scientific study.

3. Naturally occurring, repeatable events and hence fully open to scientific study.

4. None of the above.

1. Possible creative acts of God or an Almighty Being. (1)
2. Possible eternal life—meaning some form of immortality. (2)
3. Presumed transmission of life to the earth from outer space. (1)
4. Reports of transmigration of the soul; that is reincarnation or metempsychosis. (2)
5. Successful organ transplants of a heart or kidney in human beings. (3)
6. Proposed submolecular, submicroscopic spontaneous generation of life. (1)
7. Description of abortion and/or miscarriage phenomena. (3)
8. Reported resurrection of some human being. (2)
9. Application of different birth controls for purpose of eugenics. (3)

PAST	PRESENT	FUTURE
(Origin) Life	Death	(After Death)

For items 10 through 13 consider the very brief diagram given above. Now use the key to select the one entry which is most closely associated with each item:

KEY: 1. Natural (exists or occurs in physical environment) and conclusive evidence.

2. Supra-natural (man-made idea, beyond the natural)

3. Super-natural (beyond the natural associated with acts of Supreme Being).

4. None of the above entries.

10. Evolutionists have imagined a different atmosphere from the present atmosphere that they label a reducing atmosphere made up mostly of methane, ammonia, hydrogen and water vapor. (2)

11. Denial of the macrozoic idea of the origin of life on this earth was made by Redi's crucial experiment that flies come only from other flies. (1)

12. Over the centuries some scientists have believed that life on the earth was the result of Divine Intervention. (3)

13. Evolutionists believe that some gellike globs of matter absorbed the right molecules so that complex molecules formed into new units called living cells. (2)

For the following items, select from the key that one entry which is most closely associated with the entry in each item 14 through 23:

KEY: 1. Example of *circumstantial* evidence (open to several interpretations).

2. Example of *conclusive* evidence (basis for only one conclusion).

3. Either circumstantial or conclusive evidence.

4. Neither circumstantial nor conclusive evidence.

14. Macrozoic origin of first life on the earth was denied by Redi's crucial experiment that flies do not come from putrifying meat. (2)

15. Because of detection, in a controlled experiment, of color change red to yellow in the phenol test, we can deduce that yeast cells utilize oxygen. (2)

16. Laboratory synthesis of amino acids with respect to submicrozoic start of life. (1)

17. Identification of organic substances in meteors and meteorites with respect to cosmozoic beginning of life in the universe. (1)

18. Microzoic origin of first life on the earth was denied by Pasteur's crucial experiment with the swan neck flasks and growth of bacteria. (2)

19. Identification of patterns of relationships in living things with respect to theozoic start of life on the earth. (1)

20. Production of synthetic equivalents of urea, rubber, fibers for clothing with respect to spontaneous generation of living substance. (1)

21. Because of detection, in a controlled experiment, of color change of red to yellow in a phenol test, we can deduce that fish cells utilize oxygen. (2)

22. Identification of complex pattern of organelle interactions in living cells with respect to theozic start of life on the earth. (1)

23. Detection of definite pattern of exclusive left-handedness of amino acid structure in living things with respect to theozoic start of life on the earth. (1)

Attention to how scientists gain knowledge as well as attention to specific facts has been stressed. For each item 24 through 36 select from the key the appropriate entry which helps you identify each item.

KEY: 1. Example of generalization (statement about a group of things).
2. Example of process or activity of classification.
3. An analogy which is such a typical activity of scientists.
4. Example of circumstantial evidence (open to several interpretations).
5. Example of conclusive evidence (basis of only one conclusion).

24. All cells are complex. (1)
25. Laboratory synthesis of amino acids with respect to submicrozoic start of life. (4)
26. Comparison of living things to a ticking clock. (3)
27. Comparison of the cell nucleus to corporation officers. (3)
28. Comparison of a living thing to a flame. (3)
29. Cells are the units of structure and function of living things studied. (1)
30. Comparison of ribosomes and chloroplasts and factory manufacturing processes. (3)
31. Completion of a chart of results gained from phenol red tests for carbon dioxide and Winkler tests for oxygen. (2)
32. Identification of patterns of relationships and degrees of complexity in living things with respect to the theozoic start of life. (4)
33. Cellular respiration is a function of living plants and living animals. (1)
34. Comparison of the human body to an internal combustion engine. (3)
35. Completion of a chart of observations about reproductive organs and structures identified in the organisms studied. (2)
36. Green plants utilize carbon dioxide and also oxygen. (1)

4 | Origin of Humankind

When you complete this chapter you should understand how to:
1. Discuss important questions on the origin of humankind.
2. Explain fixity of species versus fixity of kinds.
3. Identify two meanings of the term *change* involved in the thinking of evolutionists and creationists.
4. Explain the real meaning of natural selection and evaluate the ideas about the relationship of changes in the natural environment and changes in living things.
5. Discuss migration-dispersal concepts as means of explaining origin of present *Homo sapiens sapiens*.

Introduction

In contrast to much of the informational content of the chapters on the origin of the universe and the origin of life on the earth, this chapter on the origin of humankind involves concepts that have been ever changing, since Charles Darwin's second book, *The Decent of Man*, published in 1871. In Chapter 2 a workable summation of the majority positions on the origin of the universe was provided by a discussion of cosmogony in contrast to cosmology with attention to the two major options of the big bang hypothesis or the steady state hypothesis. In Chapter 3 summation of the majority positions on the origin of life on the earth was presented by attention to the three major options of varieties of spontaneous generation of life in contrast to the long-standing and still viable theozoic source of first life on the earth.

Figure 27
THE CRADLE OF MANKIND

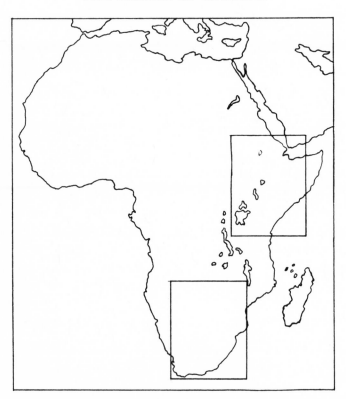

Methods of Teaching Origins

The evolutionary viewpoints can be stated with maximum brevity as: Just as cosmogonists have sought a oneness of beginning of the universe in the explosion of some dense particle, and biologists have sought a oneness of beginning of life on the earth in some unicellular life form, so megaevolutionists have sought a oneness of beginning of humankind from one common ancestor of anthropoid form.

Admittedly there have been and still are two basic conceptualizations regarding the origin of humankind: (1) the primary, initial thesis that the eternal Creator God breathed the breath of life into the dust of the earth and man became a living soul with woman made from man, and (2) the

Figure 28 — HOMINID FOSSIL LOCATIONS

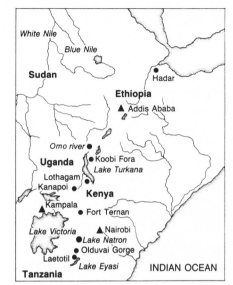

nineteenth century substitute that somehow both male and female human beings came into existence *at the same time* from the same anthropoid origin.

Although the latter animalistic concept of origin has been ever so palatable to intellectuals from the nineteenth century to present time, detailed ideas of evolutionists about an anthropoid origin of humankind have changed, and changed, and changed again. Thus, one is hard pressed to be certain of the currently adopted position, and no attempt will be made here to give a historical resume of the changing concepts of evolutionists since Charles Darwin. Suffice it to say that the early, more or less straight-line emergence of *Homo sapiens* from apelike form, and in turn from common ancestors of monkey stock has been replaced over and over again. Today the oft mentioned phrase, "the human family tree is more like a bush", can be found repeatedly as hominid fossil collections are expanded from many locales, especially from Africa (See Fig. 27 and Fig. 28) and Asia.

The animalistic view of evolutionists has become *the popular* view to the extent of seeming obliteration of the view of the supernatural, especially created origin of humankind. Yet the specially created view of first origin of humankind was *the widely accepted* view during the 18 centuries prior to Darwin; in fact, that view had been held for many centuries B.C. as can be deduced from tentative, limited translations of some of the Ebla clay tablets found in northwestern Syria since the mid 1970's. The origin of male and female human beings as given in the first chapter of Genesis is not just a recorded form of some oral tradition of early Hebrews. Evidently a long standing written record of first origin ideas has been extant in the hands of intelligent human beings since at least 2500 or 2300 B.C.

Charles Darwin stopped studying the Scriptures and turned to the *ideas of man* regarding first origins of living things, including humankind. Therefore he was not armed with broad consciousness of such unchanging answers about first origins as have been available to questing seekers since the time of Moses, if not before. Today we know that the written tradition of special creation of humankind well antedates Moses as a yardstick against which to measure changing ideas of man such as the followers of Charles Darwin. Yet in seeming disregard of this fact, evolutionists have prepared voluminous writings for world wide promotion of their ideas of anthropoid origin of humankind.[1]

Before giving attention to creation scientists' alternative views to the majority, animalistic view of the origin of humankind, let us consider a workable abbreviation of the current thinking of modern paleontologists and anthropologists; that is, the conventional wisdom about the earliest history of *Homo sapiens sapiens*.

Current Scenario on Origin of Humankind

Generally, evolutionists begin the earliest history of *Homo sapiens sapiens* within the perspective of presumed sequence of cosmic evolution, molecular evolution and organic evolution. Such an orientation was provided in the first article ("Evolution" by Ernst Mayr) in the *Scientific American* published in September 1978 and widely circulated to afford one and all with the latest status of evolutionary thinking. Likewise Richard Leakey and Roger Lewin opened their history of humankind with a chapter on "Humanity in Perspective" that they set in the context of the earth being in relation to the sun in this galaxy, which these authors presume was generated by the cosmic big bang.[2]

In briefest statement, according to evolutionists, humankind came from an animal origin. Somehow in the distant past a male *and* a female human being supposedly came into existence *at the same time* from some anthropoid origin. Human beings, then, are the end product of changes of living things that megaevolutionists think they can trace back through vertebrate ancestry to some invertebrate forms, and to changes presumably initiated in unicellular life after spontaneous generation of first life occurred on the earth from inanimate matter. According to evolutionists, human beings— that particular form of life that is fully sentient, fully conscious and self-conscious—came from an animal origin. Interestingly, human beings are that form of life that are both the subject and the object of study. Yet the answer is still negative to the question, Is it possible to scientifically study the origin of humankind? No scientist, as a scientist, was there when the first male *and* female humankind appeared on the earth. Specifically how, then, do evolutionists begin their scenario on the origin of humankind?

Old World Monkey

In the early 1980's modern paleontologists and anthropologists[3] place the roots of humanity in some common stock of Old World Monkeys from which came different forms of apes that were presumably ancestral to modern apes and ape like hominids. Usually *Aegyptopithecus zeuxis* is recognized as one of the earliest apes. A virtually complete skull was found in 1960 in the Fayum Depression, a wasteland on the eastern edge of the Egyptian Sahara. (See Fig. 29). This specimen is designated as the first ape that came somehow from the basic stock of Old World Monkeys, and has been assigned a date of around 28 million years before the present (B.P.) This form is also considered ancestral to some modern apes.

Proconsul; Dryopithecus, Gigantopithecus, Ramapithecus

Fragmental fossil evidence, called *Dryopithecus africanus*, found in 1948 on Rusigna Island in Lake Victoria and also in Europe and Asia, evidently diverged from the common monkey stock some 8-10 million years later than *Aegyptopithecus* and began another lineage of modern apes. (The name *Proconsul* has sometimes been used for this fossil ape.)

Although early beginnings of the "path of evolution towards humans" are distinctly uncertain, as stated by Leakey and Lewin, they feel that by

Figure 29
EGYPTIAN SAHARA

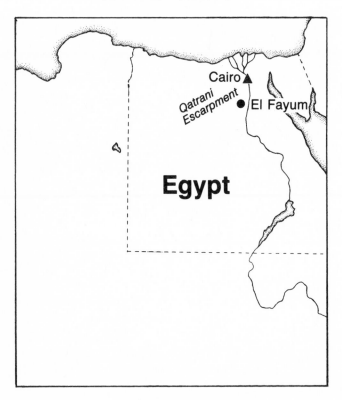

12 million years before the present (B.P.) three major genera had come into existence from the Dryopithecines which might be considered ancestral to both apes and human beings: *Dryopithecus* in Africa, *Gigantopithecus* in Asia, and *Ramapithecus* in Africa, Asia and Europe (but this interpretation is certainly not concurred in by several leading specialists).

Presumably *Dryopithecus* began a lineage of woodland apes from which modern apes have come into existence. *Gigantopithecus* became the ancestor of some very large terrestrial apes in Asia that are apparently now extinct. *Ramapithecus* is imagined as the first representative of the human family—the hominids. Although there is still only tentative agreement about assignment of individual specimens to particular genera, this tripartite pattern seems to be the main outline of very early beginnings of the scenario of the origin of humankind. (See Fig. 30). (Incidently, some paleontologists

Figure 30
RAMAPITHECUS SITES

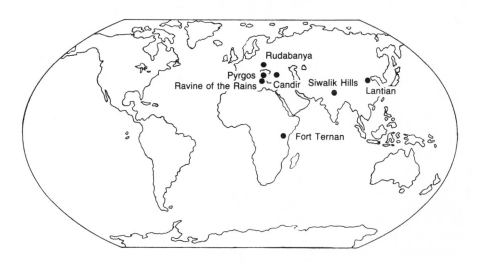

consider *Ramapithecus* an ape in all aspects morphologically, ecologically, and behaviorally.)

Multiple Forms of Australopithecus

By turning repeatedly to comparative studies of living species of many anthropoid forms and extant varieties of humankind for inspiration, modern paleontologists and anthropologists intensify their theory of the evolutionary history of humankind. Accordingly, they offer the *picture* of possibly four contemporary forms with different behavioral patterns in Africa - and possibly many other places in Europe and Asia, that lived more or less side by side some 2 to 3 million years B.P. These forms came into existence as environmental changes presumably occurred based on reasoned interpretations of geologists, paleontologists, taphonomists, paleobotanists, paleoanthropologists, and archaeologists. Evolutionist writers repeatedly stress the importance of the environment in shaping human prehistory. These evolutionists speculate that *Ramapithecus* suddenly diversified because climatic or other environmental changes formed new habitats.

"COVER WORD"
(Beware Semantic Confusion)

Trace: Megaevolutionists use this word for presumed detection of lineages of plants and/or animals, but such activities can only be deemed plausible. Such use of this term covers over the proper distinction between speculated lineages and actual events traced by careful analyses conducted by human beings, often employing technical detection equipment.

"COVER WORD"
(Beware Semantic Confusion)

Sequence: When megaevolutionists use this term in connection with discussions of rock layers they convey connotation of known cause-effect relationship. Megaevolutionists are not able to discern such relationships between fossil materials in the rocks, and hence go beyond exactness of observable conditions. Megaevolutionists regularly commit the fallacy of *post hoc ergo propter hoc* when they write or speak about rock layers or fossils as in sequences, which is the logical error of reasoning that something is the cause of something else merely because the former is presumed to be earlier in time.

In any event it is *Ramapithecus* that presumably diversified so that by 1 to 3 million years B.P. four hominid forms were contemporary in eastern and southern Africa: Some form of *Ramapithecus*, *Australopithecus* (both *africanus* and *robustus* - sometimes labeled *boiseii*, and *Homo habilis* (which may be represented by the individual skull 1470). No real consensus has been reached about these multiple forms, and different researchers use different names for the same limited, partial, fragmented fossil specimens found in Ethiopia, Kenya, Uganda and Tanzania.

How Australopithecine forms should be placed in the scenario of the origin of humankind has not been resolved. In fact, some leading specialists still hold that *Australopithecus* was nothing more than an ape, and some researchers suggest a new species, *Australopithecus afarensis*, must be considered antecedent to *Homo habilis* (See Fig. 31). Many evolutionists do agree that the gracile Australopithecine (*A. africanus*) and the robust Australopithecine (*A. robustus*) should be placed on some branch off the main family tree of modern man (See Fig. 32).

Figure 31
AUSTRALOPITHECINE SITES

The southern African sites which have yielded clues to the "evolution" of the Australopithecines.

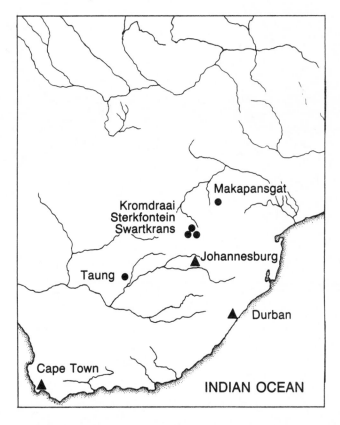

Tools

According to most evolutionists all of these hominid ancestors were upright or bipedal in their mode of locomotion with the exception of

Figure 32
EVOLUTIONARY PATH OF THE HOMINIDS

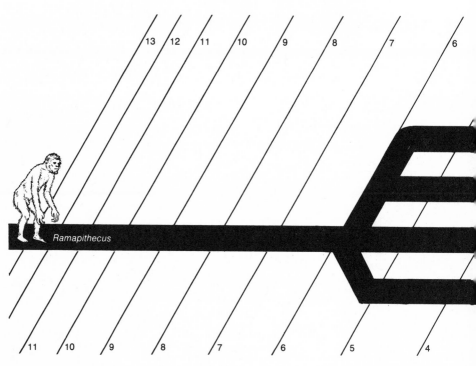

Ramapithecus that was only partially upright. (Again, some specialists conclude that even *Australopithecus* did not walk upright.) What made possible these early diversified, upright, bipedal hominids who apparently were so adaptably capable of living in a variety of habitats, such as grasslands and savannahs and along river valleys? Presumably, whatever the main pressures for diversification may have been, marked changes occurred in the hands and the eyes. Evidently the grasping hand with opposable thumb plus stereoscopic vision and detection of colors plus the upright position of bipedal locomotion were important adaptive changes that occurred during the prehistory of humankind. Such changes evidently made defense against predators and surveillance of surrounding terrain important advantages for early hominids over other competing organisms. Or so evolutionists think.

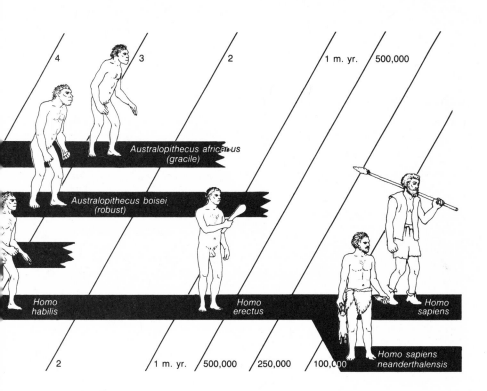

Also of great importance evidently was the possibility of carrying objects and implements or maybe tools. At many varied sites of excavation, objects have been found adjacent to hominid skeletal remains, and researchers have proposed that over a span of 1 to 2 million years B.P. extremes of tool making developed among different groups of *Homo* individuals.

Pebble tools and crude scrapers have been found in Olduvai Gorge. Also hand axes, chisels, cleavers, awls, anvils and hammerstones have been found along lake shores in Africa so that researchers think that sophisticated tool making and primitive implements were used by contemporary hominids much as modern day african neighbors have different instruments. Maybe the scenario can be revised, according to some evolutionists, such that another presumed presursor of modern humankind, *Homo erectus*, came on the scene as immigrants.

Homo Erectus

In any case by about one million years B.P. *Homo erectus* presumably was equipped to explore the whole world. Distinct behavioral differences are interpreted by evolutionists so that *Homo erectus* presumably had established home bases and developed the practice of sharing their food. Those premodern human forms were supposedly systematic food gatherers and hunters. Presumably they had developed the unique habit of collecting and cooperative sharing of food which many evolutionists take to be early signs of humanness.

Around one million to 500,000 years B.P. *Homo erectus* had so developed the unique human trait of food sharing that some may have imitated migrating activities of bird flocks and in a slow, persistent manner migrated from Africa so that they gradually occupied Asia and Europe due to a sort of evolutionary momentum (See Fig. 33). Pressure of numbers or curiosity about surrounding environments somehow resulted in changes in *H. erectus*. Evolutionists interpret skeletal finds to mean that a transition from *H. erectus* to *Homo sapiens* occurred as a steady trend of increase in size of brain and cranial capacity of the skull. With the upward shift in brain size presumably came the invention of agriculture. "The invention of agriculture was, without exaggeration, the most significant event in the history of mankind," claims Leakey and Lewin.[4] Some evolutionists claim that transitional changes from *erectus* to *sapiens* presumably occurred many times and in many places, though this seems to be contradictory to another common claim by evolutionists that early humankind migrated from Africa. Still other evolutionists claim that humankind may have originated in India.

Homo Sapiens

Nevertheless, by about 50,000 years B.P. a genetic pool of *Homo sapiens* had became widely established as represented by skeletal finds known commonly as Peking Man and Solo Man is Asia and Java, Neanderthal Man in Europe and Rhodesian Man in Africa. Clusters of mobile hunters and gatherers presumably had given way to practitioners of sedentary agriculture by individuals who had some use of language. Possibly then these mentioned prehistoric human beings were regional variations who had enough "time on their hands" to develop beginnings of complex culture, and who

Figure 33
MIGRATION OF HOMO ERECTUS

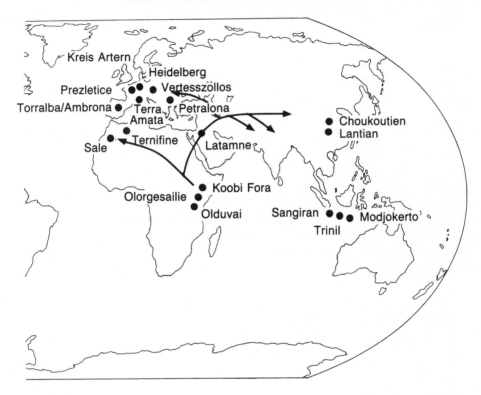

were thoughtful and sensitive to the point of deliberate burial of their dead. This remarkable independence of the environment on the part of upright hominids may have come about due to added capabilities over forest dwelling apes, such as (1) transport of food, (2) transport of water, (3) transport of fire, and (4) transport of experience by means of language.

Spirit of Humanity

Evolutionists interpret that the Neanderthals were established in various tribes some 30,000 years B.P. and for at least 20,000 years lived in Northern Europe and expanded also across France, Spain, Italy, Yugoslavia, Iraq, China, Java, Zambia and Israel. Some evolutionists presume that waves of emigrants from Africa contributed to the evolutionary momentum of *Homo erectus* with the formation of a highly variable genetic pool among *Homo sapiens*. It is noteworthy that the Neanderthals today have been assigned the special subspecies status of *Homo sapiens neanderthalensis*[5]. Out of such a mosaic of the basic *sapiens* gene pool the transition to *Homo sapiens sapiens* supposedly occurred in many different places. No single geographic center is claimed by evolutionists as the birthplace of modern man.

"COVER WORD"
(Beware Semantic Confusion)

Adaptation, adapted: These words merely refer to observed circumstances or conditions that exist, and no substantive explanation is gained as to how the recognized conditions came into existence. To write that an organism is adapted seems to explain something, but no real knowledge is gained as to how fish came to live and swim in water, or how birds came to fly in the atmosphere.

One accompanying physical change, which may have been coupled with developing culinary practices, evidently was a reduction of tooth size from the massive canines and molars of some early hominid forms. Some evolutionists believe that a growing "spirit of humanity" can be found in the widespread use of fire which came about maybe as a benefit of controlling fires in the environment due to lightning, and the possible increase of cooked food as satisfactory and palatable tastes were discovered, maybe if food was dropped in a campfire and then eaten.

Evidently there was much physical variation in early *Homo sapiens sapiens* even as is commonly evident today. Much evidence is found in caves in Europe and in caves in Africa of distinctive artistic abilities. Whether or not the use of caves as living abodes came about due to the Ice Age, at least many evolutionists think that variations in skin pigmentation in the immediate ancestors of modern man were brought about as early human beings migrated into different ecological niches on the surface of the earth.

Cro-Magnon

Presumably Cro-Magnon skeletons are fossilized remains of people exactly like human beings alive today. Did these early modern people migrate across the Beringia land bridge from Asia into the Americas, and across the Timor Straits from Java into Australia? Many artifacts, common cultural remains, and Los Angeles Man, which is given a date of 26,000 years B. P., are used to support such migrational presuppositions. And though geologists dispute whether an Ice Age occurred 70,000 or 25,000 or 12,000 years B. P. there is much agreement among evolutionists that extensive ice masses sometime ago could have functioned like great sponges and caused the ocean levels to decrease so that significant land bridges actually did exist between continents. Many, many fossil remains can be used to support migrations of a wide variety of animals as well as modern humankind. Thus the studied conclusion of most evolutionists is that by 10,000 years B.P. virtually every part of the globe was populated with humanity and agriculture was widely practiced as people lived in small villages. According to Leakey and Lewin some "combination of an abundant supply of plant food and a sufficient supplement of wild meat" contributed to controlled cultivation and farming.[6] The possible use of methods of irrigation coupled with understanding of use of seeds may have lead to the beginning of agriculture. Evolutionists feel it is evident that agriculture began in many areas—areas as different as the southeast edge of the Mediterranean, Meso-America, Peru and Thailand.

Such is one widely publicized scenario of the origin of humankind, *Homo sapiens sapiens*, to which *all* varieties of physical form and color and cultural diversity belong today.

Creationist Response to Evolutionist Scenario

Utilizing the previous sections as a plausible representation of the widely publicized scenario of the origin of humankind, *Homo sapiens sapiens*, currently promulgated by megaevolutionists, the science teacher should be prepared to offer students at least a seven part critique or rebuttal. This is not the place to argue the academic necessity of such a rebuttal, nor the constitutional civil right propriety of teaching students about possible, credible alternative aspects to the scenario presented almost exclusively by the majority, establishment oriented science teachers. Multiple references to opinions and careful analysis by legally trained specialists have been available since 1962 and continue to appear in prestigious law journals to the point that exclusive presentation of one viewpoint on the origin of the

universe and of all life therein potentially involves recognizable abridgement of civil and constitutional rights guaranteed under the Free Exercise
and Establishment Clauses of the First Amendment of the Constitution
of the United States of America.[7]

We will now consider a seven-part itemization of factual critique of aspects
of the majority scenario offered almost exclusively in public schools in this
country (and even in most schools around the world). In the last sections
of this chapter we will consider an alternative interpretation, a creationist
scenario on the origin of *Homo sapiens sapiens.*

Megaevolutionist Reactionaries Disregard Scientific Methodology and Scientific Facts

For over 120 years Charles Darwin and his popularizers have been reactionaries on a grand scale to the philosophical ground of the scientific
discipline, and in turn, have actually disregarded scientific facts.

Although not generally taught in this twentieth century, modern science
began in the 1600's because its founders believed that the universe was
contingent upon the creative acts of God. The earliest scientists acknowledged that no human being had observed the beginning of the universe, or
of life on the earth, or of the first human beings. But Charles Darwin (and
those who have followed him closely) ignored the account of origins contained in Genesis. Darwin became a reactionary to the position of Genesis
on first origins. Yet the earliest scientists knew the written tradition of first
origins (which is documented today, according to some specialists, in written
form in the Ebla tablets of around 2500 to 2300 B.C.) from their first hand
study of Genesis 1.

The founders and developers of modern science knew that they had not
created themselves and had not created the surrounding natural environment (including the celestial as well as the terrestrial aspects). Therefore
they believed and accepted the theistic account of origin, in Genesis 1. They
believed that God had created all things, and that each kind reproduced
after each kind.

Early creationist biologists such as Carl Linnaeus and John Ray once
thought God had created directly every species of organism which they
had identified. Contemporaries of Linnaeus and Ray developed the concept of fixity of species. Evidently Charles Darwin was taught that con-

cept and started his voyage on the H.M.S. Beagle believing the idea of immutability of species. It should be noted that the concept of immutability of species was an idea of Darwin's contemporaries and was not part of Genesis.

Because of Darwin's observations of the amazing variety of flora and fauna made during his trip around the world, he reacted against the idea of immutability of species which he had acquired during his schooling. He reacted against the supposed theistic position of fixity of species. Darwin evidently had stopped his Bible studies to the degree that he was not armed with the awareness that Moses had written about kinds and *not* about species.

Furthermore, when Darwin wrote his ideas of the descent of man, he was apparently unaware (and also many modern scientists with prior committment to megaevolution) that Linnaeus, at least, changed his mind after years of specific research in plant hybridization. It is true that Linnaeus wrote in 1735 in his *Classes Plantarum*: "There are as many species as there are originally created forms." From this theistic point of view he did most of his work in classification.

However, it is interesting to note what he wrote in his book, *Systema Vegetabilium* (1774), written four years before his death. During the later years of his life he carried on considerable hybridization of his own and as a result came to a definitely broadened concept of the created unit. In the book, *Stages in the Evolution of Plant Species*, Jen Clausen,[8] has translated from the Latin the following assertion made by Linnaeus in his 1774 book:

> Let us suppose that the Divine Being in the beginning progressed from the simpler to the complex; from few to many; similarly that He in the beginning of the plant kingdom created as many plants as there were natural orders. These plant orders He himself, therefore producing, mixed among themselves until from them originated those plants which today exist as genera.
>
> Nature then mixed up these plant genera among themselves through generations of double origin (= hybrids) and multiplied them into the existing species, as many as possible (whereby the flower structures were not changed), excluding from the number of species the almost sterile hybrids, which are produced by the same mode of origin.

This problem of understanding the term *kind* and the term *species* was not clarified in Darwin's time. He reacted against all living things being created kinds, turned away from the Genesis account, and opted for his own idea about natural selection. It is important to realize that the created kinds of the creation model are *not* necessarily the same as species of the modern system of classification. In addition, the term *varieties* is not equivalent to species. It is noteworthy that all such terms of classification must be used arbitrarily.

Megaevolutionists feel quite confident that a *species* is a group of inter-breeding organisms found in a particular geographic area which are reproductively isolated from other organisms. This is an arbitrary defini-tion which is often applied with considerable difficulty. (In point of fact such a definition cannot be applied to fossils.) The key concept is the aspect of interbreeding. As evolutionist E. Peter Volpe has stated, ''Only through breeding tests can the basis of the variation be firmly established.''[9]

Confident, dogmatic, committed, megaevolutionists often press for an operational definition of the term *kind*. They demand to know just what the created kinds were. Of course no modern scientist was present when the first kinds of flora and fauna appeared on the earth, and thus no clear-cut answer is possible as to the identity of the created kinds. Because of the beginning given in Genesis, biblical believers know that God has curs-ed the earth and even judged the earth and all life thereon in a catastrophic flood. Mention of such catastrophic destruction of life becomes integral to a creationist alternative on the origin of *Homo sapiens sapiens* to be presented in the last section of this chapter.

That there are rather distinct kinds, types, or forms of living things seems to be recognized even by evolutionist Ernest Mayr when he writes, ''Dif-ferent forms of life were referred to as 'types' by the comparative anatomists of the last century and even earlier. Bats, whales, birds, penguins, snails, sea urchins, and all other well known kinds of animals are such types.''[10] Apparently the terms *kinds, forms,* and *types* are really interchangeable terms. Again, however, the students should be reminded that kinds, forms, or types of living things are *not* terms of classification that are necessarily equivalent to the basic classification term of *species*.

Interestingly enough, in response to the request by megaevolutionists for an operational definition of the term *kind*, a proper, genetically oriented criterion can be suggested as a basis for identifying basic kinds, forms, or types, just as is done by those trying to identify species. Biologists do not seem to have any difficulty separating elephant and mouse, lion and leopard, buttercup and snapdragon, strawberry and apple, and so forth. Thus an operational definition of the term *kind* might be:

Kind

A kind is a distinct group of interbreeding organisms found in a particular geographic area which are genetically isolated from other recognizably different organisms.

Several creationist biologists have suggested for a number of years that the means of classification should be changed from primarily external features (from bones or impressions in stone) to more basic biological aspects of physiology and actual breeding results. (Molecular biochemists may be finally supplying just such a basis for classification of living things regarding variation within limits of recognizably different kinds.)

It is noteworthy that, of all the crosses of organisms known, only variations of basic discrete and plainly identifiable different kinds (forms or types) have ever been reported. For instance, crosses between many of the more common animals have taken place both in the natural environment and in captivity. However, offspring of such crosses usually are sterile and hence are not examples of any new kind of stable, independent existence. Crosses that have occured at least to the extent of the beginning embryonic development are listed in Fig. 34.

Figure 34
CROSSES BETWEEN DIFFERENT ANIMALS

1. lion x tiger
2. mouse x rat
3. sheep x goats
4. chicken x guinea fowl
5. chicken x turkey
6. house martin x barn swallow
7. swan x goose
8. horse, ass, zebra, kiang x onager
9. dogs, wolves, jackals coyotes x some foxes
10. ox, zebu, yak, bison, wisent, Brahman cattle x Afrikander cattle

In regard to other animals, reports are available of frequent hybrids as listed in Fig. 35.

Figure 35
HYBRIDS

1. among species of ducks
2. among species of pigeons
3. among species of pheasants
4. among species of Cecropia moth
5. among species of crows
6. among species of toads
7. among rabbits and hares
8. among species of ibex
9. among species of coyotes
10. among species of caribou
11. between purple and bronzed grackles
12. between red-shafted and yellow-shafted flickers
13. between western and eastern species of the European hedgehog
14. between house (English) sparrow and willow sparrow
15. between some species of warblers
16. between some species of gall wasps
17. between several species of freshwater fish

Likewise crosses between different plants are reported. Some of the widest crosses known are listed in Fig. 36.

Figure 36
CROSSES BETWEEN DIFFERENT PLANTS

1. wheat x wheat grass
2. goat grass, boat grass x rye
3. corn x teosinte and gamma grass
4. radish x cabbage
5. sugar cane x sorghum
6. fescue grass x Italian rye grass
7. wild tobacco x petunia
8. bean x cow pea
9. blackberry x raspberry

Actually species within certain plant genera will cross with other species of the same genera and produce hybrids. See Fig. 37.

Figure 37
PLANT HYBRIDS

1. Alder
2. Arbutus
3. Basswood
4. Birch
5. Buckeye
6. Canna
7. Carnation
8. Catalpa
9. Catchfly
10. Chestnut
11. Cotton
12. Currant
13. Gooseberry
14. Darnel
15. Dogwood
16. Elm
17. Evening primrose
18. Fir
19. Four-o'clock
20. Goat grass
21. Hawk's-beard

22. Hawthorne	32. Oak	42. Spiderwort
23. Hemlock	33. Oats	43. Spruce
24. Hickory	34. Onion	44. Sycamore
25. Holly	35. Papaw	45. Timothy grass
26. Honey locust	36. Pea	46. Tobacco
27. Larch	37. Pine	47. Vetch
28. Lily	38. Poplar	48. Wheat
29. Black locust	39. Poppy	49. Willow
30. Magnolia	40. Rose	50. Yew
31. Maple	41. Snapdragon	

Nevertheless, the position published many decades ago by Frank Lewis Marsh, Ph.D., early creationist biologist of the modern era, who has campaigned for a physiological basis of plant and animal classification, can be summarized in the following apt manner: Hybridization is important as a means of production of variation among plants and animals, but *no* crosses occur across kinds, hence diversity *within* kinds is all that is accomplished.[11] The same forceful conclusion can be expressed in another manner: A researcher studying variability of plants or animals always concludes the research study, whether in the natural environment or in the controlled laboratory, with the *same recognizable kind* of organism with which the researcher began. How, then, can modern evolutionists compose their scenario that human beings came from some animal ancestor?

Clearly the science teacher can remind students what Linnaeus learned from his empirical studies of variability and hybridization. Clearly the principles of genetics can be used to show limited variability *within* kinds as a scientifically established fact and also show a type of fixity of kinds. *Fixity of kinds* is a concept immediately associated with limited variation *within* kinds of organisms. Strictly because of known behavior of genetic materials from generation to generation, creationist geneticists can maintain full empirical support for the concept of fixity of kinds from the careful and proper science of genetics. Never does a new kind result from any breeding practices. Hence one of the most certain facts of biological science is the fact that the same kind of organism comes from a given kind, generation after generation after generation. Therefore, the concept of fixity of kinds properly represents reality: (1) in the present involving all known plants and animals during the lifetime of humankind, and (2) in the past as represented in all known fossils.

In respect to plants and animals of the present, fixity of kinds might very well be an adequate modern day equivalent expression for the root phrases in Genesis of "after his kind" and "after their kind", which are basic to modern creationist thought. Some increased understanding of part of the creation model can be gained from study of Classroom Teaching Aid 26 wherein a limited attempt is made to clarify the important question, What were the created kinds? Since no scientist was available to categorize and classify all created kinds, only limited information can be gained from listing kinds of plants and animals mentioned in Genesis. Also portions of Deuteronomy and Leviticus have been used as grounds from which to deduce some points of biblical classification. Classroom Teaching Aid 26 is at least one answer to the logical inquiry as to identity of basic created kinds.

In regard to plants and animals in the past, as evidenced in fossil materials, both specialist and non-specialist agree that many fossilized plants and animals look like plants and animals alive today. That representations of basic kinds of plants and animals are found throughout much of the so called geologic column is evident from close study of Classroom Teaching Aid 27. Quite clearly, if the historical geologist's time estimates are considered for a moment, algae have been algae for a long time, sponges have been sponges for a long time. The same may be asserted for beech trees, frogs, poplar trees, gophers, and even spiders. These charts are further support for the validity of the fixity of kinds concept, and are basic to my contention that fixity of kinds is well documented by all fossil material known. Clearly, variability of plants and animals is *not* unlimited as Darwin and many of his early followers believed.

"COVER WORD"
(Beware Semantic Confusion)

Column: used in geology when no physical referent exists with regard to the traditional geologic column anywhere on the surface of the earth; conveys connotations of reality.

To give added emphasis to the concept of fixity of kinds Classroom Teaching Aid 28 can be used. Here students can see a documented list

Classroom Teaching Aid 26
SOME POINTS OF BIBLICAL CLASSIFICATION

living beings
{
beasts (quadrupeds)
land swarmers
water swarmers
winged fliers
man
}

beasts
{
hoofed beasts
{
ungulates: deer, antelopes, cattle, sheep, goats
other ungulates plus hyraxes, pikas, rabbits
}
beasts of the earth
{
large mammals and reptiles (beasts of the field)
other beasts of the earth (large rodents)
}
}

land swarmers
{
all that goes upon the belly—lizards and snakes
all that goes on all fours—small rodents and carnivores
all that causes to multiply feet—small invertebrates
}

water swarmers
{
"fish"
{
fish with fins and scales (clean)
unclean
{
large water monsters
others (sharks, etc.)
}
}
invertebrates
}

winged fliers
{
birds, fliers of the heavens
{
clean
{
twitterers (small perching birds)
other (game birds)
}
unclean
{
screamers (birds of prey)
others (water birds, bats)
}
}
swarming fliers
{
clean—locusts, grasshoppers, crickets
unclean—all other winged insects
}
}

—from Arthur J. Jones, "A General Analysis of the Biblical "kind" (Min),"
Creation Research Society Quarterly, 9 (1): 53-57, June, 1972, p.55.

Classroom Teaching Aid 27
GEOLOGICAL RECORD FOR PLANTS AND ANIMALS

GENERALIZED GEOLOGICAL RECORD FOR PLANTS

PERIOD	Fungi	Algae	Mosses	Hepaticae	Psilophytales	Equistinae (Horsetails)	Lycopodales (Club-mosses)	Filicales (Ferns)	Pteridospermae	Cycadales	Benettitales	Ginkgoales	Cordiates	Coniferales	Monocotyledones	Dicotyledones
Present
Pliocene
Miocene
Oligocene
Eocene
Paleocene
Cretaceous
Jurassic
Triassic
Permian
Carboni-
ferous
Devonian
Silurian
Ordovician
Cambrian

Generalized geological record of plants is shown here. Solid vertical lines represent duration of existence of each plant group. Broken line portions indicate some doubt as to the earliest appearance of some groups. No common ancestors are known.

GENERALIZED GEOLOGICAL RECORD FOR ANIMALS

PERIOD	Radiolaria	Foraminifera	Spongiae	Hydrozoa	Cystoidea	Blastoidea	Crinoidea	Echinoidea	Brachiopoda	Gastropoda	Insecta	Crustacea	Arachnida	Pisces	Amphibia	Reptilia	Mammalia	Aves
Present
Pliocene
Miocene
Oligocene
Eocene
Paleocene
Cretaceous
Jurassic
Triassic
Permian
Carboni-
ferous
Devonian
Silurian
Ordovician
Cambrian

Generalized geological record of animals is portrayed in this chart. Vertical lines represent duration of existence in each animal group. No common ancestors are known.

Classroom Teaching Aid 28

"LIVING FOSSILS"

1. Crinoids:
Flowerlike echinoderms, commonly called sea lilies or feather stars. There are about 2,100 species of fossil crinoids and about 800 species of living representatives. Found in Paleozoic strata.

2. Lingula:
Within the phylum Brachiopoda, the genus *Lingula*, which currently lives in the oceans of the world, is found attached to the bottom in mud or sand by a peduncle. This same genus is found in the fossil marine fauna of the Cambrian.

3. Tuatara:
This relic of the past is the only survivor of the order Rynchocephalia, or beak-headed reptiles. Living specimens have been found only on islands off New Zealand, where they live in holes on sandy hills by the shore. The skeleton of one of these reptiles found in Jurassic deposits of Europe is almost exactly like the living tuatara. Fossil evidence of this organism is found in the Early Cretaceous, which supposedly leaves a time gap of 135 million years.

4. Coelacanth:
In 1937 a coelacanth was caught alive east of London, Cape Province, South Africa. According to the paleontological record the last coelacanth lived approximately 70 million years ago. More specimens have been taken near Madagascar and the South Africa vicinity. "The bony structures of our modern Coelacanths are almost exactly the same as those left by Coelacanths hundreds of millions of years ago." (Smith, J. L. B. *The Search Beneath the Sea.* Henry Holt and Co., New York, 1956)

5. Neopilina:
On May 6, 1952, ten specimens of this deep-sea mollusk were dredged from a depth of 3,590 meters off the Mexican Coast. According to paleontologists *Neopilina* became extinct about 280 million years ago during the Devonian period. It is not found in intervening rocks.

6. Cycads:
Zamia grows in parts of Florida, the West Indies, and South America. The East Indian genus *Cycas* attains a height of 67 feet and is 40 inches in diameter. Fossil cycads, quite abundant in Mesozoic formations, have been found in many areas with abundant remains in the Black Hills.

7. Metasequoia:
Fossils of *Metasequoia* make it the most abundant genus of the Taxodiaceae, or cypresslike family, in North America in the Upper Cretaceous to Miocene formations. Ever since 1946 many living specimens of *Metasequoia* have been found in China. (Chaney, Ralph W. "A Revision of Fossil *Sequoia* and *Taxodium* in Western North America Based on the Recent Discovery of Metasequoia," *Transactions of American Philosophical Society*, 40 (3): 171-263, 1951).

of living fossils. This combination of words may seem contradictory and incongruous. Fossils were long considered, in most cases, to represent former life forms that no longer existed on the earth, forms that had become extinct. As the science teacher can point out from this list, living examples have been found of organisms that formerly were thought to be only extinct fossils hence the term *living fossils*.

In his 1976 book, R. L. Wysong published[12] an extensive, documented list, with presumed evolutionary dates and some illustrations, which included living fossils beyond the seven documented in Classroom Teaching Aid 28. Wysong's list is summarized in Fig. 38.

Figure 38
LIVING FOSSILS

1. bat, 50 million years
2. cockroach, 250 million years
3. dragonfly, 170 million years
4. starfish, 500 million years
5. bacteria, 600 million years
6. Gingko tree, 200 million years
7. shark, 181 million years
8. nautilus, 100 million years
9. sea urchin, 100 million years
10. clubmosses, horsetails, ferns, liverworts, mosses, hornworts, 400 million years

These organisms listed in Classroom Teaching Aid 28 and Fig. 38 show fixity of kinds through time since each of these fossils have a modern day, look-alike counterpart. No one individual plant or animal has lived millions of years, but these *kinds* of organisms have evidently been on the surface of the earth for a long time, if the geologist's time scale is adopted for the sake of argument.

Furthermore, there are no true transitional forms known in the fossil materials. Yet if the broad evolutionary scenario of molecules to man occurred as evolutionists so confidently proclaim, then many transitional forms should be found easily throughout collections of fossils, plants and animals. Numerous examples of changing stages between kinds should be abundant in all fossil materials. But *no* transitional forms between kinds are known. In fact, no transitional forms are known between any level of the arbitrary classification system of plants and animals. There are none between phyla, between class, order, family, genus, and none between species. As plant and animal breeders know, new species only derive from breeding of two or more species, so there are no transitional forms between species in any fossil materials nor between species of any living plants and animals.

Evolutionists often attempt to claim existence of transitional forms in such examples as, *Neopolina*, *Seymouria*, or *Archaeopteryx*. However, these forms are *not* truly transitional but merely examples of forms that evolutionists interpret have similarities in common with more than one major kind of animal, say similar to amphibians and reptiles, or similar to reptiles and birds. Admittedly real similarities are detectable, but *no genetic* connections are demonstratable. Therefore, evolutionists merely assume that similarities manifest relationship. This reasoning of evolutionists is totally dependent on one basic assumption: *The degree of relationship depends upon the degree of similarity.* But this is only an assumption which cannot in any way be supported by genetic lineage between major kinds of organisms. There is, then, no true genetically tested transitional form known; no true transition between birds and reptiles, between reptiles and amphibians, between any other major kind of animal or between any major kind of plant.[13]

Darwin and His Followers Disregarded Two Meanings of the Term *Change* of Organisms

Ever since 1859, when Darwin helped turn intellectuals from the time honored Creator of all things, evolutionists have practiced equivocations of the term *evolution*. One very specific reason that evolutionists have written so persuasively about so called human evolution is this very equivocation of terminology. Proponents and opponents, of course, agree that the term evolution can be understood to mean change. But what kind of change is intended?

Quite often evolutionists assert that evolution means *any* change. Thus some evolutionists actually hold that a human being evolves as embryological changes occur, resulting in more and more specific manifestation of the complexity of structure and function that was set essentially at the time of fertilization (or at the time of conception, as applied to human beings). To consider human embryological changes in this way means that evolution and embryological development may be too easily accepted as synonyms.

But during all embryological development the only changes that occur are manifestations of complexity already contained in the DNA code in the zygote of each vertebrate. Thus embryological development *cannot* be the same as complex structural and functional changes of physical traits (such as, feathers for scales, or wings for forelimbs, or netted venation for parallel venation), as are necessarily entailed when evolutionists claim that all kinds of animals have a common origin, or that all kinds of plants have a common origin.

Thus a real ambiguity exists with regard to the term *evolution.* Evolutionists do not eliminate the ambiguity in any significant manner when some maintain that evolution is any change in the genetic composition of a population of organisms over successive generations. Science teachers should point out that evolutionists have the responsibility to resolve the ambiguity about the meaning of evolution, and hence the possible equivocation of embryological development and evolution. For instance:

1. On the one hand, do evolutionists mean genetic variational changes that are known or occur *within* all easily recognized kinds of organisms? (These readily documented and demonstrated changes are labeled microevolution by some specialists, but many well qualified scientists insist that the term is unnecessary since *limited genetic variation* is all that is involved.)
2. On the other hand, do evolutionists mean that over great extensions of time genetic variational changes have occurred so that totally new kinds of organisms have come into existence from existing kinds of organisms? (That is, have present kinds of organisms, including human beings, come presumably from previously existing organisms which came from other organisms with the beginning of life on the earth in some unicellular organization of living matter? Properly, this magnitude of change *between* kinds of organisms should be labeled megaevolution.)

Zealous evolutionists try to find some kind of evidence to support their contention of age long continuity between microevolution (limited genetic variation) and megaevolution (broad scope kind to kind change). In their enthusiasm to portray some continuity of change among all organisms, living and dead, megaevolutionists make multiple use of circumstantial evidence of similarities among living things or similarities among extinct, fossil things. They emphasize the circumstances of similarities of genetic materials, anatomy, embryology, cell biology, geographic distribution, protein components and behavior. Then megaevolutionists use such *comparative studies* to construct evolutionary history of past and present organisms.

Since many megaevolutionists imagine a gradual process of change of organisms, they claim that those organisms that are more similar to each other must have been more closely related than organisms less similar to each other. Thus human beings and chimpanzees are presumed to be closely related because of the circumstances of similarities. Of course all such comparative reasoning is built upon the same *basic* assumption already identified in the previous section: *The degree of relationship depends upon the degree of similarity.*

In a very candid expression Dr. Francisco J. Ayala admits that this "simple assumption is the logical basis of efforts to reconstruct evolutionary history" by means of comparative studies involving circumstances of similarities. (*Scientific American*, Sept. 1978). It is well that Dr. Ayala did not write biological basis because all such efforts to "reconstruct" evolutionary history are merely recitations of circumstantial evidence for a pattern of comparative reasoning that may be plausible to a megaevolutionist, yet is not at all biological. This is so, since no actual lineage of human beings with different kinds of organisms are established by means of the circumstantial evidence of similarities. No breeding tests establish any actual biological affinities in the sense of genetic lineages of different kinds of organisms.

Science teachers have the responsibility to show that ideas of relationship between human beings and any other animals, as proposed by megaevolutionists on the basis of circumstantial evidence of similarities, cannot be submitted to the very test of limits of variation recommended by the megaevolutionist E. Peter Volpe, namely that only through breeding tests can the basis of any variation be firmly established.

Thus many instances of diagrammatic representations (trees of life) by megaevolutionists of supposed relationships or lineages among kinds of living and extinct things may seem plausible, but they are merely circumstantial and do not represent scientifically established kind to kind lineages. Family trees of so called human evolution have been changed over and over again in the last four decades. Because of startling finds in Africa, Asia and America, specialists have been rewriting and rewriting the story of earliest humanity.[14] There is even a growing trend for imagining that the earliest ancestors of humankind came from Asia rather than from Africa as was proposed in the scenario provided in the first section of this chapter.

Actually any of these family trees or trees of life of presumed lineages found in textbooks are based solely upon arguments from homology. The term *homology* means essentially that similar structures have the same (common) gene origin. Since physical traits are the result of genetic code function, megaevolutionists claim that all vertebrates with the same basic forelimb bone pattern (including human beings) *must* have come from the same gene pool. Consequently, all vertebrates are presumed by megaevolutionists to be related in some degree (depending upon the degree of similarity, over all). The megaevolutionist argument can be extended and represented:

1. Similarities of bones—same gene source assumed.
2. Similarities of embryos—same gene source assumed.
3. Similarities of proteins, amino acids—same gene source assumed.
4. Similarities of brain form—same gene source assumed.

However, Sir Gavin de Beer remarks as follows:

> It is now clear that the pride with which it was assumed that the inheritance of homologous structures from a common ancestor explained homology is misplaced; for such inheritance cannot be ascribed to identity of genes. The attempt to find "homologous" genes, except in closely related species, has been given up as hopeless. . . What mechanism can it be that results in the production of homologous organs, the same "patterns", in spite of their *not* being controlled by the same gene? I asked this question in 1938, and it has not been answered.[15] (Emphasis in the original)

Thus the supposed lineages of different kinds of organisms that megaevolutionists present in the form of family trees or trees of life are nothing but circumstantial similarities that are completely nonnucleogenic, for two very specific reasons: (1) denial of the presumed common gene source and (2) the clear lack of any interbreeding fertility of the distinct kinds which megaevolutionists claim are related. Any *ad hoc* hypothesis about suppressor gene mutations does not alter the complete genetic gap between major kinds of organisms, or the fully recognizable discreteness of all major kinds of organisms. Paleontologists more or less readily assign all fossils to one kind of organism or another; and *researchers, in the field or in the laboratory, always conclude their research with the very same recognizable kind of organism with which they began.*

Megaevolutionists Exhibit a Predisposition or Prior Commitment to An Animal Origin of Humankind

Megaevolutionists have a prior commitment to an animal origin of human beings. Over the decades this tendency has been manifested fully in the types of reconstructions and actual fraudulent actions of evolutionists. Specifically, different evolutionists have exhibited this predisposition when they:

1. Offered Piltdown or Dawn Man as an ancestor of human beings.
2. Proposed Nebraska Man (*Hesperopithecus*) as another ancestor.
3. Built the first reconstruction of Neanderthal Man as a more recent ancestor of humankind.
4. Included Java Man and Peking Man in their presumed family tree of humankind.
5. Proclaimed *Ramapithecus*, *Dryopithecus*, and *Aegyptopithecus* as early precursers of hominoids and hominids.
6. Accepted similarities of vertebrate embryos stressed by Ernest Haeckel as support for the catch phrase ''ontogeny recapitulates phylogeny''.
7. Some evolutionary minded exhibitors transported around the country their frozen Ice Man as a human ancestor.

Megaevolutionists use the word *reconstruction* as a type of cover word; that is, the term is used in a misleading manner to gain connotative meaning of life-like existence for their imagined exterior appearances of so called apemen or near human forms. Yet the reconstructions produced are only based on minimal skeletal parts; or maybe partially articulated skeletons are all that is actually known. Often solitary skulls (or parts of skulls), mandibles, femurs, or teeth have been reconstructed into faces, arms, legs and bodies of whole apelike or humanlike individuals.

Megaevolutionists do not in any rigorous sense reconstruct animallike ancestors of human beings; rather they only generate imagined external appearances of bone and artifact remains of presumed animal ancestors.[16] Nevertheless, today, evolutionists even unfold extensive imagined scenarios about possible individual and group behavior patterns.

"COVER WORD"
(Beware Semantic Confusion)

Reconstruction: A cover word like this is used by megaevolutionists to gain connotative meaning for imagined scenarios about supposed past geologic features and/or events (or about exterior appearances of organisms when only articulated skeletons are known). The word is properly associated with such work as the reconstruction of Williamsburg, Virginia of the colonial period. In the latter reconstructive work, actual records and eyewitness reports of previously existing constructions are available, whereas no such records or reports of participants are available to megaevolutionists. Reconstruction can only follow original construction. Reconstructions by megaevolutionists are no more than imagined narratives or imagined appearances.

But reconstruction is properly associated with such work as the reconstruction of Williamsburg, Virginia, of the colonial time period. In that rebuilding work, actual records and eyewitness reports or previously existing constructions are available, whereas no such records or reports of participants are available to megaevolutionists writing some possible scenario about human ancestors. Reconstructions by megaevolutionists, consequently, are no more than imagined expressions of their predisposition or prior commitment to their idea that human beings came from an animal origin. Such commitment is well exemplified in the following examples.

Piltdown Man. Some person was so imbued with the predisposition toward an animallike origin of humankind that he purposely filed teeth and artifically stained some jaw material of a modern anthropoid and then helped another searcher "find" Piltdown Man as a possible ancient human ancestor. Admittedly many specialists were skeptical of Piltdown, but textbook authors and others seized the idea that some ancient precurser of human beings had been found; and so wrote about that conclusion for almost five decades. Not until flourine analysis was applied to the jaw material was the truly fraudulent nature of the find made known in the 1950's. Thus Piltdown Man was removed from the family tree of human beings.

Nebraska Man. The animal ancestor predisposition was so strong that fossil material of a peccary pig was initially proclaimed as manlike, and exterior reconstructions were published in newspapers in the United States and England to the effect that *Hesperopithecus* was a supposed ancestor of humankind. But Nebraska Man, too, had to be removed from the family tree of human beings when the faulty reasoning was discerned.

Neanderthal Man. Believing that human beings came from some kind of lower form, megaevolutionists formulated their initial interpretations, or reconstructions, of the bones found in the Neander Valley in Germany to portray individuals quite stooped, of low forehead, massive jaws, and hence primitive and not too intelligent. Commitment to an animallike origin for human beings was so strong that the initial reconstructions were not challenged for decades. Not until the first bones were analyzed so that their possible diseased conditions could be considered (and other bones of similar physical characteristics were found around the Mediterranean region) were the misconceptions identified and different reconstructions of Neanderthal-type beings published. Now specialists consider Neanderthal specimens so advanced and so much like modern human beings, that they are all placed in the same genus classification and assigned the scientific name of *Homo sapiens neanderthalensis.*[17]

"COVER WORD"
(Beware Semantic Confusion)

Primitive: commonly used by those attempting to show relationships between and among living and fossil organisms, in a manner that entails genetic lineage or familial relationship that commonly is totally unknown. Criteria for "primitive" is not usually given by authors who have prior commitment to evolutionary outlook. The term "lower" is often used in conjunction with primitive to convey connotations of lesser development than that of present organisms.

Java and Peking Man. Claims, counterclaims and practiced concealment of bones collected have influenced evolutionists' ideas about Java Man and Peking Man. Some experts admit that because of a combination of prejudice and a zeal for fame, a few evolutionists have confused a great many people about Java Man. Their prior commitment to the idea of an animallike origin of human beings may have significantly colored their ability to carefully evaluate fossil materials collected in different places. Absolutely no known real skulls or bone fragments (only untested reconstructions) exist presently for Peking Man. Serious questions still exist as to whether Java Man and Peking Man should be included in the family tree of human beings. They may have been apes.

"COVER WORD"
(Beware Semantic Confusion)
Advanced: commonly used by those attempting to show relationships between and among living and fossil organisms, in a manner that entails genetic lineage or familial relationship that commonly is totally unknown. Criteria for "advanced" is not usually given by authors who have prior commitment to evolutionary outlook. The term "higher" is often used in conjunction with advanced to convey connotations of greater development or improvement than that of previous organisms.

Apelike. In their search for bones of *Ramapithecus*, *Dryopithecus* and *Aegyptopithecus* specialists like Leakey and Pilbeam and others display their continuing commitment to the predisposition to an apelike origin of human beings.[18]

Embryo Development. Zealous evolutionist Ernest Heackel is a classical example in several respects of a person overcome with preconceived ideas about human origins. This German scientist, more or less contemporary with Charles Darwin, actually drew a diagram of a four week old dog embryo identical to a four week old human embryo. He drew such diagrams, evidently, to provide propaganda for his idea that similarities of vertebrate embryos were sufficient basis for claiming that the human embryo, developing from a single cell, showed a tail and gill slits; and consequently, recapitulated unicellular, fishlike and doglike stages thus repeating supposed evolutionary stages of change. The fully erroneous nature of Haeckel's drawings has been published repeatedly, but his originals still appear in some modern biology textbooks. Furthermore, embryologists have shown that the human embryo does not have gill slits. Embryologists now know that any "tail" of a very young human infant is but a temporary condition that sometimes precedes the more normal condition of the coccyx being surrounded by buttock tissue. Truly the catch phrase of "ontogeny recapitulates phylogeny" is completely denied by twentieth century scientific facts.

Ice Man Hoax. When an apelike Ice Man frozen in a block of ice was displayed in shopping centers and other exhibit places in the United States in the 1970's, the sponsors took advantage of the long standing, persuasive teachings of megaevolutionists that human beings presumably came from some lower anthropoid form. Finally science journals published admissions that the Ice Man ancestor was a perpetrated hoax. Exhibitors had taken quantities of hair and rubber and fabricated the pretend human ancestor.

Before turning to the more specific points of a four-part critique of the present popularized scenario of human evolution, it is important to understand the fact that megaevolutionists incorrectly use the terms *related* and *relationship*. When megaevolutionists employ these terms with regard to different kinds of organisms they convey the connotation of some observable, reproducible lineage of genetic relationship. Actually they can write or speak accurately, in rigorous discourse, only of mere similarities. Science teachers should make very clear that relationship of organisms is discernable scientifically *only* by means of breeding practices to determine the limit of variation.

The Popular Megaevolutionary Scenario Rests upon Extensive Extrapolation

Science teachers need to make explicitly clear to their students the fact that megaevolutionist thinking is based upon extensive extrapolation. We have already identified the broad scope of the multiple facets of conceptualization practiced by evolutionists in all major disciplines of human knowledge when we looked at the nature of total evolutionism in the Introduction.

"COVER WORD"
(Beware Semantic Confusion)

Related, relationship: When megaevolutionists employ these terms with regard to different kinds of organisms they convey the connotation of observable, reproducible lineage relationships. Actually megaevolutionists can write or speak accurately, in rigorous discourse, only of mere *similarities*, since relationship is descernable only by means of breeding practices to set the limit of variation.

From the excellently well documented meaning of the term change, which most properly should be labeled genetic variation, megaevolutionists extrapolate backward through immense time. The current, popular scenario of the origin of humankind is specifically staged within the imagined time span of millions and millions of years that supposedly have transpired since the presumed explosion of some dense substance in what is commonly called the big bang. This magnitude of time duration is fully adopted by Richard Leakey and other leading specialists trying to write the history of human beings.

In fact an excellent ''Exhibit A'' for science teachers to use as resource material with their students is the previously mentioned article by Dr. Ernest Mayr in the *Scientific American* (September 1978). In that article Dr. Mayr affords a clear indication of the grand magnitude of megaevolutionary extrapolations. Presumably biological (organic) evolution was preceded by chemical (molecular) evolution, which was supposedly preceded by atomic (cosmic) evolution. We have also noted that specialists in social studies have extended evolutionist thinking to propose social evolution as a postlude to biological evolution.

But a most candid appraisal of this type of grand scale extrapolation demonstrates that megaevolutionists go far beyond the bounds of the viewpoint or world view of naturalism. Megaevolutionists do not restrict themselves to study or consideration of only naturally occurring objects and/or events. Fully integral to megaevolutionist thinking is the repeated inclusion of catastrophic, *un*natural objects and events of truly colossal magnitude in comparison to any known naturally occurring aspects of the physical environment.

Megaevolutionists, like Richard Leakey, begin their universe with a supposed explosion of some dense substance; then accretion of celestial objects including the terrestrial globe called the earth; followed by spontaneous appearance of some living substance as progenitor of all present life on this earth; and then presumed gradual accumulation of errors due to minor mutations resulting in totally new organisms, including human beings.

However, each one of these supposed changes is essentially *supra*-natural. Each one is beyond the scope of the natural. Of course the term *natural* can commonly be understood to refer to those objects and/or events that occur and exist in the physical environment. Yet in no way does the total evolutionist possess any key in the present to help document the unnatural changes of catastrophic magnitude which are entailed in the full range of extrapolation from cosmic evolution to chemical evolution to biological evolution to societal evolution. As an important reminder of specific points on this matter presented in Chapter 1, I want to provide an itemization of some of the missing keys along with very important admissions from evolutionary-minded scientists:

1. Megaevolutionists cannot find any key in the present of some naturally occurring explosion of a dense substance comparable to the major concept of the big bang hypothesis. (Astronomer Robert Jastrow admits that no cosmogonist can scientifically study the events involved in the formation of the present circumstances of the universe.)

2. Megaevolutionists cannot find any key in the present of some naturally occurring combination of submolecular parts of matter that form into any living substance. (Biologist J. D. Bernal admits that no biochemist can apply experimental research methods to the events involved in the formation of the circumstances of existing living substance.)

3. Megaevolutionists cannot find any key in the present of any naturally occurring events involving movement of dry rock masses that result in new mountains, nor the erosion to sea level of any mountain ranges.

4. Megaevolutionists cannot find any key in the present of any naturally occurring single land mass breaking into smaller land masses that move apart.

5. Megaevolutionists cannot find any key in the present of any naturally occurring mutational changes that result in any *new* physical traits. The heavy reliance upon the concept of mutations by megaevolutionists will be given more attention in the next section of this chapter. Sufficient for the moment is the comment that some evolutionary-minded scientists are openly challenging the idea of gradual accumulation of small changes due to mutations so integral to the modern synthetic theory of evolution. Some evolutionists are openly discussing the gaps in fossil materials, and they are also proposing the concept of so-called punctuated equilibrium to explain extinction and sudden appearance of discrete and distinct kinds of fossilized organisms. Of further relevance is the admission by paleontologists Stephen Gould and David Kitts that there is no indisputable fossil evidence for gradual, megaevolutionary change of organisms in the past.

"COVER WORD"

(Beware Semantic Confusion)

Discontinuous variation (sometimes *punctuated equilibrium*): when juxtaposed, terms seem contradictory; variations are not usually counted as discontinuous or interrupted, but continuous; equilibrium usually connotes tranquil persistence.

The Popular Megaevolutionary Scenario Involves Confusion Between Natural Selection and Artificial Selection, and also Involves Multiple Errors

Second, science teachers need to call attention to the presumed role of natural selection in the scenario of human origin involving interaction of hominoids and hominids with natural environmental conditions, known and/or imagined. According to conventional wisdom, present human beings are the result of long series of events whereby organisms have successfully interacted with natural environments, resulting in appearance of totally new kinds of organisms. Human beings, then, are supposed to be products of natural selection.

Early in any discussion of presumed human evolution, science teachers should candidly point out what is really meant by the expression natural selection. In sum, the expression natural selection is a cover word for identifiable *differential survival* of some members of a kind. According to other evolutionists the expression refers to *differential reproduction* wherein the fecundity of some type of organism is an advantage in terms of numbers of offspring in successive generations. But is any selection involved? To answer this question close analysis of the analogical relationship between natural selection and artificial selection must be studied.

To illustrate relationships between natural selection and artificial selection Classroom Teaching Aid 29 is provided. A generalized diagrammatic representation of an analogy is given at the top of the teaching aid. Reference might be made at this point to the operational definition of an analogy included in Chapter 1. Of course it would be well to remind also at this point that an analogy is not identity. Based upon recognized similarities of objects and/or events, one set of properties can be associated with another

Classroom Teaching Aid 29
ARTIFICIAL AND NATURAL SELECTION

Outline of Generalized Analogy

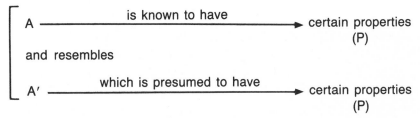

Artificial

Selection, whereby particular varieties of plants and animals survive and new characteristics result as desired by professional breeders

presumably resembles

Natural

Selection, whereby particular varieties of plants and animals survive in the natural environment and produce the most offspring, resulting in new kinds

set of properties by means of analogical thinking. Such a pattern of thought is very common to both physical scientists and biological scientists. (Review the list of examples of analogy in Chapter 1.) Known aspects of objects and/or events are compared to unknown objects and/or events. Thus the unknown seems to become knowable in terms of the known.

Analogical thinking was employed by Charles Darwin in his search for some explanation of the end result of changes in plant and animal origin about which he wrote. Darwin was familiar with artificial selection practices of professional breeders of his day. He knew that future breeding stock were changed as swine were selected for meat quality, as pigions were selected for particular apparent characteristics, as cattle were selected for butter fat content in milk produced, and so forth for dogs, cabbages and fruits. Because inheritable changes occurred from generation to generation in domesticated plants and animals as a result of selective breeding practices, Darwin reasoned by analogy that similar selective changes could have occurred in the natural environment over immense lengths of time such that new kinds of plants and animals would have come into existence. He had good reason to conclude from his fossil data that some animals had become extinct—or eliminated, although he thought they were selected against in their natural environment.

"COVER WORD"
(Beware Semantic Confusion)

Natural selection: This expression is a cover for what is really differential elimination or differential survival. The term *selection* conveys the connotation of volitional (willful) choice by human beings, and usually according to certain criteria (as in artificial selection); yet no criteria of selection exist in the natural environment. Volitional choice of the type practiced by human beings in artificial selection *does not occur* as organisms interact with each other and with the natural environment.

Use of these words with capital letters, as Natural Selection, is a further instance of anthropomorphic thinking by scientists who are committed to the naturalistic position. Such capitalization is inappropriate.

It is here that Darwin's analogical reasoning breaks down. It is true that organismal changes were directly observable as a result of selective breeding. Also differences were detectable between fossil and living organisms and hence changes over time were deducible. Nevertheless an important consideration must not be missed: in the natural environment there was (and is) *no* set of criteria by which presumed selection occurred.

The situation of organisms in the natural environment is in stark contrast to direct application of rigorous, restrictive criteria on the part of selective breeders involved with domestic organisms. In short, artificial selection involves certain specific criteria according to which professional breeders work. In contrast *there are no specific criteria* with regard to so-called natural selection. In actuality, *no* selection occurs in the natural environment. Essentially only differential survival or differential elimination occurs in the natural environment. Since the connotation of volitional choice on some basis is understood as involved with the term *selection*, then clearly no selection on a volitional basis occurs in the natural environment. There *are* specific criteria basic to selective breeding of domestic organisms. There are *no* specific criteria basic to so-called natural selection.

Thus students involved in the evolution/creation confrontation approach will be aided in their understanding if they realize that natural selection is a tautology expressible as "those that survive are those that survive". Nothing of real meaning is stated when an evolutionist suggests that human beings came from hominids, or hominids from hominoids due to natural selection. Evolutionists have thus misused the term *selection*. What evolutionists really refer to by their misused expression natural selection is differential survival, or differential elimination.[19]

Again the science teacher should identify that changes in living things as discussed by evolutionists necessarily entail two meanings of the term *change*. Evolutionists are quite satisfied that organisms, both plant and animal, change as they interact with changes in natural environments. Evolutionists are confident that organisms of successful reproductive rate survive or, as they say, are selected when changes in natural environments occur. But the crucial question that must be settled early in any evolution/creation discussion is, which meaning of the term *change* is intended?

The magnitude of change associated with artificial selection, the basis supposedly for Darwin's analogy with natural selection, is *always* a limited change. Always the variations, the modifications of plants or animals that result from artificial selection are merely changes *within* kind of organism. My previous assertion can be restated: *An artificial breeder of plants or animals always concludes all breeding practices with the same recognizable kind of organism which was used to start the selective breeding.* No new *kinds* of plants or animals result from artificial breeding. Thus one meaning of change of living things is quite accurately referred to as limited; that is, small changes *within* kind. Such limited changes, in a rigorous sense, should be referred to as genetic variation *within* limits of kind. (Some biologists insist on using the term microevolution.)

Yet proponents of Darwinism, Neo-Darwinism or modern synthetic evolution thought desire full acceptance of a much broader, more general meaning of change when they refer to natural selection and to evolution of life on the earth. Early in any evolution/creation discussion a second meaning of change must be delineated, that is megaevolution (sometimes referred to as macroevolution, or even transmutation of kinds) wherein supposedly different kinds have had common ancestors all presumably coming from a unicellular origin. Megaevolution involves broad, grand scale change of living things that evolutionists believe have occurred during geologic time. Megaevolutionary changes must always be differentiated from limited genetic variational change. Changes *across* kinds are not the same as changes *within* kinds.

How have megaevolutionists persuaded so many that they can extrapolate from empirically demonstrable, limited genetic variational change to broad, grand scale megaevolutionary change? Megaevolutionists base their thinking squarely upon *multiple errors*, that is, upon supposed fortuitious mistakes, whenever they state the following truism: Mutations are the source of the raw material upon which natural selection acts. Statement of this idea about mutations as raw material for natural selection, as a presumed analogue to artificial selection, is a central concept for all leading megaevolutionists. They always turn to mutations as the ultimate source of all genetic variation.[20]

Since a gene mutation is equivalent to a mistake, megaevolutionists have based their entire position upon some supposed gradual accumulation of minor mutations; that is, minor errors of the genetic components of living things. Presumably the genetic message has been altered over time by slow accumulation of errors. Yet there is no actual empirical evidence of accumulation of mutational changes in genetic materials resulting in the appearance of totally *new* physical traits.[21]

On the basis of careful analysis of evolutionist thinking, it becomes obvious that disciples of the late Theodosius Dobzhansky are proponents of a fallacious, deceitful position when they state that mutations are the raw materials upon which natural selection acts. The words natural selection are no more than a cover expression for the fact that differential elimination occurs as animals and plants interact with the natural environment. Since no selection, as volitional action, is involved in natural selection, then stability of kinds is *the* fully empirical datum of modern biologists. Conservation of kinds of animals and kinds of plants prevails as a result of the genetic aspects of the reproductive processes.

Science teachers can effectively set aside the often repeated claim that some mutations can be beneficial because the fact still remains that mutations are regularly identified as deleterious, debilitating and degenerative. Mutations, then, are representations of a type of *biological entropy*. Mutations commonly result in reduced viability and/or lethal conditions for affected individuals.

However, science teachers should understand that most critical to the full dependence of megaevolutionists upon mutations is the very significant fact that *no new* physical traits result from mutations. Gene mutations are no more than abberations of already existing genes. *Gene mutations result only in modifications of already existing physical traits.*

Modification of bacterial metabolism may be due to gene mutations. Modifications in wing condition or eye color, as demonstrated in *Drosophila*, may be due to gene mutations. But gene mutations result in no more than aberrations of already existing genes for wingedness or for eye color, and hence no more than aberrations of *existing* physical traits occur—*no new* physical traits come into existence. Even homeotic mutations do not result in new physical traits.

Science teachers should help students perceive that megaevolutionists exhibit an incredible dependence upon demonstrated mistakes in gene duplication (mutations) and presumed accumulation of such materials to explain their imagined transmutational scenarios about plants, animals and their imagined human evolution scenario. Such scenarios may seem plausible to persons with prior commitment to the megaevolutionist point of view, but the scenarios have no biological basis.

Gene mutations do not result in any new physical traits. Yet explanation of the origin of highly unique physical traits (such as upright bipedal locomotion, hair, mammary glands, wingedness, feathers, internal skeleton, hollow bones, dicotyledons, pollination resulting in enclosed seeds, vascular bundles, life cycles, photosynthetic processes dependent upon cholorphyll) *must* be provided by megaevolutionists, if their scenario of broad, grand scale meaning of change between organisms, including so called evolution of human beings, is to be taken at all seriously. Gene mutations, as errors, are totally lacking in any explanatory value since no new physical traits result from gene mutations. Natural selection can only refer rigorously to elimination of already existing aspects of organisms (or debilitating, degenerative changes) and cannot refer to appearance of anything new. How then could human beings come from an animalistic, evolutionary oirgin?

The Popular Megaevolutionary Scenario Involves the Belief That the Human Brain Came From an Animal Brain

Third, science teachers have a serious obligation to carefully explain difficulties inherent in the megaevolutionist claim that the human brain evolved from an animal ancestor. As presented in the first part of this chapter, it supposedly developed from *Homo erectus*, *Homo habilis*, *Australopithecus*, and so basically came from some kind of ape ancestry through *Ramapithecus*, *Dryopithecus* and *Aegyptopithecus*. Some megaevolutionists go even farther to state that the human brain is only a modified reptilian brain. According to an extended animalistic, evolutionary scenario on the origin of humankind, the human forebrain has expanded in size.[22] During such supposed evolution three basic formations have been retained that presumably reflect ancestral connections with reptiles, early mammals and recent mammals. Evolutionists definitely presume that the human forebrain has expanded in hierarchical fashion along the lines of three brain patterns that some specialists have characterized as reptilian, paleomammalian and neomammalian. (See Fig. 39) In short, evolutionists believe that they can offer a model of evolutionary and neural beginnings of a triune intelligence involving a *primal* mind, an *emotional* mind and a *rational* mind.

Science teachers should be prepared to explain to students that many evolutionists believe the complex human brain is composed of a reptilian driver component, an old mammalian brain as a site of emotional feeling, and a new brain for promotion of the preservation and procreation of ideas. Of course, evolutionists are completely unable to demonstrate any sound empirical lineage of genetic relationship between reptiles and mammals. All imagined ideas about evolution of vertebrate brains, that changes in the vertebrate brain culminated in the present great size and complexity of the human brain, are fundamentally organized upon the *basic assumption* identified twice before, that the degree of relationship depends upon the degree of similarity. Evolutionists merely arrange brain casts of organisms in a proposed continuity according to the similarities of exterior features, plus whatever information is available about neural structure and organization. No truly empirically demonstrated genetic relationship of reptilian and mammalian brains can be developed. Only particular points of structural *similarities* can be detected and hence *only* extensive imaginative, speculative ideas about relationships can be projected.

Figure 39
SUPPOSED "EVOLUTION" OF HUMAN BRAIN

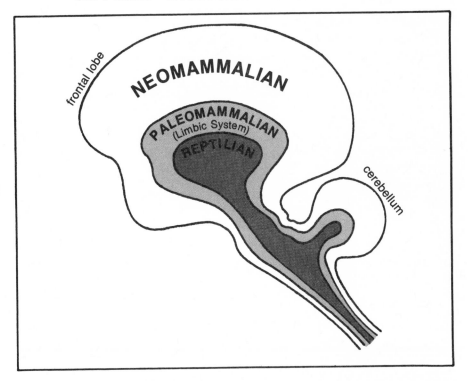

As is typically illustrated in the cited article by Paul D. MacLean, M.D., the scenario sponsored by Leakey and other megaevolutionists about origin of a tripartite brain in human beings, relies heavily upon anthropomorphic expressions. This was evident in the previous chapter on the origin of life on the earth, as detailed in the writings of Dr. Francis Crick.

With regard to human brain evolution, science teachers studying material like the MacLean article, published in a national teachers journal, should quickly detect the multiple usage of the term *nature* (in an ostensibly naturalistic scenario) as a substitute for God in the creation model. Here are a few examples:

For solutions of situations that arise in the external world, *nature designs* the neocortex so that it receives signals primarily from the (sense organs). (MacLean, p. 37, emphasis added).

Perhaps *nature*, in *placing* linguistic functions in one hemisphere, has killed two birds with one stone . . . (MacLean p. 38, emphasis added).

For some inexplicable reason, *nature* appears to have concluded that a genie— a veritable Frankenstein—had been let out of the bottle which, left unbridled, might lead to the destruction of the species. (I use the word "inexplicable" because *nature itself* seems to have given the blessing to the paradoxical principle of the need-to-die-in-order-to-live.) (MacLean, p. 39, emphasis added).

In *designing* for the first time a creature that shows a concern for suffering of other living things, *nature* seems to have attempted a 180-degree turnabout from what had been a reptile-eat-reptile and dog-eat-dog world. (MacLean, p.39, emphasis added).

Such consistent reference to strictly human activities as characteristic of the inanimate natural environment is regrettable to say the least. In this scientific age, especially, students should be helped to discern the significant difference between uniquely human mental activity and phenomena associated with inanimate matter. Nature is not a person; nature cannot design, or plan, or act as a self, or attempt to accomplish alleviation of suffering. Megaevolutionists do not propose any truly naturalistic origin of the large and very complex human brain.

The Popular Megaevolutionary Scenario Rests Upon Estimates of Time, not Upon Measurements of Time

Science teachers should be fully prepared to explain the problem of time associated with the popular scenario of so-called human evolution. Megaevolutionists presume or invoke immense time periods. They often publish expressions about time before the present (B.P.). Yet, as has been discussed earlier, proper and orderly scientific activity is limited to the present of any one investigator. Fully developed contemporary scientific theories are the result of scientific inquiries about natural phenomena in the present. Megaevolutionists must, however, deal with imagined time periods about the past since they raise inquiries about possible objects and/or events before the present. But inquiries about the past result in formulation of historical theories.

Thus time, in a sense, is the Achilles heel of *all* specialists interested in development of historical theories. No scientist is able to measure the age of the universe. No scientist is able to measure the appearance of first life on the earth. Consistent with these statements is the fact that no scientist is able to measure the age of any rock, any bone, or any artifact assumed to have been used by some postulated ancestor of present humankind.

All that any scientist can do is offer *estimates* of time before the present. Detailed analysis of accepted radiometric methods for making estimates of B.P. ages is beyond the scope of this book. Many excellent reference books are useful for clarification of potentials and limitations of radiometric estimates of time.[23] However, before closing this chapter with a succinct presentation of a creation alternative on the origin of humankind, I do want to share a few pertinent observations or comments on the terms *dates* or *dating*.

When evolutionists employ the terms *date* or *dating*, a strong possibility for semantic confusion exists. When evolutionists use these terms with respect to rocks and past events, they seek to convey the connotation of accuracy gained from specific measurments by manmade chronometers. There were, however, no human observers of the formation of rock layers or other past events commonly involved in the formation of historical theories. Therefore, there are no records of rock formations. Dates of rocks are *only* estimations. The age of a rock can only be *estimated*.

"COVER WORD"
(Beware Semantic Confusion)
Date, dating: These terms are used with respect to rocks or events of the past to convey the connotation of some degree of accuracy such as commonly results from specific measurements by manmade chronometers, or time of beginning of some manmade product. The time of commencement of a trip can be checked against a watch. The first cotton gin can be dated, as the first automobile can be dated, since some records of such manmade objects are available. Dates of rocks are *only* estimations. The age of a rock can only be *estimated*.

Frankly, the basis for the evolutionists' claim that the earth and universe are very old is found mainly in their own ideas. Even in the scientific age there are no compelling scientific measurements of the age of either the earth or the universe. However, to attempt to account for the remotest possibility of the changes imagined by evolutionists, they must postulate immense periods of time. For centuries evolutionists have upheld the idea of an old earth and universe. They have tried to support their preconceived ideas by various means of *estimating* the age of the earth by calculating various rates of change, such as cooling of the earth, sedimentation and accumulation of salt concentrations in the ocean. But none of these methods of calculation resulted in the great lengths of time evolutionists have imagined.

"COVER WORD"
(Beware Semantic Confusion)
Record: This term usually is associated with the activities of human beings; so when megaevolutionists use the terms *geologic record* or *fossil record*, they improperly convey the connotation of actually witnessed occurrances. Megaevolutionists can write and speak accurately only of the *existence* and *description* of rock layers or fossil materials.

In recent years radiometric decay of certain elements and fission tracts have been employed as a basis for estimating time. Presently the most commonly used radiometric methods of calculating the age of the earth are radioactive decay of uranium to lead, potassium to argon, and rubidium to strontium. By such methods of decay analysis the often quoted age of the earth is given as 4.5 billion years B.P.

An effective way to open any discussion of estimates of the age of the earth is to focus upon the questionable assumptions of radiometric methods.

Constant Rate. Each method involves the assumption that the rate of decay has been constant. However, there is no way to know how valid this assumption is over the immense lengths of time imagined by evolutionists. Furthermore, evidence is available that all rates involved in natural processes are changeable.

Zero Decay Elements. Each method involves the assumption that no decay elements (no lead or argon) were present at the beginning when any given rock sample being tested was formed. Yet this is impossible to know for certain, since nearly all lead in rocks or minerals might be considered primordial, and since argon is a gas that might have escaped in some quantity from an aging rock. If that were so, then uranium to lead calculations and potassium to argon calculations would be erroneous. In fact there are strong possibilities for contamination by water transported uranium salts or by apmospheric argon so that both methods of time estimation involved are subject to correction factors.

Closed System. Each method is based upon the assumption that radioactive minerals are in a closed system; that is, no parent or daughter substances have been gained or lost. Specifically, no one knows the initial or primeval ratios of the elements involved in the radiometric methods used for estimating the age of rocks. Of course, the concept of a closed system is ideal and basically nonexistent in the real world, as is brought out by Dr. Henry M. Morris in his discussion of more technical limitations of radiometric methods.[24]

Because these assumptions underlying radiometric estimates of time B.P. are open to serious challenge, evolutionists do not gain any absolute dates that they can assign to any supposed ancestor of human beings. Any dates B.P. assigned to Neanderthal, *H. erectus, Australopithecus*, or any prehistoric apes are mere estimates.

According to careful, rigorous analysis the only objective facts gained from radiometric methods are ratios of certain elements found in rocks in the *present* that are on or near the surface of the earth or on the surface of the moon. But again, no one knows the initial or primeval ratio of elements. Evolutionists, therefore, must interpret the identified present ratios of elements (uranium to lead, potassium to argon, rubidium to strontium) on the basis of certain assumptions that are open to serious challenge. Thus radiometric methods can only be used to gain *estimates* of time B.P.

Consequently, science teachers have the responsibility to bring forth evidence that both the earth and the universe may be young. There are excellent, scientifically based methods for estimating that the earth is relatively young. For example, the magnitude of the magnetic field of the earth has been observed for approximately 150 years to be decaying at a steady rate. Using reasonable assumptions and extrapolations back in time, a maximum age of the earth is calculated to be 10,000 years B.P. Likewise the accumulation of cosmic dust on the surfaces of the earth and on the moon; concentrations of nitrates in the oceans and the amount of accumulated helium in the atmosphere of the earth can be used to calculate an approximate age of the earth of 10,000 years B.P. Similarly evidence for a possible young age of the universe can be gained from studies of star clusters and from studies of short period comets.[25]

The science teacher employing the evolution/creation confrontation approach can readily help students understand that all methods of estimating time B.P. result in relative ages because all are founded upon one common assumption: What is observable about these clocks in the present has always been the same throughout the existence of the earth. In addition to already listed assumptions, any clock or chronometer of the age of the earth involves another fundamental difficulty in that no one knows the zero setting, the initial conditions of the earth. Actually, estimates of the age of the earth and the solar system vary widely over a range as great as 100 years to 4.5 billion years, and each investigator must make a decision as to which clock is most reasonably accurate. Students should realize that if an individual thinks that an old age is most logical, then methods that yield an old age will be employed. Conversely, if an investigator holds that a young age is most reasonable, then methods that yield a young age will be utilized.

A Creation Alternative: Where Did Human Beings First Appear?

Student comprehension of the problem of the origin of humankind can be broadened from the usually evolutionary interpretation. A wider understanding can be gained if science teachers lead an open and candid discussion of an interesting migration-dispersal concept that can be proposed as a creation model alternative to the accepted evolutionary scenario given in the first section of this chapter. A seven point critique or rebuttal has been offered to assist the science teacher in reaching an objective evaluation of the popular evolutionary scenario about the origin of humankind. Two further sets of data are significantly relevant to a proposed reconsideration of the conventional wisdom of modern megaevolutionists.

Important Time, Classification Considerations

Data contained in Classroom Teaching Aid 30 was prepared on the basis of work produced by M. L. Lubenow,[26] who has completed masters degree work in both theology and geological studies. Almost all of the known fossil

Classroom Teaching Aid 30
HUMAN FOSSIL EVIDENCE

H. sapiens and sapienslike fossils	H. Erectus fossils	Homo habilis	Australopithecus fossils
Neanderthal, Wadjak	Kow swamp, Rabat		Aust. africanus
Soccopastore, Omo, Solo	Temara, Peking		Aust. robustus
Fontechevade, Krapina	Olduvai hominid 28		
Rhodesian, Saldanha, Mapa	Lake Ndutu		Taung Skull
Tautaval, Swanscomb	Java, Sangiran	x	Olduvai milktooth
Steinheim, Vertesszollos	Lantian, Heidelberg		Chesowanja Ar.
Kanjera, Petralona 1M			
Kanam	Olduvai Hominid 9	x	
KNM-ER-803,737,813 (East Rudolf, Kenya)	KNM-ER-3733,3228	x	Kromdraai Ar.
	Pithecanthropus	x	Natron mandible Ar.
	Sangiran II		East Rudolf Ar.
	2M Swartkrans		Zinjanthropus Ar.
			Swartkrans Ar.
KNM-ER-1470, 1481, 1590, 1802			
(East Rudolf, Kenya) 3M			Sterkfontein
			East Rudolf
			Makapansgat
Hadar fossil hand	AL 199, AL 200		
Laetolil hominid 4	(Hadar)	x	AL 288 (Hadar)
	Laetolil (Tanzania)		
Kanapoi hominid I - - - - 4M - - - - - - - - - - - - - - - - - - - →			?
KNM-ER-329 - →			?
Lothagam 5M			

TIME IN MILLIONS OF YEARS B.P.

—after M. L. Lubenow

specimens of Australiopithecines, *Homo habilis*, *Homo erectus*, *Homo sapiens*, and sapienslike forms are mentioned in the four columns. Attention to the time scale shown results in a very striking conclusion. All of the five groups of genus *Homo* and hominid fossils must be listed *within* the first one million years B.P., if the adopted time scale of evolutionists is used as a basis of discussion. Apparently *all* forms were contemporaries of each other although admittedly at distant and scattered geographic locations. Science teachers should formulate various discussion questions to help students cope with the following important generalization: Megaevolutionists simply do not present the time dimension of all their different fossil finds in *one* integrated chart. Students should very easily grasp why some evolutionists are pointedly admitting *now* that only branches or twigs remain of any so called family tree of human ancestry.[27]

A second set of data, contained in Classroom Teaching Aid 31, can be used to further corroborate the statement that evolutionists' ideas about ancestry of the humankind have changed and changed and changed again. Whenever it has been possible the date of the original misinterpretation and the date of the correction are given for the 37 fossil remains listed by popular name along with the date of the first find.

Science teachers should carefully explain that the interpretive errors have almost always been away from modern man. Thus the corrections have almost always been in the direction of modern man. It is easy to relate this information to my previous discussion of the long standing predisposition of megaevolutionists to think that human beings came from a less than human beginning. Clearly as more and more data has accumulated, and the possibility of sampling errors has been reduced, an increasing number of fossil remains of so called hominoids have been assigned to the genus *Homo*, and to the species *sapiens*. The only fossil finds excluded from this chart are those that are still subject to serious question. Cro-Magnon Man is not included since those fossil specimens have always been considered so much like modern man that there has never been any serious problem about classification assignment.

Because of these two aids to teaching according to the evolution/creation confrontation approach to origin questions, science teachers can confidently expedite their classroom activities in complete academic freedom and responsibility. The alert science teacher can stimulate serious consideration of a creation alternative to the evolutionary scenario. But how can creationists explain the wide diversity of physical features, aspects of time span B.P. and other points of variation when *all* facts are studied openly? If some broad contemporaneity in a wide time span was identified in Classroom Teaching Aid 30, then what amount of insight might be gained from attention to the geographic distribution of Australopithecines, *Homo habilis*, *Homo erectus* and *Homo sapiens?* Before geographic distribution can be analyzed some points about the traditional cradle of mankind should be considered before stating a modern creation model about human origins.

Location of Cradle of Mankind

Prior to acceptance of evolutionary origin of humankind, scholars had generally agreed that the cradle of mankind was in Asia Minor or in some portion of the Middle East. Immense caches of data in the form of pottery and other artifacts of human activities had accumulated consequential to decades of efforts by archeologists, who had painstakingly analyzed *tells* (mounds) where clear evidence of human civilization had been found.

However, because of the efforts of the late Louis Leakey, his wife Mary and son Richard, many hominid fossil finds have been made in Africa. Thus members of the Leakey family have pushed their claim that locations in Africa (Olduvai Gorge, Lake Rudolph and other nearby sites) are possible beginning places for humankind. Yet their efforts and those of their followers have been made in spite of the interpretation of some experts that the Australopithecines were apes.

Nevertheless, because of the Leakey family successes, many intellectuals have turned away from the previously accepted interpretation that the Tigris-Euphrates river area was the cradle of mankind. It would seem that not enough is heard in the 1980's about the extensive pottery collections and other archeological finds of previous decades. The Leakeys and their supporters hold forth quite boldly for their interpretation regarding southern Africa as the cradle of mankind.

Yet the point should not be missed by evolution/creation confrontation students that *interpretations* are primarily involved. Mary and Richard Leakey, who continue very active field research programs in Africa simply seem to disregard the traditional interpretation (based upon pottery and other artifacts) in favor of their own interpretation (based upon skull features and other skeletal fragments). Hence the science teacher need not

Classroom Teaching Aid 31

THE MISINTERPRETATION OF THE HUMAN FOSSILS 1848-1964

Showing—when possible—the data of the original misinterpretation and the date of the correction. Note that the interpretive errors have almost always been away from modern man and the corrections have almost always been in the direction of modern man. All the major human fossils are included *except* those that are still open to serious question, and the Cro-Magnon fossils which are so much like modern man that they have never been a serious problem. (H.e.) refers to *Homo erectus*; (H.s.) to *Homo sapiens*; (H.n.) to *Homo neanderthalensis*; and (H.s.n.) to *Homo sapiens neanderthalensis*.

Date	Location	No.	Original misinterpretation	Correction
1848	Gibraltar	2	H.n. (approx. 1910)	H.s.n. (1964)
1856	Neanderthal Valley	1	H.n. (1864)	H.s.n. (1964)
1886	Spy, Belgium	2	H.n. (1890?)	H.s.n. (1964)
1889	Wadjak, Java	2	Homo wadjakenis (1921)	H.s. wadjakensis (1936)
1891	Java Man (Trinil)	1	Pithecanthropus erectus (1894) → Homo erectus (1940)	H.s.
1894	Predmost, Czeck.	30	Homo predmostensis (1934)	H.s.
1899	Krapina, Yugoslavia	14	Homo primigenius (1906)	H.s.n. (1964)
1907	Heidelberg Man	1	Homo heidelbergensis (1908) → Homo erectus (1963)	H.s.n. (1964)
1908	Le Moustier, France	1	Homo mousteriensis (1910)	H.s.n. (1964)
1909	La Ferrassie, France	5	H.n. (1911)	H.s.n. (1964)
1911	La Quina, France	3	H.n. (1923)	H.s.n. (1964)
1911	La Chapelle-aux-Saints	1	H.n. (1911)	H.s.n. (1964)
1914	Ehringsdorf, Germany	3	H.n. (1925)	H.s.n. (1964)

Year	Location	No.	Original name	Subsequent classification
1921	Peking Man	40	Sinanthropus pekinensis (1927)	Homo erectus (1940)
1921	Rhodesian Man	2	Homo rhodesiensis (1921)	H.s. rhodesiensis (1964)
1931	Solo Man, Java	11	Homo soloensis (1932)	H.s. soloensis (1964)
1932	Florisbad, S. Africa	1	Homo helmei (1935)	H.s. (1957)
1932	Tabun, Mt. Carmel	2	Palaeoanthropus palestinensis (1939)	H.s.n. (1964)
1932	Skhul, Mt. Carmel	10	Palaeoanthropus palestinensis (1939)	H.s. (1964)
1933	Steinheim, Germany	1	Homo steinheimensis (1936)	H.s. steinheimensis (1964)
1935	Swanscombe, England	1	Homo marstoni (1940)	H.s. steinheimensis (1964)
1936	Modjokerto, Java	1	H. modjokertensis (1936)	H. erectus (1950)
1937	Sangiran I, Java	1	Pithecanthropus II (1938)	Homo erectus (1950)
1939	Sangiran II, Java	1	Pithecanthropus IV (1939)	Homo erectus (1950)
1939	Monte Circeo, Italy	3	H.n. (1939)	H.s.n. (1964)
1947	Fontechevade, France	2	Homo (1949)	H.s.n. (1964)
1947	Cave of Hearths, S. Afr.	2	H.n. (1948)	H.s. rhodesiensis (1964)
1949	Montmaurin, France	1	H.n. (1956)	H.s.n. (1964)
1949	Swartkrans, S. Africa	3	Telanthropus capensis (1949)	Homo erectus (1961)
1953	Saldanha, S. Africa	2	Homo saldanensis (1955)	H.s. rhodesiensis (1964)
1953	Shanidar, Iraq	8	H.n. (1953)	Homo erectus (1964)
1954	Ternifine, Algeria	3	Atlanthropus mauritanicus (1954)	Homo erectus (1964)
1954	Casablanca, Morocco	1	Atlanthropus mauritanicus (1956)	Homo erectus (1964)
1956	Rhunda, Germany	1	H.n. (1957)	H.s. (1964)
1958	Mapa, China	1	H.n. (1959)	H.s.n. (1964)
1959	Petralona, Greece	1	H.n. (1960)	H.s.n. (1964)
1961	Jebel Irhoud, Morocco	2	H.n. (1962)	H.s.n. (1964)

—M. L. Lubenow

feel that the traditional Tigris-Euphrates river region as the possible cradle of mankind has been denied by megaevolutionists. The science teacher should encourage and help students interested in the roots of humankind to seek an explanation that involves *all* groups of data: pottery, skeletal fragments and other artifacts.

Traditional Interpretation Restated

Many modern creationists are convinced that the same theistic position on the origin of human beings that was accepted by the founders of modern science (see chapter 1) need not be abandoned. Those science teachers who desire to serve the academic freedom of *all* their students should understand that much evidence and fully rational explanations can be used to support a major concept of the creation model: Humankind began with the creation of Adam only a few thousand years ago.[28] Many creationists contend that eight members of only one family survived a major catastrophe by flooding that resulted in complete obliteration of all human civilization that had developed from Adam and Eve. Noah and his family of three sons and their wives survived the flood catastrophe aboard an Ark that was grounded somewhere in the highlands north of Mesopotamia. There are many, many extended traditions about a few people surviving some great catastrophe.[29]

From the initial family pattern represented in the sole survivors, in the course of time, three distinct families of human beings became established. On the basis of their patriarchal lineage the three families may appropriately be termed Japhethites, Hamites, and Shemites. In modern terminology these groups would be recognized as Indo-Europeans (Caucasoids), Mongoloids and Negroid people, and Semites (Hebrews, Arabs, and some more ancient branches of the family such as the Assyrians).

Two specialized Classroom Teaching Aids 32 and 33 could be used by science teachers to expedite understanding about these three families. As modern archaeological research continues, and there is increasing use of computers in philological (language) research, more and more information accumulates that is relevant to ancient history and to the table of nations as found in Genesis. Each of these teaching aids contains a summary of familial relationships and progenitors of earliest known nations of the Near

Classroom Teaching Aid 32
GENESIS 10—CAPSULE OF ANCIENT HISTORY?

In his *Introductions to the Old Testament* (Eerdmans, 1969) R. K. Harrison says that "the Table of Nations is unquestionably of ancient origin" (p. 559). He argues that the source of Genesis 10:2-11:10a is a typical cuneiform tablet, probably belonging to Shem's own family history, "written either from personal knowledge or from other reliable sources' " (p. 548). (p.8)

PEOPLES AND LANGUAGES

Japhethitic group:
Medes (Madai)
Greeks (Javan)
Indo-European (Gen. 10:2-5)

Nordic
Germanic }—Europe
Romans, Greeks
Early Iranians of Persia
Aryans—→ India

Hamitic group: (Gen. 10:6-20)
spoke Akkadian
Semitic language

Canaanite
Hebrew
Arabic

(oldest) Cush ———————— Ham ———————— Canaan (Gen. 10:15-20)
spoke Canaanite,

Nimrod   establ.   Egypt (Gen. 10:13)   Phoenesian
spoke   "Babel"   (Mizraim)
Akkadian   "Erech"   spoke Egyptian   Put
           "Accad"   Galla, Somal: spoke African
           in Shinar   Berber   dialects

Philistines and Minoans   related to Canaanite,
(Casluhim)   (Caphthorium) Phoenician

Shemitic group: (Gen. 10:22) from Asia Minor, thru mountains north of the Tigris to Sumerian Ur, the Persian Gulf into North India

hence famous inscriptions { Darius
{ Xerxes

(oldest) ———————— Shem ———————— Aram
Elam-Elamites   Arameans
                          \ Lud   from Kir
Asshur   Arphachshad   Lydia Kings?
Assyrians   spoke Sumerian   Isaac and
                                        Shemitic wife
Terah   Ishmael and
Abraham—South into Canaanite (Hamite) territory   Egyptian wife

—Prepared from "The Curse of Ham—Capsule of Ancient History" by Robert Brow.
Christianity Today, October 26, 1973 (pp. 8-10)

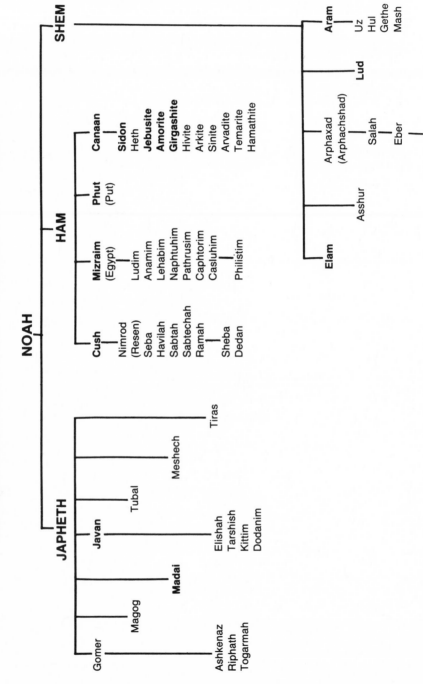

Classroom Teaching Aid 33
GENEALOGICAL TABLE OF THE DESCENDANTS OF NOAH

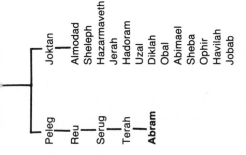

Peleg
    Joktan
    Almodad
    Sheleph
    Hazarmaveth
    Jerah
    Hadoram
    Uzal
    Diklah
    Obal
    Abimael
    Sheba
    Ophir
    Havilah
    Jobab

Reu

Serug

Terah

Abram

—Arthur C. Custance, *Noah's Three Sons* (Grand Rapids: Zondervan Publ. House, 1975), p. 56.

Note: Some mistakenly try to say blacks are the result of the curse on Ham—Which was limited to descendants, 4th son of Ham: Canaan

1. To be enslaved by brother Hamites (Canaanites under Egypt; Phoenecians under Akkadian kings of Assyria and from Babylonia)

2. To be enslaved by descendants of Shem—when Abraham's descendants defeated Amorite kings, Joshua overcame Canaanite tribes west of Jordan

3. To be enslaved by Japhethites (Indo-Europeans)—when people of Tyre, Sidon were subjected by Greeks, Hittites, Medes

   "Whether races of Africa were descended from Mizraim, or from Put, or from a mixture of Shemites and Hamites they are definitely not classed as Cannanites, and so cannot be under the curse of Ham."—Robert Brow, *Christianity Today*, 26 Oct. 1973, p. 10.

East that is drawn from research reports and interpretations by A. C. Custance and R. K. Harrison.

Now we will consider a broad overview of this creation alternative, then more detailed information in support of the general migration-dispersal model.

General Migration-Dispersal Model

At first the survivor families kept together, but very likely within a century or so they began to move away from each other due to a type of population pressure. Possibly some of the family of Shem, some of the family of Ham and even a few of the family of Japheth reached the southern section of the flat Mesopotamian Plain.[30] On the basis of evidence discussed elsewhere by Custance,[31] some creationists believe that the family of Ham became politically dominate. Evidently they initiated a movement to prevent any further dispersion by the erection of a monument high enough to be a visible rallying point on the flat plain. Thus they violated initial instruction, and brought upon themselves judgment by their Creator which led to their being forcibly and rapidly scattered in all directions on the surface of the earth.

From both sacred and secular sources the fact can be established that in every area of the world where Japhethites have subsequently settled, they have always been preceded by Hamites. This pattern can be found in every continent. In prehistoric times the pattern is manifest in that the earliest fossil remains of human beings were Mongoloid or Negroid in character and in head shape, whereas those that came last belong to the family of Japheth (i.e., Caucasoid). In early historic times the pattern of events is repeated again and again; namely, whatever cultural advances the pioneering Hamites had achieved were evidently taken over by succeeding Japhethites.

The very clear record of the more leisurely spread of the Japhethites over the earth is marred repeatedly by their destruction of the cultures which were already in existence when they arrived in sufficient numbers to conquer the people they met. This occurred in the Indus Valley, in Australia, and evidently only numerical superiority of the native population has hitherto preserved some of the peoples of Africa from the same fate.

Therefore, many creationists emphatically present the following generalization: All lines of migration of human beings, which are at all traceable or deducible, seem to radiate like the spokes of a wheel from the Middle East. (This is the reverse of claims for and implications based upon the discoveries in South and Central Africa by the Leakeys.) This generalization holds whether attention is given to fossil humankind, ancient civilization, contemporary or extinct native peoples, or the present nations of the world.

In general, according to abundant evidence, the direction of movement tends to be reflected in the gradual *loss* of cultural artifacts, which were continued in use along the migratory route, but either disappear entirely forward along the migration line or are less effectively copied or merely represented in pictures or in folklore. When several migration lines radiate from a single center, the situation is, more or less, one of a series of ever increasing circles of settlements; each settlement using fewer and fewer of the original cultural artifacts which were continued at the center. Evidently, when people moved further from the center along any routes of migration, then more new and uniquely specific items are found, which are not shared by people in other migration routes.

This is particularly true whenever complex items are found. For example, certain Minoan pottery vessels are clearly copies of metal prototypes. Where the pottery handles are joined to the vessel, little knobs of clay are found which serve no functional purpose, except evidently the artisan attempted to copy the rivets which once secured the metal handle to the metal bodies of the prototype.[32] The metal prototypes are found in Asia Minor, and thus it is clear which way the line of migration can be traced.

Logically, if the earliest migrations were quite rapid, then there would be a marked tendency toward a *loss* of cultural items common to the center as the people migrated out. Thus the general level of culture would decline at first, but in due time new centers of culture would be established with mixtures of old and new traditions.

Accompanying such cultural *losses* in the initial spread of the Hamitic peoples, creationists expect that a certain coarsening of the human physique would occur. Not only would the migrating people have been unsuited for the rigors of a pioneering life and become culturally degraded as a consequence, but the food supply very likely would have been grossly different, insufficient to maintain full body vigor, and even unsuitable to established tastes. Dietary disturbances undoubtedly affected the normal growth patterns of the young. Early students of the origin of humankind have noted that the more highly cultured an immigrant is when he arrives at a frontier, the more severly he is handicapped.[33]

That food deficiencies have definite effects upon the form of the human skull have been studied by Custance.[34] He shows that the diet of modern Eskimos is a direct causal factor in the appearance of Eskimos expressed in enlargement of bone attachment areas (zygomatic arches) of muscles used in eating blubber. Also the points of attachment on the top of the skull may be places of bone modification as musculature is involved in consuming an uncooked, unprepared diet. Custance also shows that variations in pituitary gland secretion can have direct causal effect upon body size and skull structure. Thus bone structure of so called prehistoric people that evolutionists want to call ancestors of humankind may be deformities or at least modified bone structures of normal human beings.

Straus and other investigators have shown that the earliest collection of Neanderthal bones contained significant evidence that certain individuals had had bone disease, such as ricketts or some type of osteoarthritis.[35] Evidently the curvature of some of those early bones was the basis for the mistaken *interpretations* at first that Neanderthal Man had a stooped over, bent posture. Noteworthy is the fact that dozens of skeletons of Neanderthal people have been found since—all of which had truly erect posture. Thus Neanderthal is now interpreted to have been as upright as currently living human beings. (See Fig. 40 and Fig. 41 for before and after reconstructions.)

Creationists admit that this interpretation is complex and many problems still remain. If provincial cultural centers along various initial routes of migration were the beginning points of further migrations in various directions, then there would be a highly complex pattern of cultural relationships in the earliest times. However, by and large, the archeological evidence available can be used to support the contention that a cradle of mankind was located in the Middle East, from which successive waves of pioneers moved out into strange and different territories.

But those migrants were almost certainly *not* Indo-Europeans (i.e., Japhethites). They were Hamitic pioneers, either Mongoloid or Negroid in type for the most part but with some admixture. Those pioneers blazed trails and opened up territories in every inhabitable part of the earth— evidently at great loss to their cultural heritage and also to the detriment

Figure 40
EXAGGERATED APELIKE RECONSTRUCTIONS
OF NEANDERTHALS

These three representations of Neanderthal are actually misconceptions as recognized today due to artists' constructions from very limited numbers of skeletal parts. The adult man on the left, the younger individual in the middle, and the woman carrying a child are each examples of exaggerations of hunched shoulders, dangling arms, and apelike posture that early experts thought would be representative of these supposed ancestors of modern man. These diorama figures were produced for display in 1929.

Courtesy, Field Museum of Natural History, Chicago.

Figure 41

RECENT RECONSTRUCTIONS OF NEANDERTHALS

These constructions of Neanderthals were produced in 1972 as "corrections" of the stooped portrayal of Neanderthals offered by experts in 1929. The change to the upright position and the alteration of facial expressions has come as the result of hundreds of skeletal finds. Specialists now conceive that Neanderthals were so much like modern man and the differences so few that they are hard to explain. Thus these forms have been assigned to the same genus and species as modern man but with a different subspecies name: *Homo sapiens neanderthalensis.*

Courtesy, Field Museum of Natural History, Chicago.

of the refined physique still found in their relatives who remained at the point of origin. In each new locality the pioneering migrants either established a way of life according to resources they found, or they were overwhelmed by the circumstances of isolation. In the second case only a few scattered remnants survived, and their physical remains may be evidence of the severe affect of the strange environment.

When the Japhethites followed the early waves of migrants, they took advantage of the established cultural practices, as the European immigrants did in North America. Sometimes the Japhethites displaced other people entirely, sometimes they absorbed other people so that the two populations were combined, or sometimes the people they met were educated in new ways and then left. All three patterns can be found in India. The Indus Valley people were overwhelmed and entirely displaced or absorbed, and then thousands of years later this admixture was once more educated in new ways by a further influx of Japhetic settlers, who have since surrendered their dominant status.

A possible general condition of degeneration and degradation of migrating people can be referred to now. If early migrants were in isolation and suffered deprivation of food, clothing and shelter, then any possibility of their living for a hundred years or perhaps even longer would add further complications. Evidence can be found that early human beings lived for long spans of time, although declining after the flood catastrophe. In fact, the skull structures are almost obliterated in some fossil specimens, which might reasonably be interpreted as evidence of very extreme old age. Might the conventional apeman form be a consequence of isolation, deprivation and old age?

Such is the broad conceptualization of the creation alternative of the origin of humankind: (1) That the dispersal of human beings took place from a center somewhere in the Middle East and that this dispersal accounts for the disposition and patterning of unequivocal fossil remains of early man, and (2) That those who formed the vanguard were of Hamitic stock, using the term *Hamitic* to mean all descendents of Noah who were not in the line of Shem or Japheth.

Time Problem Considered

Of course megaevolutionists do not consider this creation alternative to be credible primarily because it violates their time scale. The time frame involved in this creation view of human origin is much different than that of the evolutionary scenario involving millions of years B.P. We have already noted real problems regarding radioactive methods for estimating time. It is noteworthy that the time factor in so many prehistoric sequences has tended to be reduced rather than extended. The rule of reduction is almost unbroken when the following severe cuts can be listed: a date (i.e., estimate) of 10,000 years is reduced to 3,000; a date of 18,000 is reduced to 10,000; a date of 1,000,000 is reduced to 50,000! The Magdelanian culture that was once assigned the dates of from 50,000 to 18,000 years is now estimated to have been 15,000 to 8,000 years B.P.

Other examples of reduction could be cited with respect to carbon-14 estimates of Niagara Falls, desert lakes, and Neolithic cultures. The periods supposedly occupied by Paleolithic Man, Mesolithic Man, and Neolithic Man were once used to derive an estimated sum of the time involved for all such peoples. It is now recognized, however, that various ages may have been contemporaneous, just as the Indians of North America were still in a Stone Age when the Industrial Revolution began in Europe, and some Australian aborigines were still in a Stone Age when the first atom bomb was dropped on Hiroshima. So the time problem remains.

Evolutionists also had problems, at one time, fitting increasing numbers of fossil finds of prehistorical hominids into their evolutionary scenario. In point of fact at the time that the evolutionary scenario (in early form) was accepted by anthropologists, a problem was quickly recognized; namely, the supposed ancestors of modern man all too often seemed to turn up in the wrong places. That is, the earliest fossil hominid remains were found in places quite removed from the Middle East. Therefore, one authority argued that human and animal inhabitants of Europe had migrated to that region from Asia and from Africa.

Analysis of Geographic Distribution

Although the problem of time still is not totally resolved, the science teacher can help students consider this plausible and reasonable creation alternative on the origin of humankind question by leading a brief classroom analysis of geographical distribution of *four* major groups of fossil materials that have been found around the world from the mid-1900's to the present; as follows:

Australopithecus. The sites of fossil finds of *Australopithecus* (the most primitive in the evolutionary framework) are located in South Africa and East Africa. (See Fig. 42). Considering the location of these sites, they are clearly in an area peripheral to the Middle East region. The Australopithecines are found furthest away from the center of the Tigris-Euphrates river area. If Australopithecines are part of the human ancestry, might they have been some that migrated first from a center of civilization, changed the most and suffered the greatest loss of cultural practices and physical degeneration? Also noteworthy is the fact that some experts maintain that these forms were simply extinct apelike animals because of the small brain capacity, the lack of true tools and apparent specializations. If they were apes, then they could not be part of the human lineage according to all known principles of genetics.

Homo habilis. Likewise the sites of fossil finds of *Homo habilis* are located in South Africa and East Africa. (See Fig. 43). Were they some of the earliest migrants from the Middle East area? However certain specialists question the legitimacy of this fossil material as separate species of man.

Homo erectus. The sites of fossil finds of *Homo erectus* are located in Java, China, East Africa, North Africa, and in Europe. Though these forms are widely scattered they are notably peripheral to the Middle East area, but they are somewhat closer than the Australopithecines. There seems to be a more even distribution of *Homo erectus* than the Australopithecines, since they are found on all the large land masses of the Old World except Australia. (See Fig. 44).

Homo sapiens. Although the sites of fossil finds of *Homo sapiens* are also widely scattered and located on all the large land masses, most of the fossil materials have been clustered in Europe and to the west and north of Mesopotamia, along with more isolated finds toward the periphery in Australia and North America. (See Fig. 45). Were *Homo erectus* and *Homo sapiens* (that is, Neanderthal, Swanscombe, Mt. Carmel and Solo forms) those individuals who migrated last from the Middle East area, pushing out *Homo habilis* and *Homo erectus* from previously occupied areas?

The problem of time still remains. Creationists have no complete answer on the origin of humankind. No scientist ever really measures the date

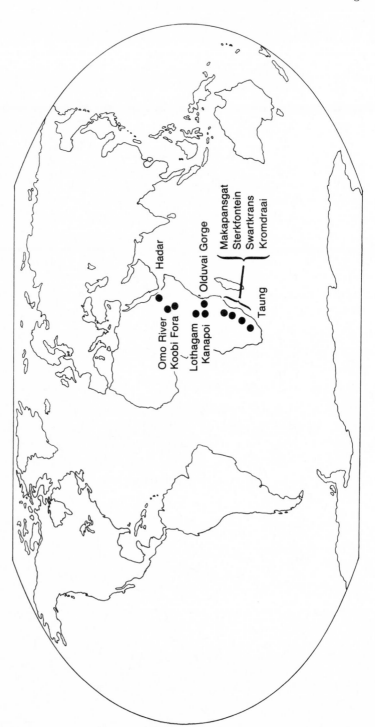

Figure 42
FOSSIL FINDS OF AUSTRALOPITHECUS

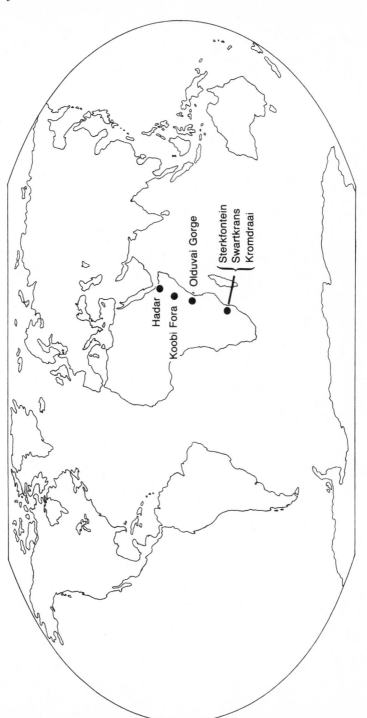

Figure 43
FOSSIL FINDS OF HOMO HABILIS

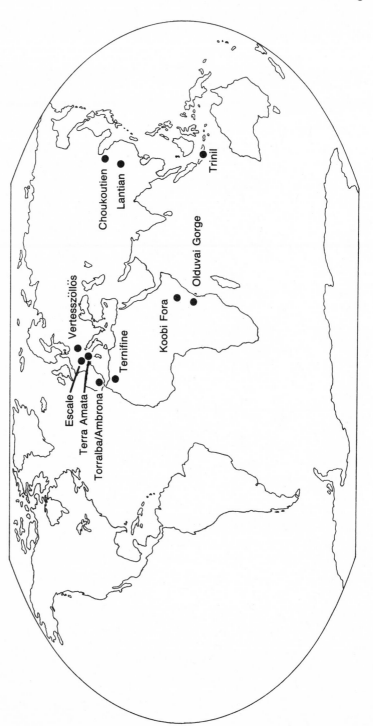

Figure 44
FOSSIL FINDS OF HOMO ERECTUS

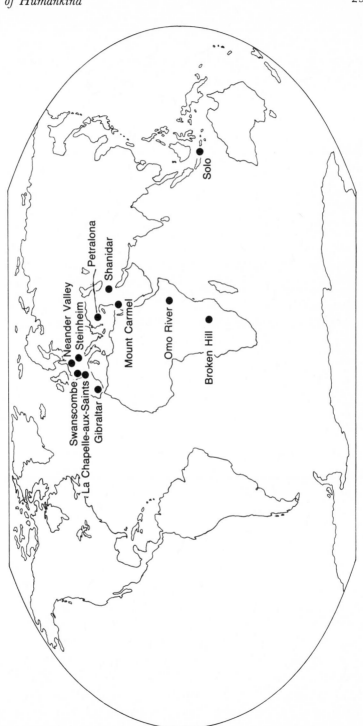

Figure 45
EARLY TYPES OF HOMO SAPIENS

of any fossil. Only estimated ages B.P. have been offered by megaevolutionists in their scenario of the origin of humankind. However, it is possible to explore further lines of evidence, and in doing so science teachers
can instruct their students in a pertinent exercise of inductive reasoning.

Another Line of Inductive Analysis

Science teachers should direct student attention to some aspects of population analysis at this point. Some specialists have observed that wide variation in physical appearance is often found in small groups of people living
in comparative isolation and have found a marked conservatism in cultural
development. In contrast, when human beings are found living in large
conglomerations, there is a strong tendency for the physical appearance
to be fairly uniform. But then a rather wide diversification is noted in the
culture.[36]

Stated in general terms, the above duality of concepts means that when
a population of human beings is small (as many creationists hold to have
been the case after Noah's family survived the flood catastrophe), members
of a single family vary widely in physical appearance, but the group tends
to remain highly conservative in culture and social behavior. Whereas,
when the human population becomes large, then the physical form becomes
more or less uniform but marked cultural variability becomes apparent.

Small pioneering (i.e., migrating) groups necessarily must live somewhat
precariously; and, in turn, must be cautious about innovations. It seems
rather obvious that a group of people on the brink of starvation would not
dare to risk much change in their social behavior. But, of course, as each
settlement of pioneers became established with expected increase in local
population, then more freedom in cultural behavior could be allowed.

The above described features of dispersal of peoples in small groups would
thus account for two facts: (1) the remarkable uniformity of cultural artifacts
in every part of the world where early man has been found; and (2) the
extraordinary resistance to change that is so characteristic of contemporary
primitive people whose margin of survival always seems to remain so slim.

Two famous authorities could be quoted to advantage. Sir W. LeGros
Clark commented on high variability of fossil material in this manner:

High variability (in type) may be correlated with the fact that (at that time) the rate of hominid evolution was proceeding rather rapidly with the development of relatively small and often contiguous populations into widely dispersed areas with contrasting and changing environments.[37]

The fact of initial variability has been noted as a nearly universal phenomenon by Richard B. Goldschmidt:

The facts of greatest general importance are the following. When a new phylum, class, or order appears, there follows a quick explosive (in terms of geological time) diversification so that practically all orders or families known appear suddenly and without apparent transitions.[38]

Such facts have been acknowledged in recent years by numerous megaevolutionists among whom are Stephen J. Gould and Niles Eldredge. Also science teachers can use principles of modern genetics to help students realize that in any small population where *inbreeding* occurs, the genes for all characteristics contribute to the appearance of a marked variability in physical form. This principle of variability of physical form in any small inbreeding population, especially when introduced into a new environment has been very widely observed in plants and animals, including human beings. From all this the science teacher can help students inductively generalize, as follows:

1. A species is more variable when it first appears.
2. A small population is more physically variable than a large population.
3. When a species (or just a few members of it) shifts into a new environment, wide variation appears again that only becomes more uniform after some time period.
4. Small populations are likely to be highly conservative in their culture.

Inductions Applied

Remarkable variableness in physical appearance is observed in fossil hominids when finds from all the various widely scattered geographic sites are compared. The range of skull forms is amazing. In short, fossil hominid remains fit remarkably well with the reality of the four factors just enumerated. Creationists assert that the facts of variability are best accounted for when three assumptions are made: (1) that a small population of human beings began at some central area, (2) that successive waves of migrants of probably only a few individuals in any one group moved along migration lines to establish a succession of centers, and (3) this migration-dispersal pattern was repeated again and again until early man had spread into every inhabitable part of the world.

Creationists who are aware of the geographical distribution analysis for four groups of fossil forms, which megaevolutionists now consider so favorably in developing their scenario for the origin for humankind, are very prone to agree with the following statement supported factually by A.C. Custance:

> The most primitive fragments which had been pushed furthest to the rim might logically be expected to have the greatest proportion of shared culture elements, so that links would not be surprising if found between such peripheral areas as the New World, Europe, Australia, South Africa, and so forth—which is exactly what has been observed. Such lines of evidences force upon us the conclusion that we should not look to these marginal areas for a picture of the initial stages of man's cultural development nor a picture of his original appearance. It is exactly in these marginal areas that we shall *not* find these things.[39] (Emphasis in the original)

In other words, the prehistoric forms of presumed human ancestry could very well be examples of diseased, degenerate, degraded inbred and isolated survivors of waves of migrations as previously proposed.

Of course creationists admit that all this contradicts evolutionary constructions. But along with Custance many creationists are familiar with the facts that support the contention that lines of migration of humankind do not radiate from some point in Africa or the Far East. Rather, based upon (1) archaeological evidence about cultural patterns, (2) consideration of physical diversity of fossil hominids, and (3) known principles of genetics relevant to small inbreeding populations, science teachers can give evidence of the migration-dispersal pattern presented here as a creation alternative. There is excellent logical sense and reasonableness that human beings were making long treks to the uttermost parts of the world *at the very same time* that civilization was blossoming at the center, i.e., the Middle East (still the most logical cradle of mankind, when *all* facts were taken into consideration).

Undoubtedly the way a person views the present multiplicity of fossil finds is colored significantly by the individual's world view. (See Fig. 46 for a summary of the two origin alternatives.) Nevertheless, on the basis of the geographic distribution analysis provided and the principles just reviewed, science teachers should be able to present the following objective points:

1. The most primitive, degraded types of hominid fossils have been found at the margins. An extraordinary example of the tremendous variability that an early, small isolated population at the periphery can show is found at Choukoutien in China. Expert Franz Weidenreich recognized that the range of variation in this group includes a representative Neanderthal Man, a ''Melanesian'' woman, a Mongolian type, and another similar to the modern Eskimo.
2. Examples of *Homo erectus*, including Vertesszolles Man in Hungary, Ternifine Man in Algeria, Olduvai Man in Tanzania, and Lantian Man in China, are all more or less peripheral to the traditional cradle of mankind.
3. Neanderthal Man, including Swanscombe Man, Steinheim Man, LaChappelle Man, Gilbralter Man, Shanidar and Mount Carmel Man, are intermediate for cranial, facial, and dental characteristics between *H. erectus and Homo sapiens sapiens.*

Of course megaevolutionists, who follow the primary emphasis upon skeletal data utilized by the Leakey family (again, they seem to summarily disregard the abundant archaeological and philological evidence), will continue to bring into question the geographical position of the cradle of mankind contained in the creation alternative presented here. Custance offers the following:

Evidence accumulates daily that, culturally speaking, the place of man's origin was somewhere in the Middle East. No other region in the world is as likely to have been the Home of Man if by man we mean something more than merely an intelligent ape. ....
Many speculations exist as to the routes taken by Caucasoids, Negroids and Mongoloids, as the world was peopled by the successive ebb and flow of migrations, and while not one of these really establishes with certainty *how* man originated as *man*, almost all of them make the basic assumption that western Asia is his home as a creator of culture.

From this center one can trace the movements of an early migration of Negroid people, followed by Caucasoid people, in Europe. From this same area undoubtedly there passed out into the East and the New World successive waves of Mongoloid people, and the time taken need not have been so great.[40] (Emphasis in the original)

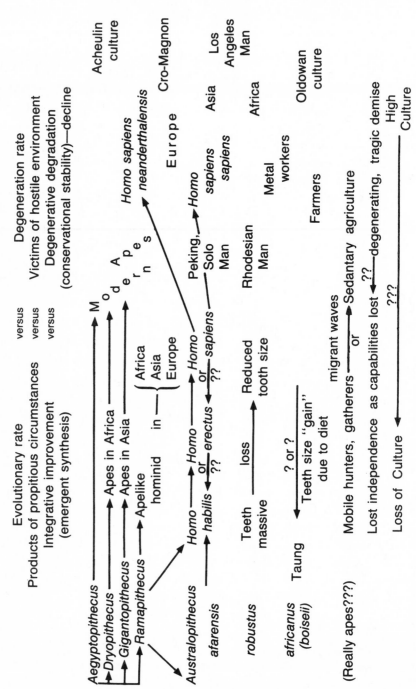

Figure 46
ORIGIN ALTERNATIVES DIAGRAMMED

Custance then provides plausible estimates given by researchers that the time dimension truly need not be a great problem. One specialist estimates that human beings might have covered the 4,000 miles from Harbin, China to Vancouver Island in just 20 years. Another expert reports that 600,000 people under constant threat of attack and during the winter moved 2,100 miles from a point in Mongolia to China in just five months.

CONCLUSIONS

Acknowledging that many primitive people have recollections of a former higher cultural standing, Custance concludes that *all* the peoples of the world, prehistoric and historic, came from the family of Noah. Thus for some creationists the events described in Genesis 5-10 are a reasonable historical account of the ancient peoples of the world; consequently, a person can believe that modern man did not begin with the stature of an ape and did not reach a civilized state after a long evolutionary history.

The following brief summary about the origin of humankind as presented by Custance concludes presentation of the creation alternative:

1. The geographical distribution of fossil remains is such that they are most logically explained by treating them as marginal representatives of a widespread and, in part, forced dispersal of people from a single multiplying population established at a point more or less central to them all, which sent forth successive waves of migrants, each wave driving the previous one further towards the periphery.

2. The most degraded specimens are representative of this general movement who were driven into the least hospitable areas where they suffered physical degeneration as a consequence of the circumstances in which they were forced to live.

3. The extraordinary physical variability of their remains stems from the fact that they were members of small, isolated, strongly inbred bands; whereas the cultural similarities which link together even the most widely dispersed of them indicate a common origin for them all.

4. What is true of fossil man is equally true of vanished and of living primitive societies.

5. All these initially dispersed populations are of one basic stock—the Hamitic family of Genesis 10.

6. They were subsequently displaced or overwhelmed by the Indo-Europeans (i.e., Japhethites) who nevertheless inherited or adopted and extensively built upon their technology and so gained the upper hand in each geographical area where they spread.

7. Throughout this movement, both in prehistoric and historic times, there were never any human beings who did not belong within the family of Noah and his descendents.

8. Finally, this thesis is strengthened by the evidence of history, which shows that migration has always tended to follow this pattern, has frequently been accompanied by instances of degeneration both of individuals of whole tribes, and usually results in the establishment of a general pattern of cultural relationships, which are parallel to those that archaeology has since revealed from antiquity.[41]

FOOTNOTES

[1]In past decades some evolutionists have even asserted that human beings came from apes as expressed by anthropologist Ashley Montagu and others in Appendix G. And in the mid-1970's a specialist at the Yerkes Primate Research center at Emory University even claimed that apes came from human beings! (See Discussion of "Evolutionist Declares: Apes Evolved from Man!", *Acts and Facts* 5 (8): 1-2 and 7 Aug. 1976).

[2]Richard Leakey and Roger Lewin, *Origins* (New York: E. P. Dutton, 1977).

[3]The ideas presented in this section divide into eight parts and provide a skeletal outline that generally follows that offered by Richard Leakey and Roger Lewin, *Origins* (New York: E. P. Dutton, 1977). Publication of *LUCY The Beginnings of Humankind* by Donald Johanson and Maitland Edey (N. Y.: Simon and Schuster, 1981) since final revision of this section does not alter significantly the discussion provided.

[4]*Origins*, p. 123.

[5]Erik Trinkaus and William W. Howells, "The Neanderthals", *Scientific American*, 241 (6): 118-133. Dec. 1979. Descriptive abstract: "They were not so different from modern man, but the differences still remain to be explained."

[6]*Origins*, p. 144.

[7]As representative references see California Attorney General's Opinion, No. 53-266 of June 21, 1955. Wendell R. Bird, "Freedom from Establishment and Unneutrality in Public School Instruction and Religious School Regulation, *Harvard Journal of Law & Public Policy*: 125-205, June 1974; Wendell R. Bird, "Freedom of Religion and Science Instruction in Public Schools", *Yale Law Journal*, 87:515-570, Jan. 1978 and John W. Whitehead and John Conlan, "The Establishment of the Religion of Secular Humanism and Its First Amendment Implications", *Texas Tech Law Review*, X (1): 1-66, Winter 1978.

[8](Ithaca, N.Y.: Cornell University Press, 1951) pp. 4-5.

[9]Peter Volpe, *Understanding Evolution*, 3rd ed. (Dubuque, Iowa: Wm. E. Brown Co. Publishers, 1977) p. 4.

would not have predicted stasis from population genetics, but I am now convinced from what paleontologists say that small changes do not accumulate' '' (in) Research News: "Evolutionary Theory Under Fire", *Science*, 210:884, 21 Nov. 1980.

[22]The following paragraphs are based upon a typical evolutionary article: Paul D. Machean, M.D., "A Mind of Three Minds: Evolution of the Human Brain", *The Science Teacher*, April 1978, pp. 31-39.

[23]See the following references: Harold S. Slusher, *Critique of Radiometric Dating*, Technical Monograph No. 2, San Diego: Institute for Creation Research, 1973 and Thomas G. Barnes, *Origin and Destiny of the Earth's Magnetic Field*, Technical Monograph No. 4, San Diego: Institute for Creation Research, 1973.

[24]Henry M. Morris, *Scientific Creationism*. Public School Edition (San Diego: Creation Life Publishers, 1974).

[25]See each of the following by Harold S. Slusher: *Age of the Cosmos*, Technical Monograph No. 9 (San Diego: Institute for Creation Research, 1980); *The Origin of the Universe: An Examination of the Big Bang and Steady-State Cosmogonies*, Technical Monograph No. 8 (San Diego: Institute for Creation Research, 1978).

See also Harold S. Slusher and Stephen J. Duursma, *The Age of the Solar System: A Study of the Poynting-Robertson Effect and Extinction of Interplanetary Dust*, Technical Monograph No. 6 (San Diego: Institute for Creation Research, 1978) and Harold S. Slusher and Thomas P. Gamwell, *The Age of the Earth*, Technical Monograph No. 7 (San Diego: Institute for Creation Research, 1978).

[26]Marvin L. Lubenow, "The Human Fossil Evidence and the Origin of Man," Unpublished paper, 1976.

[27]Charles E. Oxnard, "Human Fossils: New Views of Old Bones," *American Biology Teacher*, 41 (5): 264-276, May 1979; and David Pilbeam, "Rearranging Our Family Tree," *Human Nature*, 1 (6): 38-45, June 1979.

[28]The following pages are based heavily upon the reasoning of anthropologist A. C. Custance, *Genesis and Early Man* (Grand Rapids: Zondervan Publishing House, 1975.) The reader should understand that Dr. Custance does not share my position regarding the extent of the Noachian Flood, or its bearing on modern historical geology and the age of the universe.

See also R. Daniel Shaw, "Fossil Man: Ancestor or Descendant of Adam?", *Creation Research Society Quarterly*, 6 (4): 172-181, March 1970.

[29]There is much circumstantial evidence for a world wide flood. The most ubiquitous type of rock is sedimentary rock found in multiple layers on all major continents. Sedimentary rocks are supposed to have been formed under water. Also multiple examples of polystrate fossils add to the evidence for a worldwide flood. See Appendix C for a long list of arguments for a worldwide flood catastrophe.

[30]V. G. Childe, *New Light on the Most Ancient East* (London: Kegan Paul, 1935) p.18, and *What Happened in History*, (New York: Penguin Books, 1946) p. 81).

[31]A. C. Custance, *Noah's Three Sons*, Part I: The Part Played by Shem, Ham, and Japheth in Subsequent World History; Part IV: The Technology of Hamitic People (Grand Rapids: Zondervan Publishing House, 1975) and *Time and Eternity*, Part V: The Confusion of Tongues (Grand Rapids: Zondervan Publishing House, 1977).

[32]See J. D. S. Pendelbury, *The Archeology of Crete* (N.Y.: Methune, 1939) p. 68 and V. G. Childe, *Growth of Civilization*, 5th edition (London: Kegan Paul, 1950) p. 19.

[33]Sir Wm. Dawson, *The Story of the Earth and Men* (London: Hodder and Stoughten, 1903) p. 390.

[34]A. C. Custance, *Genesis and Early Man*, Part II: Primitive Cultures: A Second Look at the Problem of Their Historical Origin; Part IV: The Supposed Evolution of the Human Skull; Part V: The Fallacy of Anthropological Reconstructions. (Grand Rapids: Zondervan Publishing House, 1975).

[35]Straus, William L. Jr. and A. J. E. Cave, "Pathology and the Posture of Neanderthal Man," *Quarterly Review of Biology*, 32: 348-363, Dec. 1957. See also Rush K. Acton, "Bone Disease Simulating Ancient Age in 'Pre-Human' Fossils", *Acts and Facts*, Vol. 7, No. 5, May 1978.

[36]See A. C. Custance, "The Lebzelter Principle: A Generative Idea," *Creation Research Society Quarterly*, 11 (3): 157-159, Dec. 1974. The following paragraphs are based extensively upon this article.

[10]Ernst Mayr, *Animal Species and Evolution* (Cambridge, Mass.: The Belknap Press of Harvard University Press, 1963), p. 588.

[11]See his chapter on "Hybridization", *Evolution, Creation and Science* (Washington, D.C.: Review and Herald Publishing Association, 1947).

[12]R. L. Wysong, *The Creation-Evolution Controversy*—Implications, Methodology and Survey of Evidence, Toward a Rational Solution (Midland, MI: Inquiry Press, 1976).

[13]This is admitted in *Science*, 210:883, November 21, 1980: "The absence of transitional forms between established species has traditionally been explained as a fault of the imperfect record, . . . if sedimentation and fossilization did indeed encapsulate a complete record of prehistory, then it would reveal the postulated transitional organisms. But it isn't and it doesn't."

[14]This is most evident in the title of the article by David Pilbeam, "Rearranging Our Family Tree", *Human Nature*, 1 (6): 38-45, June 1978.

[15]Gavin de Beer, *Homology*, The Unsolved Problem (London: Oxford University Press, 1971, p.16.) Also *Oxford Reader Series*, No. 11 (Burlington, N.C.: Carolina Biological Supply Company).

[16]Dr. Richard E. Dickerson provides an extensive example of scenario reconstruction in his article "Chemical Evolution and the Origin of Life" (*Scientific American*, Sept. 1978). He clearly writes about a five part scenario (one of his own words), which I have given much attention to in Chapter 3, regarding raw materials, monomers, polymers, isolation of living substance and reproductive continuity as he considers "the problem of the evolution of living cells". Of course Dickerson admits early in his article (p. 73) that it is one thing to propose *scenarios* for the origin of life that *might* have been and another thing to demonstrate that such scenarios are either possible or probable.

As a further point with regard to reconstructions of the past, the science teacher can use the September, 1978 issue of *Scientific American* for application of the criteria of scientific writing to evaluate the story of the beginning of life on the earth that Dickerson admits he provides. Another author in the same issue writes of the story of presumed evolution of animal behavior (p. 191). Science teachers should ask students to decide whether these stories are fully credible examples of scientific writing.

[17]Erik Trinkaus and William W. Howells, "The Neanderthals", *Scientific American* 241 (6): 118-133, December 1979.

[18]See Appendix G for a set of quotations to support the contention that megaevolutionists *do* believe that human beings evolved from apes or monkeys or both, although not from any living anthropoid.

[19]Ichthylogist Donn Eric Rosen reviews the book, *Introduction to Natural Selection* by C. Johnson (Baltimore: University Park Press, 1976) and includes this remarkable statement: "Although natural selection theory fails to explain the origin of evolutionary novelties, its greatest shortcoming in terms of evolutionary theory is that it fails to explain evolutionary diversity." (*Systematic Zoology*, 27 (3): 370-373, September 1978, p. 37.

In reviewing another book, Norman Macbeth included the following in closing:" . . . one might say that the frailty of natural selection seems to be regarded as a *trade secret*," (*Systematic Zoology*, 27 (2): 266, June 1978, emphasis in original.)

Embryologist Arnold W. Ravin wrote on "The Amorality of the Gene", in *Medicine on the Midway*, 33 (3): 12, Spring 1979 as follows: "But it is a misnomer to apply the term 'selection' to the world of unconscious creatures. It is all too easy to see in the metaphor of 'nature' a guiding, selecting, winnowing entity choosing among possibilities and even creating possibilities themselves. My point is that there is no selection in the domain of nonhuman creatures, certainly not of the sort we associate with choice and that is practiced by man."

See also Randall R. Hedlke, "An Analysis of Darwin's Natural Selection - Artificial Selection Analogy", *Creation Research Society Quarterly*, 16 (2): 89-97f, September 1979; and T. Bethell, "Darwin's Mistake," *Harper's Magazine* 252: 70-75, February 1976.

[20]Just such a statement is made by Dr. Francisco J. Ayala (*Scientific American*, Sept. 1978, p. 58). On the same page Dr. Ayala recognizes that a mutation can only be considered an *error* in duplication of DNA.

[21]Recognition of this situation is found in this statement: "In a generous admission of Francisco Ayala, a major figure in propounding the Modern Synthesis in the United States, said, 'We

[37]Quoted by Custance from Wilfred LeGros Clark, "Bones of Contention," Huxley Memorial Lecture, *Journal of the Royal Anthropological Institute*, 88 (2): 301, 1958.

[38]Richard B. Goldschmidt, "Evolution As Viewed by One Geneticist," *American Scientist* 40-97, Jan. 1952. See additional material on this point in A. C. Custance, *Genesis and Early Man*, Part IV: "The Supposed Evolution of the Human Skull" (Grand Rapids: Zondervan Publishing House, 1975).

[39]A. C. Custance, *Genesis and Early Man*, p. 46.

[40]A. C. Custance, *Genesis and Early Man*, p. 55.

[41]A. C. Custance, *Genesis and Early Man*, pp. 56-57.

Chapter 4

General Discussion Questions

1. What are the stated goals of this chapter?
2. State briefly the traditional viewpoint on the origin of male and female human beings.
3. Briefly what is the animalistic, evolutionary scenario of the origin of humankind?
4. On what basis might megaevolutionists be considered "reactionaries" to the century-old traditional view of the origin of human beings?
5. How do creationists contrast the phrase "fixity of kind" with "fixity of species"?
6. What is an operational definition of the term "kind"? To what division(s) of modern classification might "created kinds" compare?
7. Explain the apparently contradictory combination of these words: "living fossils".
8. How can different meanings of change be made clear with regard to the term "evolution"?
9. List the missing "keys" that are problems for megaevolutionists who believe the "present" contains clues of the "past".
10. Discuss the tendency of megaevolutionists toward misinterpretations of skeletal remains.
11. Consider briefly various methods for estimating old age of life and the universe favored by megaevolutionists; now do likewise for various methods for estimating young age of life and the universe favored by creationists.
12. What is the basis for the interpretation by creationists that prehistoric skeletal materials are from diseased, degenerate, isolated inbred individuals of small populations of human beings?
13. Explain the words: "cradle of mankind".
14. Discuss possible implications of an analysis of geographic distribution of fossil hominid remains.

15. Discuss a migration-dispersal Creation Alternative to the majority scenario of human origins.

Class Projects or Individual Assignments

1. Prepare a topical outline of this chapter.
2. List "cover words" that could cause semantic confusion.
3. Make an illustrated wall chart of the analogy between "natural selection" and "artificial selection".
4. Collect photographs of "living fossils".
5. Collect illustrations or drawings of reconstructions of imagined ancestors of human beings—both those accepted today, and those that are now discarded by evolutionists.
6. Prepare a diagrammatic illustration of the physique and culture of small populations of human beings as compared to large population conglomerations.
7. Prepare a wall chart of examples of the comparative method utilized by evolutionists. (Suggestion: Consider comparisons of skeletons, embryos, and brain casts.)
8. Draw arrows on a world map to illustrate the "Cradle of Mankind", and show: (a) the migration-dispersal pattern of *descendants* long accepted by traditionalists, and (b) the migration-dispersal pattern of *ancestors* of human beings proposed by megaevolutionists.
9. Work out a set of answers for the evaluation items provided at the close of this chapter. Now prepare a set of similar evaluation items for this general subject matter area.

Read: Duane T. Gish, *Evolution the Fossils Say No!* (Public School Edition). 1978. See especially Chapter VI, "The Origin of Man". San Diego: Creation-Life Publishers.

Donald Johanson and Maitland Edey, *LUCY The Beginnings of Humankind*. 1981. New York: Simon and Schuster.

Harold Slusher, *Critique of Radiometric Dating*. 1973. Technical Monograph No. 2. San Diego: Institute for Creation Research.

John C. Whitcomb, *The World That Perished*. 1973. Grand Rapids, MI.: Baker Book House.

On the Use of Scripture in Parochial Schools
1. Ask Students to read Genesis 5 and Genesis 10. Discuss the increasing veracity of the "Table of Nations" given by the author of Genesis, which also is the basis for a time scale of only a few thousand years rather than millions of years claimed by evolutionists.
2. Ask students to count the number of times they find the phrase "after his kind" or "after their kind" used in Genesis 1. Compare these phrases to the phrase "fixity of kinds".
3. Also give attention to 1 Cor. 15:39 in context of each kind having a definite body.
4. Discuss the two previous suggestions in relation to known, established limits of genetic variation developed by specialists in the study of heredity.
5. Ask students to read Genesis 7:10-12, 17-24. Review all possible physical changes of the surface of the earth. Include attention to "overthrust" ideas of modern geologists and fossil existence and fossil formation.

EVALUATION QUESTIONS

For items 1 through 5 select the entry in the key which most properly matches the definition provided.
KEY: 1. Microevolution
        2. Megaevolution (macroevolution)
        3. Mutation
        4. Natural selection
        5. Artificial selection
1. Inheritable alterations of existing DNA (genic) materials. (3)
2. Volitional (that is, willful) choice by some human being according to some definable criterion or criteria. (5)
3. Changes in the genetic composition of a population with the passage of each generation. (1)
4. Differential elimination or differential survival of some organisms without regard to any criterion or criteria. (4)
5. Changes in the genetic composition of organisms such that all populations have come from some beginning population(s). (2)

For items 6 through 14 select from the key the one entry which you recognize as being most closely associated with each item:

KEY: 1. A possible means for estimating an old earth.

2. Might be an uncertainty with regard to radioactive estimates.

3. A possible means for estimating a young earth.

4. Certain criterion for a chronometer.

5. None of the above.

6. Cosmic radiation may have varied over past time. (2)

7. There is a limited amount of helium in the atmosphere of the earth. (3)

8. Decay of uranium to lead, or potassium to argon. (1)

9. Differences in original isotope concentrations in rocks than is assumed. (2)

10. The timer must be sensitive and accurate, and readable in units of time. (4)

11. There is a very low amount of nickel in the sediments of the ocean basins. (3)

12. We must know when the timer was started and whether it was started at zero time. (4)

13. The magnetic field of the earth is decaying. (3)

14. The timer must run at a uniform rate and must not have been disturbed or reset. (4)

For items 15 through 33, select the entry from the key below which will indicate that you understand, according to the particular point of view of this course, what *actually* is involved in each item; that is, the *real* "situation that prevails" regardless of what some people might suggest.

KEY: 1. Natural, circumstantial evidence for the evolution model.

2. *Supra*-natural, circumstantial evidence for the evolution model.

3. Natural, *conclusive* evidence for genetic variation within kind.

4. *Supra*-natural, circumstantial evidence for the creation model.

5. Natural, circumstantial evidence for the creation model.

15. Data establishing "races" and "varieties" of organisms. (3)

16. Redshift of light spectra and background radio noise and radiation. (1)

17. Data of polymorphism in Tay-Sachs disease. (3)

18. Data of polymorphism associated with sickle cell anemia. (3)
19. Formation of folded mountains and block mountains. (2)
20. Proposed transitional form such as Seymouria. (2)
21. Example of breeding activities of peppered moths in England. (3)
22. Data of similarities of proteins as detected in vertebrate organisms. (1)
23. Example of polymorphism in cystic fibrosis. (3)
24. Proposed transitional form such as Archeopteryx. (2)
25. Direct Creator involvement in human activities. (4)
26. Data of similarities of embryos of vertebrate organisms. (1)
27. Example of breeding activities of frogs in one or several regions. (3)
28. Complex patterns of organelles and organ systems. (5)
29. Data on human blood groups in Rh disease. (3)
30. Use of the Founder Effect with regard to religious isolates. (3)
31. Appearance (beginning) of original, stable (though variable in a limited sense) kinds of plant and kinds of animals. (4)
32. Use of concepts of genetic drift and gene flow. (3)
33. Data of similarities of skeletons of vertebrate organisms. (1)

For items 34 through 45, select the entry from the key that will indicate that you understand, according to the particular point of view of this course, what *actually* is involved in each item; that is, the *real* "situation that prevails" regardless of what some people might suggest.

KEY: 1. Natural, circumstantial evidence for evolution model (total evolutionism).

2. *Supra*-natural, circumstantial evidence for evolution model (total evolutionism).

3. Natural, *conclusive* evidence for genetic variation within kind.

4. *Supra*-natural, circumstantial evidence for creation model (scientific creationism).

5. Natural, circumstantial evidence for creation model (scientific creationism).

34. Studies of hybridization and mechanism of speciation by polyploidy in wheat. (3)
35. Data of similarities of proteins as detected in vertebrate organisms. (1)

36. Studies of facial angles by scientists in the 19th century to try to show origin of blacks. (1)
37. Life appeared as a result of spontaneous generation. (2)
38. World wide catastrophic changes modified greatly the land surface of the earth. (4)
39. Studies of factors in diversification of finches and competitive exclusion. (3)
40. Consideration of the so-called cave people as inbred, isolated, diseased degenerate descendents of fully human contemporaries. (5)
41. Studies of disease and glandular disorders in living human beings. (5)
42. Data of similarities of skeletons of vertebrate organisms. (1)
43. Discussion of conquest of the land following invasion of the land and leading to adaptive radiations of different organisms. (2)
44. Present matter came from explosion of some dense, eternally existing substance. (2)
45. Stable groups or kinds were established (made) "in the beginning". (4)

To show your understanding of the meaning and reality of two degrees of change with regard to both living and dead organisms and concepts associated with "selection", select from the key the entry which is *most closely* associated with each item 46 through 64:

KEY: 1. *Micro*-evolution
2. Neither of these degrees of change.
3. *Mega*-evolution (macroevolution)
4. Natural selection
5. Artificial selection

46. Pictorial representation of different cabbage type plants from the same species. (1)
47. Pictorial representation of various sized horses from large draft type to small knee-high or "apartment size". (1)
48. Pictures of different finches and different pigeons. (1)
49. Changes in the genetic composition of a population with the passage of each generation. (1)
50. A chart of the historical record of plant life on the earth as presented by Volpe in his chapter on history of life. (3)
51. Random mating as discussed by Volpe regarding genetic equilibrium. (1)

52. Various pictures of constructions of animals based upon actual complete skeletons found in the La Brea tar pits in California. (1)
53. Pictorial representation of the geneology of dogs. (1)
54. Differential elimination or differential survival of some organisms without regard to any criterion or criteria. (4)
55. Comparison of Gingko leaves or birch leaves found in sedimentary rock strata with gingko leaves and birch leaves found alive today. (1)
56. Selective breeding resulting in appearance of an auroch like animal similar to those known to have existed 300 years ago. (1) (5)
57. Study of these changes involves proper, orderly science, which is based clearly upon observational, quantitative practices. (2) (1)
58. A chart of the historical record of animal life on the earth as presented by Volpe in his chapter on history of life. (3)
59. Mutational change that might have been the cause of multilegged frogs. (1)
60. Comparison of an ant found in amber with ants alive in the present natural environment. (1)
61. Changes in the genetic composition of organisms such that all populations have come from some beginning population(s). (3)
62. Comparison of bat skeleton found in sedimentary rocks with bat skeleton found in natural environment. (1)
63. Selective breeding resulting in appearance of a tarpan-like animal similar to those known to have existed in the late 1800's. (1) (5)
64. Pictorial comparison of various embryo and larval stages of complex organisms. (3)

For items 65 through 80 select from the following key that one entry which is most properly associated with each item:

KEY: 1. Circumstantial evidence for *mega*-evolution
        2. *Conclusive* evidence for *micro*evolution.
        3. None of the entries stated here
        4. *Circumstantial* evidence for *micro*evolution
        5. *Conclusive* evidence for *mega*-evolution

65. Skeletons of lions, horses, vultures found in La Brea tar pits and bears, larger than lions, horses, vultures and bears known to be alive today. (4)
66. Data establishing "races" and "varieties" of organisms. (2)

67. Data of polymorphism in Tay-Sachs disease. (2)
68. Data of polymorphism associated with sickle-cell animals. (2)
69. Proposed transitional form such as Seymouria. (1)
70. Example of breeding activities of peppered moths in England. (2)
71. Data of similarities of proteins as detected in vertebrate organisms. (1)
72. Data of similarity of Gingko leaves and horseshoe crabs in fossil materials with gingko leaves and horseshoe crabs alive today. (4)
73. Example of polymorphism in cystic fibrosis. (2)
74. Proposed transitional form such as Archaeopteryx. (1)
75. Data of similarities of embryos of vertebrate organisms. (1)
76. Example of breeding activities of frogs in one or several regions. (2)
77. Data on human blood groups and Rh disease. (2)
78. Use of the Founder Effect with regard to religious isolates. (2)
79. Use of concepts of genetic drift and gene flow. (2)
80. Data of similarities of skeletons of vertebrate organisms. (1)

To show your careful understanding of the reality of the concepts of two degrees of change with regard to both living and dead organisms, select from the key the entry which is *most clearly* associated with each item 81 through 93:

KEY: 1. *Micro*-evolution
       2. Neither of these ideas of change
       3. *Mega*-evolution

81. A chart of the historical record of plant life on the earth as presented by Volpe in his chapter on history of life. (3)
82. Random mating as discussed by Volpe regarding genetic equilibrium. (1)
83. Gingko leaf or birch leaf of supposedly millions of years ago. (1)
84. Mutational change that might have been the cause of multilegged frogs. (1)
85. An ant trapped in amber supposedly millions of years of age. (1)
86. Pictorial representation of the geneology of dogs. (1)
87. Pictorial representation of different cabbage-type plants from the *same* species. (1)
88. Selective breeding resulting in appearance of an auroch-like animal similar to those known to have existed 300 years ago. (1)
89. Bat skeleton supposedly millions of years of age. (1)

90. Selective breeding resulting in appearance of a tarpan-like animal similar to those known to have existed in the late 1800's. (1)
91. A chart of the historical record of animal life on the earth as presented by Volpe in his chapter on history of life. (3)
92. Various pictures of constructions of animals based upon actual complete skeletons found in the La Brea tar pits in California. (1)
93. Study of these changes involves proper, orderly science, which is based clearly upon observational, quantitative practices. (2) (1)

5 | Summary

When you complete this chapter you should understand how to:

1. Illustrate the fact that all scientists (evolutionist and creationist) utilize the same data regarding origin questions.
2. Maintain that creation teaching is legal and constitutional.
3. Explain that creation can be taught objectively and is now included in major textbooks.
4. Present major generalizations of the evolution/creation confrontation approach to teaching about first origins.

This is a how to book for those teachers seeking methods and classroom materials to implement their teaching about the origin of the universe, origin of life on earth, and origin of humankind.

There is no private scientific information or exclusive data about the physical environment available to evolutionists or creationists only. Both camps must utilize essentially the same scientific data. In other words, objective findings concerning all portions of the natural environment (terrestrial and celestial) are the same for evolutionists and for creationists. To summarize the empirical basis of these assertions I have developed Classroom Teaching Aid 34 to help the science teacher show students how the *very same basic categories of information or data* are used by all persons developing evolution/creation interpretations of origin questions. As usual I recognize the two positions of greatest contrast (megaevolution vs. scientific creationism). We will now consider seven categories of scientific data.

Evolutionists and creationists emphasize available data in markedly contrasting manner. The former place great emphasis upon *similarities*, whereas the latter put much emphasis upon *differences*. This is not to say that evolutionists ignore differences or that creationists ignore similarities. Yet a summarizing generalization may be repeated again: *evolutionists generally stress*

Classroom Teaching Aid 34: CATEGORIES OF INFORMATION

Classes of Scientific Data	Emphasizes similarities	Emphasizes differences
	Summary of ways scientific data are used to support evolution uniform model	Summary of ways scientific data are used to support catastrophic creation model
Genetics and Variation	Imagined broad change: kind from kind; across kind. Differences due to recombinations and beneficial mutations that have accumulated; slow change.	Known limited change: only variation within kind. Mutations mostly harmful; result in no new traits; definite breeding gaps; no connections between kinds.
Classification	Similarities are basis of grouping; due to supposed common gene pool of similar genes; supposed history of kinds.	Fixity of kinds; no connections between distinct groups as due to persistence of basic characteristics due to varieties from different beginnings.
Comparative Form of Anatomy	The degree of similarity is basis for degree of relationship; common gene pool, supposed common ancestry.	No real connection of kinds; similarities could be due to common plan by Creator God; consistence of master plan pressed.
Comparative Embryology	Similarity of structure is result of genetic relationship, supposed common gene pool, supposed common ancestry.	No real connection of kinds; similarities could be due to common plan by Creator God; consistency of master plan pressed.
Geographic Distribution	Supposed descent with change due to modified environments.	Barriers, breeding resulted in centers of population growth; no new kinds; continental drift idea could be relevant.
Fossil Evidences	Presumably successive layers provide evidence of succession of life forms; so-called actual history of related organism groups.	Definite gaps between kinds, no intermediate forms; no real geological column; worldwide flood possible cause; n.b. living fossils = fixity of kinds.
Dating Estimates	Data interpreted to mean long ages based on certain assumptions of constant decay rate, no contamination. Use radiometric and nonradiometric estimates plus geologic column.	Radiometric dating assumptions are erroneous; evidences of young earth noted; rapid burial likely, catastrophism.

similarities and creationists generally stress differences. A comment on each category or class of scientific data is in order with regard to relationships of groups of organisms:

Genetics and variation. Evolutionists *assume* changes across kinds have occurred, whereas creationists have *conclusive* evidence that only variations *within* kinds can be scientifically documented.

Classification. Evolutionists *suppose* that similar groups came from common gene pools, whereas creationists have *conclusive* evidence that natural classificatory categories reflect absence of genetic lineage between kinds.

Comparative anatomy. Evolutionists *suppose* that the degree of relationship depends upon the degree of similarity, whereas creationists have *conclusive* evidence that similarities are not the result of genetic connections.

Comparative embryology. Evolutionists *suppose* that similarity of embryos is evidence of common ancestry, whereas creationists have *conclusive* evidence that embryos, which are only immature stages of growth and differentiation prior to adult stages, are not similar because of any genetic connections.

Geographic distribution. Evolutionists *suppose* that organisms in different parts of the world have been selected due to interactions with the environment, whereas creationists have *conclusive* evidence that the fundamental barrier between kinds is the genetic discreteness and distinctiveness due to DNA arrangements.

Fossil evidence. Evolutionists *presume* without regard for logical fallacy (i.e., *post hoc ergo propter hoc*), that fossil organisms evidenced in upper rock layers are descendents of fossil organisms in lower rock layers, whereas creationists have *conclusive* evidence that even fossilized kinds are distinct.

Dating estimates. In making statements about time before the present (B.P.), evolutionists *interpret* ratios of radioactive elements in the present as evidence for their estimates for long age of the earth (hence life on the earth), whereas creationists have *conclusive* evidence that no zero setting is known for any radiometric clock.

To further augment the fact that all persons developing evolution/creation interpretations about origin questions utilize the *same* fossil materials and breeding data, Classroom Teaching Aids 35 and 36 have been devoloped. At first glance these may appear to be identical charts; however, different subheadings and causes are involved. The first chart makes explicit that even the evolutionists' camp is not a monolithic, unified

Classroom Teaching Aid 35
TWO EXPLANATIONS OF SAME EMPIRICAL DATA

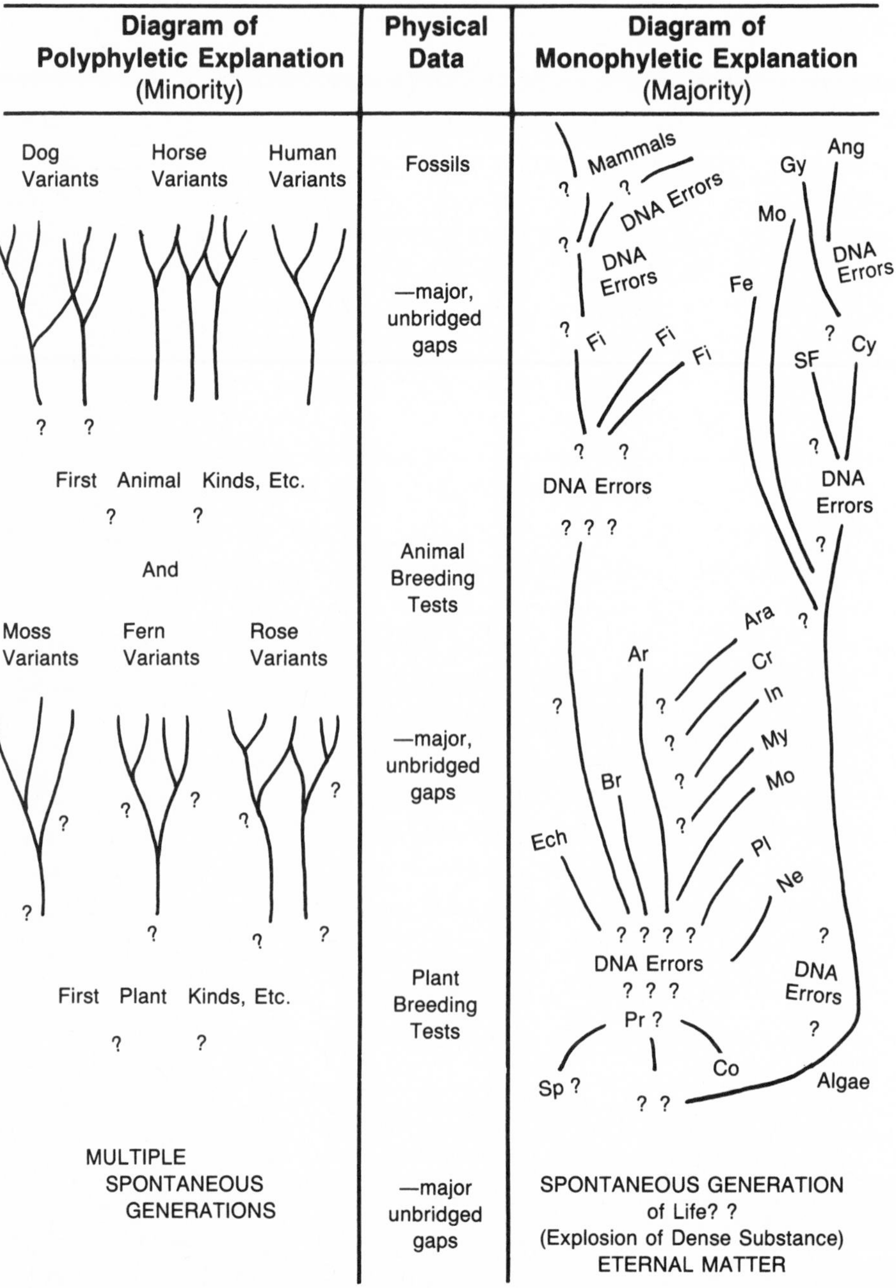

Diagram of Polyphyletic Explanation (Minority)	Physical Data	Diagram of Monophyletic Explanation (Majority)

Dog Variants   Horse Variants   Human Variants

?   ?

First   Animal   Kinds, Etc.
?   ?

And

Moss Variants   Fern Variants   Rose Variants

?   ?   ?   ?
?   ?   ?   ?

First   Plant   Kinds, Etc.
?   ?

MULTIPLE
SPONTANEOUS
GENERATIONS

Physical Data column:

Fossils

—major, unbridged gaps

Animal Breeding Tests

—major, unbridged gaps

Plant Breeding Tests

—major unbridged gaps

Monophyletic Explanation (diagram labels):

Mammals   Gy   Ang
? ?   DNA Errors   Mo
?   DNA Errors   Fe   DNA Errors
? Fi   Fi   Fi   SF   ? Cy
?   ?   ?

DNA Errors   DNA Errors
? ? ?   ?

Ara   ?
Ar   Cr
?   ?   In
?   My
Br   ?   Mo
Ech   ?
Pl
Ne
? ? ? ?   ?
DNA Errors   DNA Errors
? ? ?
Pr ?   ?
Sp ?   Co
? ?   Algae

SPONTANEOUS GENERATION
of Life? ?
(Explosion of Dense Substance)
ETERNAL MATTER

Classroom Teaching Aid 36
TWO CONTRASTING EXPLANATIONS
OF THE SAME EMPIRICAL DATA

Modern Creationism	Empirical Facts	Modern Evolutionism

Dog Variants   Horse Variants   Human Variants

Created Animal Kinds

AND

Moss Variants   Fern Variants   Rose Variants

Created Plant Kinds

FIXITY OF KINDS

ETERNAL GOD

Empirical Facts:

Fossils

—major gaps

Animal Breeding Tests

—major gaps

Plant Breeding Tests

—major gaps

Modern Evolutionism:

Mammals   Ang   Gy

DNA Errors   M

DNA Errors   F

F   F   F

DNA Errors   Cy

SF

DNA Errors

Ara   Cr   In   My   M

Ar

Br

Ech   Pl   N

DNA Errors
Pr ?
Sp   Co

DNA Errors

SPONTANEOUS GENERATION
of Life? ?
(Explosion of Dense Substance)
ETERNAL MATTER

position—both majority and minority variations can be found in scientific literature of the past three decades.

In Classroom Teaching Aid 35 a diagrammatic representation of both the minority position (on the left), and the majority position (on the right) is given which is expressed by evolutionists in prestigious scientific journals. The *polyphyletic* explanation is based on the presumption by a minority of evolutionists (like Keosin, Nuttall, Schindewolf and others) that divergencies are noted between major groups (phyla) of organisms due to separate origins of each group from separate spontaneous generations of living substance. (And probably because of negative connotations, the terms *biopoesis*, *abiogenesis*, or *neobiogenesis* are often employed as substitutes for the words spontaneous generation.)

The contrasting *monophyletic* explanation is based on the presumption of the majority of evolutionists (once led by the late Julian Huxley and the late Theodosius Dobzhansky and now by G. G. Simpson, Franscisco Ayala and others) that all phyla of animals and all phyla of plants have come into existence through mutational changes in previously existing organisms, from a single cell, from the first noncellular living substance on the earth, which arose spontaneously from inorganic matter.

The prime difference then between the polyphletic and monophyletic explanations authored by supposedly naturalistically oriented evolutionists is the scope or magnitude of spontaneous generation of living substance imagined. Yet spontaneous generation is definitely *not* a naturally occuring phenomenon. (See Chapter 3). Each of these explanations entails supposed positive mutational changes—that is, accumulation of helpful DNA replicative errors. Yet mutations are no more than that—errors of DNA replication; and absence of accumulation of small changes has been admitted by evolutionists.[1]

Classroom Teaching Aid 36 is essentially a contrasting formulation. The diagrammatic entry on the left represents the position of modern creationism with fixity of kinds as established by God as the initial stages (in stark contrast to multiple instances of spontaneous generation imagined by polyphletic evolutionists). The diagrammatic entry on the right represents the position of the majority of evolutionists (monophyleticists) with one spontaneous generation of living substance as an initial stage, which resulted supposedly from some inherent propensity of matter, after formation of the earth, after some big bang explosion of eternal matter. With this teaching aid the science teacher may show students digrammatically the nature of the most contrasting positions that scientists take when utilizing the same empirical data (fossils, plus plant and animal breeding records), which is of course a potential reinforcement of the main thrust of Classroom Teaching Aid 34.

Classroom Teaching Aids 35 and 36 also contain two different approaches to what has been called by some textbook authors the tree of life. For most megaevolutionists there has been one and only one tree of life throughout time. For most modern creationists there have been and actually still are whole forests of multiple examples of a tree of life. In other words, megaevolutionists see humankind as that one particular mammalian vertebrate that interacted with the natural environment in such a selective manner as to evolve from some other anthropoid form that had a common ancestry somehow with other vertebrates, which presumably had a common ancestry with unicellular life. Thus for megaevolutionists there has been *one huge* tree of life.

Modern creationists, on the other hand, see each major kind of plant and each major kind of animal represented by a *separate* tree of life, such that each major kind has a created beginning form, which contained a high potentiality for variability of life *within* the basic created kind. Thus humankind would be represented by one tree, which seems to fit all known empirical data, since all living human beings are potentially interfertile—all are the *same* species, or different varieties of the *same* created kind.

Evolutionists often propose that belief in *one* spontaneous generation of living substance is more simple (hence more parsimonious) than belief in multiple creative acts of omnipotent God. However, the science teacher can simply point out that modern evolutionism entails imagination of *multiple* occasions of supposed positive, helpful mutations (actually DNA errors), whereby new physical traits have come into existence.

Yet, *not a single* new physical trait has ever been known to arise from a mutational change! A mutation is only a change in an already existing physical trait. A mutation only results in a different variable expression of an already existing physical trait.

Hence there is no gain of simplicity with regard to speculations about spontaneous generation by evolutionists. Modern creationism involving specially created plant and animal kinds, all with potentialities for variability and hybridization (always *within* kind), is the most straightforward explanation of available empirical data; i.e., all fossilized plant and animal materials, and all plant and animal breeding records. All of these data can be used to support *conclusively* the statement that real gaps have existed and continue to exist between different kinds of organisms, and the existence of gaps demonstrates the *fixity of kinds*.

In Chapter 4 we studied the "gaposis" of fossil materials. Let me summarize further the actual ideational gaposis which regularly confronts evolutionists. Classroom Teaching Aids 37 and 38 make this ideational gaposis visually comprehendable. These two charts were designed relevant to plants and animals, respectively, to summarize visually the dependence of megaevolutionists upon the concept of mutations.

Classroom Teaching Aid 37
GAPOSIS OF EVOLUTIONISTS — REGARDING PLANTS

Filamentous plants	*M U T A T I O N S*	Unicellular plants
Chlorophyll		Nonchlorophyll
Land plants		Aquatic plants
Enclosed seed bearing		Exposed seed bearing
Broad, netted venation		Narrow, parallel venation

Classroom Teaching Aid 38
GAPOSIS OF EVOLUTIONISTS — REGARDING ANIMALS

Life	*M U T A T I O N S*	No life
Cells		No cells
Multi-cellular forms		Single-celled forms
Vertebrates		Nonvertebrates
Skeletal forms		Nonskeletal forms
Human consciousness		No human consciousness

In brief, evolutionists must imagine that filamentous plants came from unicellular plants by some mutation or series of mutations. Likewise, they must imagine that chlorophyll appeared in plants where there had been no chlorophyll as the result of some mutation or series of mutations, and so with the other cited physical aspects: land plants from aquatic plants, enclosed seeds from exposed seeds, and broad, netted leaves from leaves with narrow, parallel venation. But these are just a few of the changes in highly unique physical traits that must be explained by megaevolutionists, if their broad, grand scale meaning of change between plants is to be taken at all seriously. Megaevolutionists have *no real* explanation for such supposed changes in plants. The same all encompassing summary conclusion can be stated with regard to the representative physical traits for animals listed in Classroom Teaching Aid 38.

It is fully legal and constitutional to teach scientific creationism in any school, whether it be public or parochial, secular or sectarian. Because of all that has gone before in previous chapters, the science teacher should no longer have any serious doubt that the creation model is a viable, scientifically based alternative to the evolution model about first origins. Any science teacher can teach the creation model in this pluralistic society because it is plainly fair and lawful to do so. No special ruling is needed to teach the creation model; no new laws are required. In fact attorney generals in state after state have formulated opinions that scientific creationism may be taught in the public schools. A straightforward presentation of the creation point of view *and* the evolution point of view about first origins is fully within responsible edification of the young. *No religious worship is involved.* Thus there is no violation of so-called separation of Church and State.[2]

Since the creation model can be discussed effectively on scientific grounds and since evolutionism is fundamentally a philosophy, a world view, then it is patently unsound educational practice and even unconstitutional for megaevolution to be taught and promoted exclusively in the public schools. I have reviewed constitutional protections of public school students. So exclusive presentation of evolutionary explanations of first origins in effect amounts to compulsory, selected indoctrination in a state endorsed world view. The only fair, legal, constitutional solution of this problem is to teach *both* the evolution model and the creation model, strictly as scientifically based *interpretations* of origins, whenever and wherever the subject of first origins is under discussion.[3]

Furthermore, the fact that this recommended two-model evolution/creation confrontation approach to teaching about origins is manifestly possible is evident even beyond publications of staunch proponents. Several secular publication firms have released books wherein the authors give limited attention to the antithetical positions of evolutionists and creationists regarding questions of first origins. In contrast to almost complete lapse since the mid-1040's of any attention by textbook authors to explanatory ideas of creation scientists, science books published by Allyn-Bacon,

McGraw-Hill and Macmillan Publishing Co. contain specific recognition
of the position of creation scientists.[4]

Noteworthy is the fact that the first edition of Stanley Weinberg's high
school book, *An Inquiry into the Nature of Life* (Boston: Allyn-Bacon, Inc.),
was published in 1971. When I presented a paper, along with Dr. Duane
T. Gish of the Institute for Creation Research, before the 1972 annual
convention of the National Association of Biology Teachers (see *The American
Biology Teacher*, January 1973 and March 1973, respectively), and discussed
the entire matter with author Weinberg, he was most specific about his
opposition to inclusion of creation concepts in a biology textbook or science
classroom. Yet while preparing the 1974 edition of his book, author
Weinberg evidently *changed his mind* and decided to include a section called
"Creationists say—" in his textbook. (See Fig. 47). Secondly, McGraw-
Hill textbook editors agreed with author Davis and Solomon that their 1974
college textbook should contain the major arguments that creationists use
to support their point of view, as shown in Fig. 48. Thirdly, the fact that
a rather low key presentation of creationist concepts and arguments has
been approved by textbook editors of Macmillan is evidenced by material
from their college textbook, *The Science of Evolution* by William D. Stansfield.
(See Fig. 49.)

Thus the creationist position can be taught objectively along side the
evolutionist position in a two-way confrontation manner. In fact I taught
a scientifically based creation model of origins along with my presentation
of megaevolutionary ideas (noting the specifically circumstantial support)
for most of the past decade in my general education natural science classes
at Michigan State University. This was accomplished in accordance with
academic freedom and responsibility.

I definitely taught about the nature of scientific knowledge, and I explained the scientific processes throughout my courses as three specific
themes were implemented: (1) explication of observation versus explanation; (2) discussion of the structure of scientific theories; and (3) attention
to interaction of science and society.

In one course untitled "Changing Concepts of the Universe", the subject
matter (selected from astronomy, chemistry and atomic physics) was utilized
to implement these three themes. The lecture topics included belief systems
and world view, definition of science, science versus scientism and criteria
for evaluating scientific writing. The difference between scientific theories

Figure 47
CREATION CONCEPTS IN HIGH SCHOOL BIOLOGY TEXTBOOK

EVOLUTIONISTS SAY—	CREATIONISTS SAY—
The theory of evolution need not be accepted because most scientists support it. Since no one was present at the creation, neither creation nor evolution is provable. Therefore both theories are equally reasonable.	Agreed. Evolution should be accepted only as long as the evidence supports it. No scientific theory is ever proven. It only becomes probable to the extent that it fits the facts. Evolution fits the evidence; creation does not.
The earth is only a few thousand years old. Radioactive dating, giving an age in billions is inaccurate.	Radioactive dating is essentially accurate. The earth is at least 4.5 billion years old.
Lyell's theory of slow change in the earth's surface is incorrect. Geological features such as the Grand Canyon were formed quickly by catastrophies such as the flood of Noah's time.	Geological evidence supports Lyell's theory of a slowly changing earth.
Worldwide dating of rock strata is incorrect. Some evidence comes from human footprints in Utah and Texas, found in the same strata as trilobite and dinosaur fossils.	Rock strata are dated correctly. Geologists find that the so called footprints in Utah are simply rock formations. Many of those in Texas were hand carved.
No undisputed fossils are found from the so called earliest period in earth history.	A considerable number of fossils have been found in Precambrian rocks.
If various animal phyla evolved from each other, they should have appeared at different times. Actually all major phyla except chordates appeared together at the beginning of the Paleozoic era.	Correct. As yet we have no explanation for this. Despite this gap, the theory of evolution is supported by enough other evidence to be reasonable.
If evolution occurred, there would be transitional forms between the major groups of animals and plants. There are no such forms.	Thousands of transitional forms are known including intermediates between the various vertebrate classes. Many gaps remain. The evidence is clear that evolution occurs, but not as to all details.
Similarities such as those between the forelimbs of vertebrates do not mean relationship.	Similarities of development and of structure do indicate relationship.
Because mutations are generally harmful, they cannot be a factor in evolution.	While most mutations are harmful, many beneficial ones are known. These are materials for evolution.
Plants and animals do change, and new species may even develop. But change never goes beyond the limits of the original created *kinds*.	We know what species are, but *kinds* are not defined. The same process that forms new species also forms new families and larger groups.
Evolutionists deny the creative power of God.	The hand of God is just as evident in evolution extending over billions of years as in creation occurring in an instant or a few days.

From Stanley L. Weinberg, *Biology: An Inquiry into the Nature of Life.* Copyright © 1977 by Allen and Bacon, Inc. Reprinted with permission.

Figure 48
CREATION CONCEPTS IN COLLEGE BIOLOGY TEXTBOOK

In general, the majority of creationists support their view with most or all of the following arguments:

1. Evolutionary theory rests on the concept of uniformitarianism, which assumes that events proceeded in the past at the same rate as they do today. But uniformitarianism can be neither proved nor disproved. Because man was not around to record events that supposedly occurred before his time, we cannot prove that mutations occurred at the same rate as they do in the present. We cannot be sure that sedimentary rock has always been deposited at the same rate that is observed today, and thus we cannot calculate with certainty the age of a fossil in sedimentary rock.

2. Morphologic and biochemical similarities may reflect an economy of design on the part of the Creator; whereas, major differences would indicate different types of organisms made for different purposes. Moreover, organisms that are morphologically similar are *not* always biochemically similar. Evolutionists arguments about similarities are sometimes convincing but cannot constitute proof; they are only more or less plausible.

3. Many supposedly vestigial structures have minor or even major functions. The human appendix, listed as a vestigial remain of a cecum, more fully developed in our vegetarian ancestors, appears to be a sort of intestinal tonsil and may be important in the early development of immune mechanisms. At one time the thyroid gland was considered vestigial and was removed by surgeons for reasons we would now consider frivolous.

4. Nonharmful mutations occur seldomly and at random. The number of very specific mutations needed to make one radical change in an organism is large. Thus the probability is minute that mutations could lead to the development of new phyla.

5. Dating fossils is not easy. While it is doubtless true that, in general, younger sedimentary rocks are deposited on top of older ones, the original relationship is easily disturbed by geologic events, and this disturbance is not always easy to detect. Even dating by the technique of radioactive decay is not above criticism. How can we be sure that a given rock contained none of the products of radioactive decay to begin with or that none of them (such as argon, a gas) has subsequently leaked away? In any case, results of the various dating methods tend to conflict. If they are valid, they should agree, at least roughly. Even *general* evolutionary sequences can be disturbed by unreliable dating. In human "evolution", for instance, it now appears that the most recent *Australopitheous* is geologically younger than the oldest known *Homo*. How, then, can the existence of *Australopithecus* be considered evidence for the evolution of *Homo*, as it is usually supposed to be?

   Such fossil evidence as exists might be explained by the view that organisms were created in timed sequence. Another view is that organisms were destroyed in a universal flood and that the segregation of distinct communities of fossil organisms in separate strata may be explained ecologically. A marine community, for example, might be the first to be buried by a catastrophic sedimentation, followed by a swamp community, followed by a terrestrial lowland community washed over both, etc.

6. In the final analysis, evolution is inherently incredible. All geologic time is actually too short to develop man from an organic soup by microevolutionary processes without the purposeful intervention of a Creator.

From *The World of Biology* by P. W. Davis and E. P. Solomon. Copyright © 1974. Used with the permission of the McGraw-Hill Book Company.

Figure 49
CREATION CONCEPTS IN ADVANCED COLLEGE TEXTBOOK

Human cultural evolution has now matured to the stage at which science is part of everyday life. The scientific concept of evolution by natural selection has been ranked as one of the greatest philosophical achievements of all time. The human mind has become so complex that it can comprehend notions of its own origins through natural processes. How valid are these evolutionary theories? Are they so rigorous and so highly predictive that they virtually solve all biological problems? A partial answer to these questions is presented in the next two sections.

Mathematical Challenges to the Evolutionary Theory

It would be quite wrong for the student of evolution to obtain the impression from reading this or any other text on evolution that adequate answers have now been found to all the problems in this field. Nothing could be further from the truth! Many of the questions that troubled Darwin are still raised today. Are the processes of random variation and natural selection really sufficient to account for the diversity of life that we see around us? One of the most widely publicized recent debates of this age-old question took place in April 1966 at the Wistar Institute of Anatomy and Biology in Philadelphia between a group of mathematicians and biologists. The mathematicians charged that if natural selection had to choose from the astronomically large number of available alternative systems by means of the mechanisms described in current evolution theory, the chances of producing a creature like ourselves is virtually zero. . . .

More Critique

. . . In the remainder of this section, a sampling of quotes, remarks, and criticisms will be presented from a book by Norman Macbeth entitled *Darwin Retired* (1971). No attempt will be made either to justify these excerpts or to argue in rebuttal. They are simply presented to give the reader some feeling for the kinds of challenges being directed at neo-Darwinism. (Here followed an itemization of 36 excerpts from this book available from Gambit Incorporated, Boston.)

From *The Science of Evolution* by William D. Stansfield. (Copyright © 1977 by William D. Stansfield). Used with the permission of Macmillan Publishing Co., Inc.

and cosmogonies was pointed out as circumstantial evidence for some big bang explosion, steady state and oscillating ideas about origin of the universe was contrasted with circumstantial evidence for the creation of the universe. (See Fig. 50: Table of Circumstantial Evidence.) The second half of this course included controlled experimentation on derivation of the gas laws, laws of chemistry, static electricity and magnetism.

Figure 50
TABLE OF CIRCUMSTANTIAL EVIDENCE

A. Big bang Origin of the Universe:
1. Red shift of light spectra
2. Nova, supernova
3. Background radiation and radio noise

B. Spontaneous Generation of Life:
1. Synthesis of amino acids (only building blocks of living substance)
2. Production of synthetic equivalents of urea, rubber, fibers

C. Animal Origin of Human-kind:
1. Similarities of skeleton, embryo, muscle, brain form
2. Similarities of components of DNA, RNA, hemoglobin, etc.
3. Emotional, territorial and aggressive animallike behavior in reaction to signs, signals, and perceptual thought

AA. Creator Origin of the Universe:
1. Orderly arrangement of stars in constellations
2. Orderly pattern of planetary motions
3. Orderly pattern of comet motions

BB. Creator Origin of Life:
1. Definite pattern of exclusive left-handed amino acid structure
2. Complex pattern or organelle and organ inter-actions in living organiza-tions

CC. Creator Origin of Human-kind:
1. Self-conscious awareness and metaphysical concern
2. Personality involving moral, ethical concern; reflective, symbolic, conceptual thought
3. Reports of direct Creator involvement in human activities

In a second course entitled "The Nature and Continuity of Life", students studied subject matter (selected from cell biology, aspects of knowledge of sexual reproduction and genetics) to again implement the three themes stated above. The confrontation of creationist and evolutionist ideas was interwoven with controlled experimentation about cell functions and discussions of DNA, heredity and the nature of living things. Specifically I covered such topics as the artificial synthesis of amino acids, arguments from probability, mutation rates and the circumstantial evidence for creation found in the order, pattern and complexity of life.

In my third course entitled "Human Biosocial Evolution of Man", I engaged in a grand scale confrontation between the creation model and the evolution model regarding origin of humankind. The three main themes of my teaching were implemented through selected scientific topics from geology, comparative biology, molecular biology, population genetics and paleontology. The course began with definition of the term *evolution* and lead into the two-model approach to show students that the evolution model can be challenged scientifically.

The middle section of this third course focused on contrasting *interpretations* of scientific evidence. Topics such as mutations, natural selection, fossil materials, biogenesis, continental drift and a creationist migration-dispersal alternative to the majority animalistic, evolutionary origin of human beings were included. I concluded the course with some examination of the societal impact of evolutionary thinking in social darwinism, history, political science and all main areas of human knowledge. Certain practical scientific implications of the creation model were also summarized.

Classroom Teaching Aid 39 is a skeletal outline of these courses, which have been presented under varying titles. The classwork was designed for freshmen and sophomore nonscience majors and transfer students, who took the courses to satisfy a graduation requirement. Following is a summary list of some of the generalizations that I stressed, which also have been stressed in this book. (I also included in my teaching the common theses of the majority evolutionary thinking.)

SUMMARY GENERALIZATIONS

1. Observation, plus repeated observation, is at the very center of precise scientific activity. Therefore, since ideas formulated about origin of the universe, origin of life on the earth, and origin of humankind involve

Classroom Teaching Aid 39
COURSE OUTLINES

FALL TERM	WINTER TERM	SPRING TERM
What do men say today about the place of the earth in the universe?	What do men say today about life, regarding origin and continuity?	What do men say today about origin of living things and origin of humankind?
MOTION	**LIFE**	**CHANGE**
Can the origin of the universe be studied scientifically? NO!	Can the origin of life be studied scientifically? NO!	Can the origin of humankind be studied scientifically? NO!
Astronomy Size of the universe Geometry of the universe Order, pattern	Reproduction Asexual Sexual Genetics — (variability in stability)	Geological changes Biological changes (within vs. across) Evidences—circumstantial vs. conclusive
Cosmology versus Cosmogony Evolutionism vs. Theism World views	Sub-microscopic origin (spontaneous generation) versus Theozoic origin (created pattern) Mutational errors	Evolution Model versus Creation Model (Physical Sciences Biological Sciences) (Earth Sciences Social Sciences)

unobservable, unrepeatable events, then those ideas are outside precise *scientific* activity.

2. Precise *scientific* activity is restricted to empirical, quantitative, mechanical and correctable studies.

3. Most commonly, evolution is understood to mean molecules to man, hydrogen to human beings, particles to people, or amoeba to man changes.

4. Most modern creationists believe that all that is in the heavens, on the earth and in the seas originally came into existence by creative acts of God the Creator.

5. If first origins are presented in any course, then a two-way treatment of concepts of the creation model *and* the evolution model is required to protect the academic freedom and civil and constitutional rights of all persons involved in the educative process.

6. The terms *kind* and *species* are difficult to define but they are *not* equivalent. Possible created kinds could refer to arbitrary classification divisions of order, family, or genus.

7. All scientists use the same main categories of evidence, but the evidences are interpreted differently, such that proponents of the evolution model emphasize *similarities*, whereas proponents of the creation model emphasize *differences*.

8. The entire system of evolutionary thought rests upon one *basic assumption*: The degree of relationship depends upon the degree of similarity.

9. There are two meanings of the term *change* that must always be made explicit when discussing origins of plants and animals: (a) change *within* easily recognizable kind of organisms which is most adequately called genetic variation (*within* kind); and (b) supposed change *across* recognizable kind, which is appropriately called megaevolution or macroevolution (the amoeba to man thesis).

10. There is a fixity of kinds that may be supported *conclusively* from plant and animal breeding records. This phrase could well be the twentieth century equivalent of the biblical phrases ''after his kind'' and ''after their kind''.

11. There are no compelling scientific reasons for maintaining that the earth (or the universe) is billions of years old. All proposed methods of dating only result in *estimates* of age. There are sound reasons for claiming that the earth and the universe are young.

12. Each of the adopted radioactive methods for estimating age are based

upon limiting assumptions. No one can determine initial ratios of elements when the earth began, nor determine actually whether decay rates have always remained constant.

13. Although uniformitarian geologists refer repeatedly to the concept that the present is the key to the past, they regularly imagine forces about mountain building, mountain range erosion and continental glaciation that are unobservable. Uniformitarian geologists, therefore, really include *supra*-natural events in their thinking, and hence contradict their own desire to refer only to events that occur naturally.

14. There are no known truly intermediate or transitional forms, with actual genetic connections, between recognizable kinds of plants and animals in the fossil materials.

15. The concept of fixity of kinds can be supported by a long list of living fossils, organisms once thought to have been extinct, but now are known to be alive.

16. Attention might be called regularly to the empirical nature of cosmology and the highly speculative, imaginative nature of cosmogony.

17. Conceptual formulations of big bang expansion and steady state existence of components of the universe are examples of nonscientific speculative (imaginative cosmogonal) thinking outside the scope of empirical *and* theoretical activities of *contemporary* scientific work.

18. Some scientists still believe that life came into existence by spontaneous generation, that is, by chance coming together of submolecular parts of matter.

19. Life is known *only* in complex organization, although admittedly in single cell (as well as multiple cell) patterns, but never in simple form.

20. Megaevolution, that is, amoeba to man (or molecules to man), is mathematically impossible and really quite irrational. The fact that proteins in living things are composed *only* of left-handed amino acids makes more difficult the problem of credibility of evolutionist thinking.

21. All efforts directed at production of living material in the laboratory utilize already existing materials, and thus, *synthesis*, rather than creation, is involved.

22. If scientists ever are successful in producing synthetic living substance, then they will have demonstrated that intelligent planning was involved; hence, by analogy, then an Intelligence (God the Creator) was responsible for the initial pattern of organization of first life on the earth.

23. Although physical features of plants and animals may well be the result of the DNA code, there is no known "code of the code" to explain how the patterns of the DNA codes found in plants and animals ever came into existence.

24. Mutations (changes in already existing genes) do not result in any new physical traits, but *only* in characteristically *variational* changes of already known physical traits. Usually mutational changes result in debilitating conditions, or loss of viability, or death.

25. Every field and laboratory researcher always concludes research work with the *same* easily recognizable *kind* of organism with which research started.

26. At no time do human beings ever have any functional tails or gill slits. Any claims for existence of such features are based upon abnormal conditions that usually disappear during development of an individual.

27. No anthropoid ancestor of human beings is known. There are pronounced differences between human beings and any form of animal life.

28. Constructions of so-called prehistoric man have really been the result of preconceived ideas that human beings came from some anthropoid origin.

29. Some anthropologists have turned away from an evolutionary interpretation of human ancestry and now propose that the widely scattered, so-called prehistoric fossil forms might have been isolated, inbred migrants from a Near East center of civilization.

30. The concept of evolutionary origin of humankind has been accepted in every major discipline of human knowledge. The broad scope of such acceptance is specific evidence of the multiple impact of the unobservable, undemonstrable total evolution model of origins.

31. Significant consequences of belief in an evolutionary ancestry of human beings, instead of descent from an original pair (Adam and Eve), are the lack of identity, and the problem of explanation of the source of human personality.

32. Serious misapplications of evolutionary thinking in the nineteenth century were practiced by Social Darwinists, and numerous examples of similar misapplications are committed today by twentieth century Social Darwinists.

33. Teaching the creation model versus the evolution model of origin is the only direct guarantee that selected indoctrination during first origin

instruction will be avoided. Such teaching about different beliefs of first origins is fully consistent with Supreme Court rulings concerning teaching *about* beliefs of different people.

34. Fundamentally the issue involved in the creation/evolution confrontation controversy is a spiritual matter. What is the relationship of the individual with God, the Creator, with Jesus Christ as Redeemer and Savior?

FOOTNOTES

[1]See Roger Lewin, "Evolutionary Theory Under Fire", *Science* 210: 884, 21 Nov. 1980.

[2]In reference to my science teaching at Michigan State University, in December 1977, Dr. Clifton R. Wharton, Jr., then President of Michigan State University was quoted as follows in *Scientific American* 237 (6):87: "The argument that Professor Moore violates the concept of separation of church and state seems not to apply here. We do not have a situation in which there is control, or attempted control, over the education programs by the church."

[3]See Wendell R. Bird, "Freedom of Religion and Science Instruction in Public Schools", *Yale Law Journal* 87: 515-570, January 1978; and "Freedom from Establishment and Unneutrality in Public School Instruction and Religious School Regulation", *1979 Harvard Journal of Law and Public Policy*, 125-205, June 1979.

[4]Two other examples of limited recognition of the position of creationism are: Francisco J. Ayala and James W. Valentine, *Evolving: The Theory and Processes of Organic Evolution.* (Menlo Park, CA: The Benjamin/Cummings Publishing Company, 1979), and Douglas J. Futuyma, *Evolutionary Biology* (Sunderland, Mass.: Sinauer Associated, Inc. 1979).

Chapter 5

General Discussion Questions

1. What are the stated goals of this chapter?
2. Explain that there are no ''private'' data for evolutionists nor for creationists.
3. How do creationists emphasize data differently than evolutionists?
4. What is the polyphyletic explanation of the origin of plants and animals?
5. What is the monophyletic explanation of the origin of plants and animals?
6. What is the essential difference between a polyphyletic explanation of the origin of all life and the position of modern creationism?
7. Discuss the fact that *not a single* new physical trait has ever been known to come from gene mutations.
8. What is meant by the concept of ''gaposis of ideas'' of evolutionists?
9. Explain the difference between circumstantial evidence and conclusive evidence.

Class Projects or Individual Assignments

1. Prepare a topical outline of this chapter.
2. List *all* ''cover words'' given in this book that could cause semantic confusion.
3. Prepare a large wall chart of categories of data used by evolutionists *and* creationists.
4. Prepare large charts of phylogenetic ''trees'' (mono-and poly-, plus modern creationist) and locate cut-out pictures of plants and animals in proper places.
5. Prepare large charts of the ''gaposis of ideas'' of evolutionists with regard to plants and animals—adding more aspects than included in this chapter.
6. Prepare a large wall chart of the circumstantial evidence for a Creator origin of all things.
7. Prepare a large wall chart of the circumstantial evidence for an explosion-accident-mistake origin of all things.

Read: R. T. Clark and James D. Bales, *Why Scientists Accept Evolution.*
1966. Grand Rapids, MI: Baker Book House.
First Amendment of the Constitution of the United States of
America.
John N. Moore, *Questions and Answers on Creation/Evolution.* 1976.
Grand Rapids, MI: Baker Book House.
John W. Whitehead, *The Separation Illusion* (A Lawyer Examines
the First Amendment). 1977. Milford, MI: Mott Media.
Paul A. Zimmerman, Editor, *Darwin, Evolution and Creation.* 1959.
St. Louis: Concordia Publishing House.

6 | What Difference Does It Make?

Introduction

The scope of this book is limited mainly to consideration of methods and classroom materials to aid science teachers interested in the two-model confrontation teaching approach to origin questions. My treatment of the creation model and the evolution model about first origin questions is designed to afford the greatest contrast of interpretations by scientists who represent fully antithetical world views. Thus the ramifications of various modifications of the creation model mentioned in the Introduction, and minority and majority variations of the evolution model given in Chapter 5, have been discussed only briefly.

However in this closing chapter I want to give particular attention to possible moral and ethical consequences of total evolutionism. To do so I must eventually give attention to the inhumanity of human beings doing good through the sanction of might makes right, when applied through war, concentration camps, ballot box contests, or similar competitive natural selection means.

Modern Science Replaced by Scientism

Modern science was begun by great physical scientists and by leading biological scientists, such as Galileo, Kepler, Newton, Linnaeus, Ray, Clerk-Maxwell, Faraday, Kelvin, Pasteur, Mendel and Virchow. All were theists and many of them were Christians. These great scientists accepted the world view of Theism. They believed that the universe and the earth were created by God. Further they believed that, since they were created in the image of God, they had abilities for observation, search and reason such that they could, as Kepler expressed, "think God's thoughts after Him".

But these scientists also realized that their abilities were limited; thus, they confined themselves to studies that were empirical, quantitative, mechanical and correctable. I maintain that these aspects of their work are limiting principles of careful, proper scientific endeavor. I discussed these limiting principles at some length in chapter 1 to help science teachers appreciate that inquiries by scientists differ and that there are necessary limitations of scientists and the discipline of science.

Nevertheless, many scholars in approximately the past 150 years have changed those limiting principles of science into dogmas, into various forms of scientism. Science, as a professional endeavor, has been explained in this book as limited to studies of naturally occurring phenomena; that is, natural scientists do not attempt to study the supernatural. Professional scientists properly limit themselves to studies of *interrelationships of matter and energy*. In contrast, modern practitioners of scientism are motivated by the viewpoint that the *only reality is matter and energy*. Scientism is a belief that only the methods of the natural sciences can be used fruitfully in the pursuit of knowledge. According to scientism there is only up-to-date scientific knowledge, and all else is nonsense. As a consequence many scholars are proponents of empirical scientism, psychological scientism and sociological scientism.[1]

Typical of empirical scientism is the attempt to reduce all of being to nature. Darwin described human intellect in terms of animal intelligence, and moral faculty was traced to instinct and pleasure in animals. Marx and Freud used this reductionism to make human beings candidates for the mass society. Yet proponents of such reductionism commit the genetic fallacy when they claim that some object or event can be logically identified with or fully explained by some supposed remote origins.

As practitioners of psychological scientism, Hobbes and Rousseau began with naturalism to give importance to the group, along with accompanying suppression of individual liberty and natural rights for real freedom and self-fulfillment. Feuerbach followed by holding that modern man had abandoned faith in favor of science; and Freud came along with his theory of absolute psychic determinism.

By employing sociological scientism Comte divided intellectual history into three stages: theological, metaphysical and positive or scientific, which have not replaced each other but have been superimposed. Through the rejection of all that is nonphysical, Marx and Lenin dogmatically held that matter is eternally evolving by applying Darwin's ideas on organic evolution to the historical process as a whole. These ideas have definite consequences in totalitarianism. If moral (universal) obligations are rejected, then the only realistic alternative for the maintenance of law and order rests with the state as the absolute arbiter of right and wrong.

Therefore, many leading "idea persuaders" in a great variety of disciplines of human knowledge have *not* carefully followed continued use of the aforestated limiting principles of science. Because of their failure to abide by proper limiting principles characteristic of the founders of modern science, proponents of multifaceted scientistic dogmas have helped nurture a certain mindset evident in the present milleu, that scientists have practically unlimited capabilities to attack and eventually solve any problem turned over to them. Therefore, I maintain that the former limiting principles that are characteristic of the works of scientific greats have been perverted into universal dogmas, which have even become separate world views, because of extremism in application of the concept that the only reality is matter and energy. Let me list some specific examples:

Empiricism. The empirical limiting principle of science has been ignored, hence empiricism is not emphasized in keeping with the viewpoint that the only proper source of information is scientific methodology; hence intuition and revelation are completely ignored or discarded.

Materialism. The quantitative limiting principle of science has been ignored, hence empiricism is now emphasized in keeping with the viewpoint that matter is the primary reality and that spiritual aspects of human existence are either not important or nonexistent.

Determinism. The mechanical limiting principle of science has been ignored, hence determinism is emphasized as a viewpoint that all events, including human behavior, are controlled by impersonal forces over which human beings have no control.

Utopianism. The correctable principle of science has been ignored, hence utopianism, which has been called the perennial heresy, is stressed to press forward the thought that human beings can be self-corrective enough to bring about an ideal society.

Total Evolutionism

Today this hope is propagandized in public school through an almost exclusive presentation of total evolutionism. Classroom Teaching Aid 40 is a graphic organization of ideas about the replacement of science by scientism in modern society. I call attention to the arrows pointing from the four identified limiting principles of science to the extreme universal dogmas. I claim there is a one-to-one correlation, and these universal dogmas are essentially subsumable under the one all encompassing rubric, total evolutionism, which I have explained in detail in the Introduction.

But what difference does it make whether scientism has replaced science in modern society? To be more specific, scientism today is basically an ideology, and it is held tenaciously and applied systematically by many leaders in an authoritarian manner. Essentially, scientism is a twentieth century version of eighteenth century Deism; and, like the deists, proponents of scientism have denatured God. In doing so they have deified nature; they have anthropomorphized nature; they have assigned to scientism an omniponent role in solving all problems, in clarifying all things.

I do believe there is a profound difference whether someone acknowledges and follows as guidelines the necessary limitations of scientists, or whether someone's actions are guided by *the* overriding form of scientism, the world view of total evolutionism. Admittedly, physical and biological scientists study pheonomena in the *natural* environment. They certainly do *not* attempt to study the supernatural. However, the supernatural might be a useful presupposition for a scientist, as a complete person. The supernatural might be a useful presupposition *again* for modern scientists in certain instances with regard to ultimate origin questions: origin of the universe, origin of life on the earth, or origin of humankind.

Thus the choice between limiting principles of science and universal dogmas of scientism are significantly relevant to first origin questions. As a human mind thinks, so is the individual inclined. He who will not have God the Creator, must have a substitute. Today that substitute is found in the mental constructs and the ideational formulations of naturalistically oriented scientists. But in the twentieth century real options are still possible.

The reader should understand that I collected many arguments by scientists *against* megaevolutionary ideas for most of a decade before I accepted

Classroom Teaching Aid 40
TRENDS FROM SCIENCE TO SCIENTISM

In historical times, we identify,

Theistic beliefs dominant	Scientific Era	Nontheistic (atheistic) beliefs dominant

Bacon	Steinmetz	Faraday	Marx
Galileo	Clerk-Maxwell	Linnaeus	Freud
Kepler	Einstein	Ray	Huxley (T. H. and Julian)
Newton	Von Braun	Pasteur	Positivist
			philosophers
	(thinking thoughts after God of		Monod
	their theistic outlook)		Skinner

SCIENCE—with limiting principles

SCIENTISM—with universal dogmas becoming world views because of extremism

1. Empirical—observation, sense perception $\longrightarrow$ 1. Empiricism—Science alone gives the truth and this truth is absolute.

2. Quantitative—measurement, numerical symbols $\longrightarrow$ 2. Materialism—Matter is the primary reality.

3. Mechanical (materialistic)—use of machinelike models $\longrightarrow$ 3. Determinism—All behaviour, including that of human society, is determined by impersonal force.

4. Corrective—all aspects are subject to re-test and examination $\longrightarrow$ 4. Utopianism—The coming of the ideal society is guaranteed.

all
based on
TOTAL EVOLUTIONISM

Cosmic (stellar) evolution	Molecular (chemical) evolution	Organic (biological) evolution	Social (cultural) evolution

TOTAL or GRAND SCALE EVOLUTIONISM

Jesus Christ as my Savior. I became fully aware of weaknesses and deficiencies in Darwinism, Neo-Darwinism, and modern synthetic evolutionism published by scientists in the scientific literature in every decade after the appearance of Charles Darwin's book, *The Origin of Species*, in 1859. I found in the early 1960s that the primary choice I had to make about the cause of the universe and all that is therein was in regard to the questions, Who do you say Jesus Christ is? Was He Creator of all things?

But before I could face those questions, I had to answer these questions: (1) Is it rational to believe that all the orderliness of the universe came from an imagined explosion of a dense particle of absolutely unknown origin? (2) Is it rational to believe that the first life on the earth came by chance, as molecular parts (also of unknown origin) combined into building blocks that became living substance that somehow became cellular? (3) Is it rational to believe that humankind, which is the only life in the universe (as far as we know) that is conscious of consciousness, came from mutational changes (fortuitous mistakes) that occurred in some subhuman form? To me, each one of these questions is answered most accurately with an unqualified "no". Megaevolution is totally irrational. Total evolutionism is completely irrational. Until these three questions are faced fully they are common stumbling blocks to acceptance of Jesus Christ as Creator of the heaven and the earth, who *was* accepted as Savior by many founders of modern science.

What Difference: Evolution or Creation?

But what difference does it make whether human beings were created or had a megaevolutionary origin? I believe it does matter profoundly what one believes in general answer to that question.[2] The way we behave toward other human beings depends upon who we think *they* are, and who we think *we* are. If we believe other human beings are purposeful creations of a loving God, then we take a different view of human beings and ourselves than if we believe we are all megaevolutionary accidents. If we believe we are descended from animals, then we will tend to behave like animals.

Animal behavior is well ordered and quite appropriate for their nature. Animals live by simple rules - might makes right, the fittest usually survive, the superior killer dictates to the less fit. Animals are regimented in groups according to their relative strength and cunning. Animal societies are primarily materialistic; success in an animal society is based usually upon the ability to gather food and occupy the most advantageous natural surroundings suitable for the particular kind of animal involved. Fish do well in water. Birds succeed in the air and animals succeed on the land. All of these conditions result in efficient, orderly organizations of living creatures which usually prosper under their systems.

Most significant is the fact that when human beings think of themselves as superior animals, they tend to live according to animal principles. But animal behavior is *not* apprioriate for human society. I can easily show that human totalitarian societies *exaggerate* animal behavior.

Totalitarian leaders seek to dominate territories beyond their own needs; they try to establish control over peoples of other nations. Powerful political leaders seek to organize the less powerful into oppressed minorities. In general, the more powerful human being tries to force the less powerful into a subordinate position. Whereas "live and let live" might be an appropriate motto in animal societies, dictatorial regimes of human beings of whatever degree are not above utterly eliminating the less powerful— by total victory, or by majority dominance over the minority. Yet human beings do not tolerate well the reign of the superior killer. They have a gut-level distaste for dictatorship and control.

The oppression of people—like Jews, blacks, Kulaks, the underprivi- ledged—by other peoples is actually beneath the level of animal behavior. Nevertheless, oppression seems justified by evolutionary thinking, by sur- vival of the fittest thinking, by "might makes right" thinking, since the persecuted ones are supposedly not the fittest, and so they simply are not worthy of survival. Dictation, oppression, eliminating the less powerful—the minority, the weak—seems totally natural.

Communistic ideology, as propounded very early by Lenin, depended heavily upon use of Darwin's ideas as filtered through acceptance of them by Karl Marx, who felt Darwin's natural selection concept fit his ideas about human society as nothing but rivalry between competitive classes of human beings. Darwin and Marx lived in a time when domestic breeders were learning how to refine methods for selecting superior strains of vegetables, swine, cattle and so forth. Nietzsche assumed that superior human beings could be selected in the same way.

The selection practices of breeders were very successful in producing increased butterfat content in milk and leaner swine. As was pointed out in the discussion of Darwin's analogy between artificial selection and natural selection, the system worked well because breeders usually agreed upon what they preferred regarding particular characteristics of vegetables and animals.

What a difference when human beings began to select other human beings! Human beings are not cattle or swine (though Hitler called inferior people *Schwein*, meaning swine). Breeding human beings, to produce physical trait variations that somebody considers more desirable, interfers with human dignity and self-respect; interfers with human rights and opportunity for self-development.

Clearly, evolutionists believe, and teach others to believe that natural selection determines the survival of good cattle, good crops, and for that matter, good human beings. However, evolutionists forget that breeders select qualities in domestic organisms according to their tastes, which is an artificial, more or less arbitrary selection. But the analogy between artificial selection and natural selection breaks down just at this point of application of selection qualities, or criteria of choice.

True, peoples of different nations struggle. Evolutionists say that is "the nature of the beast". Marx observed competition among human beings, and he assumed that one class of human beings could dictate or select the movements and thoughts of other classes in the ongoing competition of human existence. Then that controlling class could possibly begin selecting the fittest human beings—*or at least the fittest human beings in the opinion of the controlling class.*

But this process of central control of human beings by other human beings, this artificial (not natural) selection of human beings, brought nothing but trouble. According to Marx, Nietzsche and Lenin we were supposed to get superior human beings. Instead we got such men as Hitler and Stalin and those who have followed their mold in other nations in every decade of the twentieth century.

At least Hitler and Stalin were very frank in admitting that they set themselves up as selectors of other human beings. Hitler was especially frank. He said that the so-called Aryan race was superior to the Jews. Considerable attention could be given by the evolution/creation confrontation teacher to the fact that the term *race*, when applied particularly to human beings, has been a direct consequence of the application of evolutionary thinking. In fact in the nineteenth century many scientists taught that the blacks were inferior to whites.[3]

Hitler conducted breeding experiments with human beings in strict consistency with the artificial selection activity of a superior group committing oppression, selectively killing other human beings. The Lebensborn project of the Hitler regime, the subject of a 1975 public television program, was based on the concept that it was a virtue for select unmarried Aryan women to become pregnant by elite Nazi military officers. Centers of breeding were actually established where men and women were sent to make their supposed contribution to a future superior race. Many of the unfortunate children of such liasons—the innocent victims of *perverted* artificial selection—are still alive. One wonders if those that are aware of their parentage have any illusions of superiority.

Stalin considered the members of his own political party to be the "fittest" human beings, and he was the dictatorial overseer of the cruel oppression of hundreds of thousands of other human beings. Much of his thinking and methods have been applied in Cuba, Viet Nam, Cambodia, North Korea and Red China. During every decade of the twentieth century these applications of the *artificial* (not natural) selection principle, taken over by totalitarian dictators from evolutionary thinkers, has resulted in disappearance of massive numbers of human beings. Thousands of Jews, Kulaks (Russian peasants), and other "undesirables" in nation after nation have been spirited off to starvation camps, forced labor and work-to-death prisons as one group of human beings has dictated to other human beings.

Of course Stalin and those who followed him have had no biological excuse for their selections; their criteria were what men *thought* rather than how they looked. Those human beings least able or willing to absorb the teachings of Communism in Russia, Red China, Tibet, Estonia, Latvia, Ukrania, Bessylrabia, Veit Nam, Cambodia and North Korea have been conveniently eliminated. All in accordance with might makes right thinking, or survival of the fittest thinking, or struggle for existence thinking of the oppressive over the oppressed. Somehow Darwin's *The Origin of Species* led to events as detailed in Solzhenitsyn's *The Guleg Archipelago*—that mind-numbing report of the torture and murder of millions of human beings.

Many people are sickened by the tyranny over human beings seemingly sanctioned by the selection of the fittest. The evolution/creation confrontation teacher in the natural sciences, social sciences, or the humanities can see now that it has made a difference if one holds to the animalistic origin of human beings propounded by evolutionists. Of course, not everyone who believes the evolution model is a potential Hitler or Stalin. But it should be clearly evident that totalitarian regimes, or political majorities—with their ruling ''selectors''—do seem to have roots in the evolutionary way of thinking. If one believes that human beings are evolved animals and responsible to no Creator but are subject to improvement by artificial (not natural) selection, then it is only a short step to believing that pure materialism and selective breeding would be good for all human beings. Signs of this latter approach are evident today in the thinking of proponents of genetic manipulation and proponents of mercy killing of the aged, deformed and mentally defective.

Impact of Survival of the Fittest Thinking

It is unfortunate that schoolchildren are taught evolution (megaevolution) as if it were fact. Evolution is taught as fact, however, due to the extensive indoctrination of modern intelligensia in the modern total evolutionary point of view as described in the Introduction. It is important to realize that a certain respect is attached to a fact; there is at least a certain behavior of human beings to conform to it. Thus, each child who comprehends the idea of survival of the fittest wishes naturally to become the fittest. I do not mean that the child becomes bestial, but children can compete with one another in the cold and unforgiving manner of animal competition.

Remember that animal competition is influenced by restraining rules of instinct and proportion, but the creative human being can be a more cunning competitor. By the time children become teenagers, they have experienced a prolonged exposure to evolutionist thinking and the implications of the survivalist point of view in course after course in science, social studies, sociology, anthropology and the humanities. They begin to see themselves and other human beings as animals rather than as creations of a caring Creator.

The finished adult emerges as a fierce competitor, covetous and materialistic; ready to use others as means to ends; ready to overkill, to overcompete. Thus the sin nature of human beings—the natural tendency toward acquisitiveness and selfishness—is encouraged by evolutionary thinking. In the same manner that evolutionary philosophy gave Hitler and Stalin and those who have followed after them *excuses* for their system, so the idea that human beings are improved animals gives materialistic persons an *excuse for excess*.

Does it make a difference with regard to social result if people believe the biblical account of the origin of human beings rather than megaevolution? If it makes a difference, then those believing creation ought to behave differently. It is true that no one human being has ever carried out the letter of the Scripture, but changes do occur in the person who deliberately seeks to live according to the Bible.

Believing in creation requires, of course, belief in God, the Creator, and in the order of creation set forth in the Bible. (Recall the earlier discussion of theistic evolution.) In accordance with the creation point of view there is no substance to the concept of the fittest. All persons are human beings, whatever the color of skin, height, or other physical difference. There is no one valid criterion for selection for survival of one human being over another in a physical sense. I agree that God chose a man, Abraham, and a nation, Israel, to accomplish His special purpose, but there are two vital differences between those selections by God and selections between human beings attempted by other human beings.

First, the selector with regard to Abraham was the Creator and therefore a perfect selector by definition. Second, Abraham was not chosen for his particular mission because he was more fit in some natural way than other men. One searches in vain for any evidence that Abraham was physically superior to any of his contemporaries. In fact, one could suggest that God's point in choosing Abraham was to demonstrate that *any* human being, however fit or unfit, may accomplish a great deal by following the will of God. By studying the life of Abraham and the history of Isreal one can conclude that each prospered or failed according to how God was followed, but not through any human superiority or through any special human effort.

Since human beings have *not* evolved into anything superior since creation, there is no point to the struggle over survival of the fittest. Everyone survives according to God's plan for each individual.

According to the creation point of view, human beings were given dominion over a created world. From this comes an emphasis for respect for all fellow human beings regardless of skin color or other physical characteristics; and also a respect for the natural environment as well, since human beings are the caretakers of the world. Pollution, overutilization of natural resources and overpopulation, which usually causes famine, are all serious concerns to those human beings who see themselves as entrusted with dominion over the world, over their natural environment, which today extends way out into space.

According to evolutionary thinking, the excesses of human beings and the ruination of natural resources are real phenomenological expressions of the animal inclinations of human beings. These are the excuses for human behavior offered by Lorenz, Ardrey, Morris—Social Darwinists of the twentieth century (as followers of nineteenth century Social Darwinists)—and ethologists and sociobiologists like E. O. Wilson. Yet according to the creationist point of view these matters become serious moral concerns.

When human beings have taken God's view of themselves and others, then love and trust are characteristic of their activities. Schools, hospitals and beneficent governmental relationships have been recognizable outcomes in all areas on this earth—in Europe, in the Americas, in Africa and in Asia. Selection of human beings with accompanying inequities have been unthinkable by teachers, preachers, doctors, lawyers and politicians who have been working and living according to the biblical positions, which are basic to the creation point of view. Persecution of any human being has been repugnant to those imbued with the respect for individuals and freedom inherent in created human beings.

The creation point of view entails a future since God's Word accounts not only for the beginning of all things but also the ending as well. When the future is very hazy to anyone trying to apply evolutionary thinking (What kind of organisms can be predicted when no change of kind into kind is part of reality?), the creation point of view leads to quite explicit ideas about the future. The current extremely materialistic and totalitarian way of life seems but a prelude to the end times told of by ancient Hebrew prophets and the author of the Book of Revelation.

Trusting in the total view of creationist thinking, which includes the salvation of believing men and women can make a real difference. According to the Scriptures, those persons believing in God, obtaining their salvation through the sacrifice of Jesus Christ, have eternal life. Men differ on the timing and fulfillment of prophecy, but the promise of eternal life to believers is most clear in the Scriptures.

Death has a big impact on the evolutionist. At death his sojourn on the earth comes to an end. The pointlessness of accidental life followed inevitably by death becomes confounding to the materialistic evolutionist. The individual spark of life is snuffed out, with no reason whatsoever announced for having existed, and no reason given for the demise of the meaningless life.

However the believer in God, the Creator, and His Son and co-Creator Jesus Christ, continues. The Creator remembers, as He remembered Noah and his family. Just as surely as each believer was created for a purpose, so each believer is appointed to go on with his Creator eternally. Those human beings who are not believers thus never come to the hope for reunion with their Creator.

Obviously the outlook of eternal life is not included in evolutionary thinking. Thus the concept of eternal life is surely the greatest difference between the evolutionist point of view and the creationist point of view; and the concept of eternal life surely has the greatest impact on the individual. Human beings can and do live differently when each believes that what he does will have an everlasting impact upon others.

FOOTNOTES

[1] These terms are fully developed and discussed by Dr. G. Owen, *Scientism, Man, and Religion* (Philadelphia: The Westminster Press, 1952). See also A. H. Hobbs, *Social Problems and Scientism* (Harrisburg, PA: The Stockade Company, 1953).

[2] These concluding pages represent a paraphrasing of material found in Zola Levitt, *Creation: A Scientist's Choice* (Wheaton, IL: Victor Books, 1976; San Diego: Creation-Life Publishers, 1981, pp. 8-15). In that book the author describes how I helped him, a practicing Hebrew Christian, escape from his self-imposed position as a "closet evolutionist."

[3] John S. Haller, Jr., *Outcasts from Evolution,* Scientific Attitudes of Racial Inferiority, 1859-1900 (Urbana: University of Illinois Press, 1971). See also William Stanton, *The Leopard's Spots,* Scientific Attitudes Toward Race in America 1815-59, (Chicago: The University of Chicago Press, 1960); George W. Stocking, Jr., *Race, Culture, and Evolution* (N.Y. The Free Press, 1968); and Winthrop D. Jordan, *White Over Black* (Chapel Hill: The University of North Carolina Press. 1968).

Chapter 6

General Discussion Questions

1. Define: "modern science", "scientism", "universal dogma", and review all terms defined in the Glossary.
2. What are some of the consequences of the adoption of "scientism" by many modern intellectuals?
3. What has been the possible impact of "natural selection" in the twentieth century history of nations?
4. Which questions did the author of this book really have to face before clarifying his position with Jesus Christ?
5. What difference does it make if a person believes he or she is an evolved animal or a specially created being?
6. In what manner has evolutionary thought been used to give sanction to the concept of "inferiority" among human beings?
7. What is the *real* difference between the evolutionist viewpoint and the creationist viewpoint?

Class Projects or Individual Assignments

1. List as many names as possible of scientists of any century who have been either theists or Christian theists.
2. Prepare a large chart to represent Total Christotheism.
3. Prepare a large chart to represent Total Evolutionism.
4. Examine the Appendices for suitable material for large classroom charts.
5. Work out a set of answers for the "final examination" provided at the close of this chapter. Now prepare a similar composite examination for all the origin questions discussed in this book.

Read: Mortimer Adler, *The Difference of Man and the Difference It Makes.* 1967. New York: Holt, Rinehart and Winston.

G. Marian Kinget, *On Being Human.* 1975. New York: Harcourt Brace Jovanovich.

Terrence Des Pres, *The Survivor* (An Anatomy of Life in the Death Camps). 1976. New York: Oxford University Press.

Walter E. Lammerts, Editor, *Why Not Creation?* 1970. Nutley, N.J.: Presbyterian & Reformed Publishing Co.

Zola Levitt, *Creation: A Scientist's Choice.* 1976, 1981. San Diego: Creation-Life Publishers.

C. S. Lewis, *The Abolition of Man.* 1947, 1965. New York: Macmillan.

Norman Macbeth, *Darwin Retried: An Appeal to Reason.* 1971, 1979. Boston: Gambit Incorporated.

Henry M. Morris, "Introducing Scientific Creationism into the Public Schools" (Pamphlet). 1975. San Diego: Institute for Creation Research.

On the Use of Scripture in Parochial Schools

1. Have students prepare handwritten copies of the following "beware" verses: Matt. 7:15, Matt. 24:11, Mark 13:5, I Cor. 15:33, Eph. 4:14, Eph. 5:6 plus Psa. 118:8 and Isa. 55:8, 9. Consider possible relationship of each verse content to the evolution/creation confrontation.

2. Different groups of students might be asked to read and discuss Genesis 1 (Group A), John 1-3 (Group B), and Colossians 1:15-17 (Group C) in order to consider the question: How does each particular passage relate to first origin questions? Then ask a leader or recorder to summarize the discussion of each group.

3. Some Christians maintain that the "thesis" of evolution can be combined with the "antithesis" of creation to formulate the "synthesis" of theistic evolution. Ask students to search the Bible for verses with concepts such as "you are with me or against me" or "set your hand to the plow and don't look back". Discuss relationship of these to the previous "synthesis".

4. Help students know how to witness to those who believe megaevolution.

5. Teachers might recall "out loud" whether the teaching of evolution that they experienced strengthened their belief in the Biblical record, or were they confused in their beliefs.

FINAL EXAMINATION

Presented here are 55 final examination questions for evolution/creation confrontation teaching approach. Acceptable answers are shown in parentheses at the end of each item (occasionally more than one answer is acceptable).

Consider the KEY for items 1 through 5 in such a manner as to show how you realize that each item is evidence that would be used by a proponent of the evolution model. Use each key item only once.

KEY: 1. Improvement of living things results from natural selection.
  2. Changes in the physical environment results in living form changes.
  3. Populations can diverge to degree of forming new subpopulations.
  4. Comparative anatomy is a basis for evolutionary thinking.
  5. Long time has passed through which living forms have changed.

1. Homologies of skeletons among a wide variety of living and extinct animals. (4)
2. Different clocks based upon different assumptions and involving different sources of error can be used to gain convergent data. (5)
3. Phenotypes are a compromise resulting from conflicting selection pressures operative in ecological niches. (1) (possibly 3)
4. Reasoned reconstruction of the Grand Canyon was basic to conclusions that ecological niches have changed and selection pressures have been altered. (2)
5. Examination of natural selection experiments in the laboratory and in complex interactions of animals and plants in the natural environment. (3) (possibly 1)

Consider the KEY for items 6 through 10 in such a manner as to show how you realize that each item is evidence that would be used by a proponent of the creation model. Use each key item only once.

KEY: 1. The Ultimate Cause of all patterns and order is the Creator.
2. All basic kinds of living things were created and lived contemporaneously.
3. Human beings did not have an animal origin.
4. Kinds of animals and plants are basically fixed and separate.
5. The universe, and hence, the earth and all things are relatively young.

6. Some circumstantial evidence has been found that dinosaurs and human beings may have made tracks in the same sedimentary material. (2)
7. The entire geological column does not exist and radiometric dating methods yield only estimates of time, and hence, there is no scientifically compelling reason to accept billions of years proposed by evolutionists. (5)
8. There are no known genetically determined transitional forms between kinds and "living fossils" represent evidence of significant continuity of certain kinds. (4)
9. Reconstructions of prehistoric men have really been the result of preconceived ideas as evidenced in the changing classifications and interpretations of Neanderthal. (3)
10. Because of the basic assumption of cause and effect all evidence of regularity must be due to a Coder or Planner. (1)

For items 11 through 15 select from the KEY the entry that is most closely associated with the material in each item. A key item may be used more than once.

KEY: 1. Use of scientific data to support the creation model.
2. Use of scientific data to support the evolution model.
3. Use of scientific data to support either model.
4. Use of scientific data that supports neither model.

11. Imagined broad change such that differences are due to recombinations of genes and accumulation of beneficial mutations. (2)
12. No real connection between kinds of embryos as similarities are due to common plan of organization of parts. (1)

13. Supposed common gene pool of similar genes results in classificatory groups of organisms from common ancestry. (2)
14. Presumably successive layers contain evidence of succession of life forms as "actual history" of related organism groups. (2)
15. No connection between kinds is evidenced by the limited changes within known kinds of organisms of the present and of the past. (1)
16. Which of the following can reasonably be included in the heading of total evolutionism? (5)
    1. Stellar evolution and molecular evolution
    2. Molecular evolution and organic evolution
    3. Organic evolution and societal evolution
    4. Only 1 and 2 listed here
    5. Actually all included in 1, 2 and 3 above
17. Which of the following would a creationist lecturer find acceptable? (5)
    1. Presentation of creation ideas about origins is the teaching of religion.
    2. Teaching about evolutionary origins of life and human beings is the presentation of precise, contemporary scientific theory.
    3. Presentation of creation ideas about origins is a study of beliefs of people.
    4. Teaching about evolutionary ideas of origins is a presentation of a "historical" argument.
    5. Actually 3 and 4 as stated above
18. As you might discuss the creation/evolution controversy with another person you could mention which of the following anomalies cited by creationists as "out of order" aspects of evidences now known. (4 or 5)
    1. Presence of spores (special reproductive units) of complex plant forms in the Cambrian, one of the lowest layers of the geological column used by evolutionary geologists.
    2. Lists of living fossils as organisms that were once thought to have been extinct but are now known to be represented by living specimens.
    3. Polystrate tree trunks that extend across multiple layers of rock strata.
    4. Only 1 and 2 as stated above
    5. Only 1 and 3 as stated above

For items 19 through 24 select from the key the entry that could be used most closely to illustrate to another person how some Darwinian ideas have been used in major disciplines in human knowledge even though supportive evidence for evolution has always been circumstantial.

KEY: 1. Sociology and social studies
2. American history and political science
3. Education and psychology
4. Anthropology (cultural)

19. Excuse of sweat shops and child labor practices during an early period of industrialization. (1)
20. Assertion that skeletal remains of Neanderthal and other forms were ancestors of present living human beings. (1 or 4)
21. Argumentation that the Constitution of the United States of America was passed as a consequence of class warfare during the colonial times. (2)
22. Acceptance of the human child as the product of evolutionary change. (3)
23. Acceptance of the concept of inheritance of acquired characteristics as useful in explanations of human personality. (3)
24. Presentation of the argument for development of an improved human society through the interplay of classes, even political forces, as centers of power. (2)
25. At this point you should be able to list a number of convergent evidences that evolutionists use to support their position, such as similarities of (5)
1. embryos.
2. skeletal structures.
3. dating estimates from different methods.
4. 1 and 2 here plus amino acid components of proteins.
5. All of the above plus animal and human behavior patterns.
26. Of course you also should be ready to recognize that a creationist would respond to convergence listed in the previous item, as (5)
1. erroneous overstatement of facts.
2. possibly the result of use of common design template by the Creator.
3. conclusions based upon adoption of similar assumptions.
4. 1 and 2 above.
5. 1, 2 and 3 above.

27. The creationist proponent at this point in the end of the term would logically take which one of the following positions? The evolutionist spokesman has (4)
    1. concentrated upon attention to aspects of vertebrates.
    2. repeatedly presented his position as an argument, a picture, a story.
    3. apparently assumed that if his ideas about vertebrates are acceptable, then his ideas about megaevolution (amoeba to man) change also are supported.
    4. all of the above.
    5. only 1 and 2 as given above.

28. Typically, explanations offered by evolutionists involve a basic assumption (the degree of relationship depends upon the amount of similarity), as in the (5)
    1. study of vertebrate embryos.
    2. study of vertebrate hearts and kidneys.
    3. study of the skeletal pictures.
    4. 1 and 2 above.
    5. 1, 2, and 3 above.

29. Creationist scientists commonly argue in support of a world wide flood by referring to which of the following as primary evidence? (5)
    1. Worldwide distribution of flood traditions.
    2. Worldwide occurence of water laid sediments and sedimentary rocks.
    3. Comparatively recent uplifts of major mountain ranges and marine fossils on mountain crests.
    4. Evidence of worldwide climate.
    5. All of the above.

30. Evidence for the deductive nature of the reasoning of Charles Darwin as he developed his ideas of evolution by means of natural selection is found in the fact that he formulated which of the following? (5)
    1. Postulated that populations possess the potential to increase at geometric rate, but also that the size of populations remains more or less constant.
    2. He concluded that members of a population engage in a struggle for existence.
    3. Observed that members of a population are not identical due to inheritable variations, and so concluded that the best adapted variants are naturally selected.

4. Postulated that the time available for evolutionary change is the immensity of geological time, and concluded that natural selection produces naturally improved forms.
5. All of the above.

31. Now you should be able to engage in conversation on specific points concerning the creation/evolution controversy. Opponents to whatever position you take in the controversy might employ which of the following fallacies of reasoning and argument? (5)
    1. Assumption that whatever discredits a person (some personal shortcoming) also discredits his evidence or his position.
    2. Supposition that one position wins by default when the other position cannot be established.
    3. Appeal to popular sentiments; that is, stating that if the majority holds a position then that position is true.
    4. Begging the question by assuming the very point to be proved as proof for that point.
    5. All of the above, plus use of humor as a diversion or as a substitute for evidence.

32. When discussing the creation/evolution controversy contradictions between facts and theory are sometimes treated in which of the following ways? (5)
    1. The contradiction is ignored.
    2. The person responsible for the contradiction is declared a poor researcher.
    3. Some small part of an existing theory may be modified after much testing.
    4. More than one theoretical formulation may be considered tenable for a time.
    5. All of the above plus, finally, one theory may completely replace another.

33. A creationist would use which of the following to support his position? (5)
    1. Evidences of order and pattern and regularity in space, in life forms, and in the human body are basic to recognition of actions by a Planner, Creator.

2. Agreement with the law of biogenesis (that life comes only from life) of all known facts about appearance of plant and animal life.

3. Identification of gaps of major proportions in the fossil record and gaps in the animal and plant breeding records such that discrete, separate kinds exist.

4. Agreement with the laws of thermodynamics in conservational processes and mainly detrimental, undesirable changes due to gene changes (mutations).

5. All of the above.

34. In turn, an evolutionist would use which of the following to support his position? (5)

1. Similarities of earth changing processes today to those active in the past, such as continental drifting.

2. Similarities of comparative anatomical features such as bones, proteins, embryos, brains.

3. Convergence of estimates of ages through use of different methods.

4. Acceptance of these different aspects by a majority of scientists.

5. All of the above.

35. Evolutionists justify the use of chemical and physical clocks on the basis that (3)

1. estimates arrived at by various methods converge.

2. uniformitarianist isolation of marsupials by continental drift.

3. interlab agreement on the same sample is good.

4. 1 and 2 above.

5. all of the first three.

36. The fact that Australia had only native marsupial mammals is explained by evolutionists as resulting from (2)

1. a climate too severe for placental mammals.

2. geographic isolation of marsupials by continental drift.

3. the migration of marsupials to Australia during the last Ice Age.

4. 1 and 2 above.

5. 2 and 3 above.

37. Why do evolutionists reject the interpretation of polystrate tree fossils as indicative of the flood of Noah? (2)
    1. All evolutionists are agnostics or atheists and do not believe in God.
    2. These fossils have been interpreted by evolutionists as indicating local floods which occurred at different geological periods.
    3. Evolutionists suppress evidence which does not fit their theory.
    4. Creationists are the only people who have seen these polystrate fossils.
    5. Evolutionists account for the fossils by saying that reconstructions of the past must be in error because there was no human present to leave a written account.

38. Consider Mayr's statement that ''the phenotype is a compromise.'' One deduction would be that the forelimb which is *least* specialized would be adapted to the *greatest variety* of tasks. Which of the following forelimbs best meets this criterion? (5)
    1. bird wing
    2. whale flipper
    3. Allosaurus forelimb
    4. frog foot
    5. human hand

39. Creationists criticize evolutionist models of natural selection because (4)
    1. a human experimenter intervened to start the experiment.
    2. natural selection to a creationist means only ''natural survival.''
    3. creationists can demonstrate that evolutionist models are wrong.
    4. 1 and 2 above.
    5. 2 and 3 above.

40. Evolutionists reply to the creationist criticisms in the previous question by saying that (5)
    1. predictions made from the natural selection models have been correct.
    2. the basic assumption of the evolutionist is that the same set of physical and chemical laws are at work in the laboratory and in the natural ecosystems.
    3. natural selection is a term which includes differential survival and differential reproduction due to all factors in an ecological niche.

4. 1 and 2 above.
5. 1, 2 and 3 above.

41. Evolutionists study changes in gene pools as a measure of micro-evolution because (4)
    1. evolutionists study species on a gene-by-gene basis.
    2. fixity of gene pools is the essential indicator of evolution.
    3. a change in gene frequencies may be apparent before a change in phenotype frequencies.
    4. 1 and 3 above.
    5. all of the first three.

42. The search for life on Mars is based upon the evolutionist assumption(s) that (5)
    1. the same laws of chemistry and physics that may have given rise to life on earth could also have done so on Mars.
    2. studies of the formation of proteins during laboratory experiments can give us clues as to how these events could have taken place on earth 4.5 billion years ago.
    3. if life exists on Mars, it probably would be entirely different than life as it exists anywhere on earth.
    4. 2 and 3 above.
    5. 1 and 2 above.

43. In fish, gills develop from gill slits during embryological development. In mammals, structures of similar appearance develop at the same point, but do not perforate (break through); instead structures other that gills develop. What possible interpretations can be made? (4)
    1. The Great Designer used a common design for both fish and mammals up to this point in their embryological development.
    2. Mammalian ancestors were related to ancestors of modern fish; this common ancestry is reflected in the similarities of embryos up to the stage specified.
    3. The observations are complete coincidences which cannot be explained by evolutionists or creationists.
    4. 1 and 2 above.
    5. all of the first three.

44. Reptiles have a mesonephros (mid-kidney) whereas mammals have a metanephros (third kidney). What possible interpretations can be made? (4)
    1. The Grand Designer used a different design for reptiles than for mammals.
    2. As embryos mammals develop a mesonephros and thus show reptilian ancestry.
    3. The two kinds of kidneys cannot be fitted into either evolutionist or creationist theory.
    4. 1 and 2 above.
    5. 2 and 3 above.

45. Different groups of animals have hearts of different degrees of complexity. What possible interpretations of these data can be made? (5)
    1. The Grand Designer used different hearts in different groups of animals.
    2. The differing complexity of hearts exactly parallels the sequence postulated by evolutionists for the evolution of animals.
    3. The creationist can show that the kinds of hearts found in various animal groups tend to contradict the evolutionist sequence.
    4. 1 and 3 above.
    5. 1 and 2 above.

46. If a series of hominid skulls were arranged in an order such that the teeth went from *small* to *large*, then (2)
    1. the associated tools would range in the same order from pebble tools to arrowheads.
    2. the first skulls in this series would have associated indications of fire, while the latter ones would not.
    3. the first skulls in this series would have the earlier ^{40}K-^{40}Ar dates, while the latter skulls would have the most recent dates.
    4. 1 and 3 above.
    5. 2 and 3 above.

47. With respect to the previous question, at what geographic location would the skulls be found? (3)
    1. All skulls would be found at sites around the world.
    2. The first ones would be found in Africa only, while the latter ones would be found in Asia and America as well.

3. The first ones would be found in Europe and North America, while the last ones would be found only in South Africa and East Africa.
4. 2 and 3 above.
5. None of the above.

48. With respect to the two previous questions, what can you say about the brain size of these hominids? (1)
   1. The first ones in this series would be skulls with the largest cerebral capacity, while the latter ones would be those with the smallest.
   2. There would be no relationship between brain size and the order in which the skulls are placed.
   3. The larger the size of the teeth, the larger the size of the brains.
   4. 2 and 3 above.
   5. 1 and 3 above.

49. You could expect a creationist scientist to evaluate the activities of Washoe and Lana as (5)
   1. examples of organisms responding essentially to signs and signals.
   2. demonstrations of the use of conditioned reflexes and imitation to establish a pattern.
   3. examples of preliminary behavioral patterns employed by ancestors of human beings.
   4. all of the above.
   5. 1 and 2 as stated above plus insistence that no real use of symbols or full conceptual thought were demonstrated.

50. The very concrete and specific language patterns used by chimpanzees such as Washoe (in American Sign Language) and Lana (in Yerkish) (2)
   1. are wholly unrelated to human language patterns, according to the creationist.
   2. are very similar to language patterns of young children, according to psychologists.
   3. indicate that chimpanzees are fully human.
   4. 1 and 2 above.
   5. All of the first three.

51. Based upon the theory of evolution, which of the following pairs would have a common ancestor that would have lived closest to the present? (2)
    1. butterflies and buttercups
    2. baboons and chimps
    3. fish and flies
    4. toads and frogs
    5. sponges and starfish

52. With respect to the previous question, which of the pairs would have a common ancestor that would have lived the farthest back in time (the longest ago)? (1)
    1. butterflies and buttercups
    2. baboons and chimps
    3. fish and flies
    4. toads and frogs
    5. sponges and starfish

53. Which of the following methods could be involved in an attempt by an evolutionist to control the course of changes in the human species? (5)
    1. attempts to remove harmful genes from the human gene pool
    2. attempts to select for genes held to be desirable
    3. attempts to make genetic copies of persons held to be superior
    4. 1 and 2 above
    5. All of the first three.

For items 54 and 55 consider the following paragraph:

A paper by R. L. Dennis in *Science*, (April 2, 1976, p. 66) reports the discovery of a Pennsylvanian (Carboniferous) fungus which has some of the features of modern Ascomycetes and some of the features of modern Basidiomycetes, two different major kinds of modern fungi. You are to assume that Dennis' description of the fossil plant is correct, both as to his observations and to his descriptions of similarities of each of the modern types of plants.

54. How would an evolutionist react to the Dennis paper? (2)
    1. He would be astonished that fungi appear in the rock record as
       early as the Carboniferous.
    2. He would argue that Dennis' fossil plant probably is—or is closely
       related to—the ancestor of both kinds of modern fungi.
    3. He would argue that Dennis' fossil plant probably resulted from
       a cross between Ascomycetes and Basidiomycetes which lived in the
       Carboniferous.
    4. He would increase his efforts to find both Ascomycetes and Basi-
       diomycetes in the Cambrian.
    5. He would concede that this fungus—having some features of two
       major modern fungi—overthrows much of evolutionary theory.

55. How would a creationist react to the Dennis paper? (2)
    1. He would argue that this fungus—having some features of two major
       kinds of modern fungi—overthrows much of evolutionary theory.
    2. He would say that the discovery of this plant does not significantly
       add to our view of creation one way or the other.
    3. He would argue that the ancestor of Ascomycetes and Basidiomy-
       cetes should have occurred much earlier in the Cambrian.
    4. He would concede that the discovery of this fungus overthrows the
       idea of fixity of kinds.
    5. He would argue that Dennis' plant probably resulted from a cross
       between Ascomycetes and Basidiomycetes which lived in the Carbon-
       iferous.

Appendix A

"EVOLUTION IN EVERYDAY LIFE" from Students' Projects

Following are unedited copies of material submitted by students to satisfy requirement of recording noted uses of evolutionary thinking in everyday events:

All through my primary schooling, I was taught the origin of man, the earth and the universe, by the concepts of the evolution model. In Junior and Senior High school, we were shown many films in science classes concerning the ideas of evolution (i.e., Darwin's Finches; Dr. Leakey's archaeological expeditions; and movies on the Galapagos Islands). At the time, these films were quite interesting and believable. But since I've been exposed to the two sided teaching techniques of some of my college professors, my ideas of evolution as a means of origin have discontinued. I feel that because of the one-sided teaching techniques of primary school systems, young people are being trained to think the way the majority of society thinks and little if any consideration is given to the beliefs of minorities.

One day in my social science class, my professor went into a lecture about why wars occur. Part of the lecture dealt with comparisons between apes and man. Also there was a section on how man had evolved and how his culture and habits had also evolved. My teacher went into great detail about how although we were direct descendents of the apes, man had developed certain characteristics that led to, among other things, war. He (the professor) made comparisons between the anatomy and brain sizes of man and ape. One of his statements went like this: "We have evolved . . . and we have basic instincts." He also in a way, seemed to contradict himself when he said that only man could pass on knowledge to succeeding generations.

I remember the professor "demonstrating" how primitive man walked with a stooped gait, his hands dragging on the ground. He also talked of social and cultural evolution.

At first I just was taking my regular notes, but all of a sudden it dawned on me that his lecture was very evolution oriented. I looked back into my notes and found the word evolution four times, plus various other references to evolution. It really showed me how at least this social science teacher was very evolution biased in his lecture.

Last week there was a special on television called "Primal Man". I
watched this show and I'm going to talk about how they used evolution.

The men on the show were supposed to represent Neanderthal man. These
men were portrayed as hairy creatures which were bent over.

Later in the show they represented Cro-Magnon man. These men were
not quite so hairy and stood up straighter. They also portrayed these men
as beginning to think. They began asking questions about the world in an
attempt to understand it. They said that through the mind the world becomes
suitable to human habitation.

The producers of the show brought in the aspect of survival of the fittest
and that men must adapt to society. This shows the evolutionary idea because
the good and the strong survive and carry on and the bad things disappear.
This is sort of the idea of Darwin's natural selection.

The producers also used evolution in saying that thinkers evolved from
nonthinkers. The early men created symbols with which he could communicate. Without worldwide symbols and when men were illiterate, problems arose because tribes could not communicate with other tribes.

I think that this thinking evolving from nonthinking is another form of
the unfolding society. These men weren't changing that much, they were
just developing what they already had. This is parallel to a child growing
into adolescence.

I am enrolled in Psychology 170. The class entails study of the basic
methodology and understandings of the psychology (defined in the text as
"the science of the behavior of organisms"). The book is entitled *Introduc-
tory Psychology*—a mastery coursebook with performance objectives and is
written by Walter M. Vernon of Illinois State University.

Throughout the text many references are made to evolution, even to the
point of basing some major beliefs on the truthfulness of the evolutionary
model.

On pages 71-77, there is a section entitled "*The Evolution of Behavioral
Tendencies*". This section includes comments like, "Man is a biological
organism with an evolutionary history . . . when one examines the patterning and similarities in both the behaviors and the structural characteristics
of the various living species, including man, one is inclined to accept an
evolutionary view as at least one of the causative factors in human behavior."
Although Vernon refers to the idea that evolution is not proven, he leads
the student to an acceptance of the model through his wording.

He makes assumption upon assumption throughout the text and passes them on as fact. "Evolutionary changes are very gradual." "Gradually, over thousands of years, with the process of natural selection favoring the larger, swifter animals, the species as a whole began to take on the form it has today." For a book which is supposed to be science, Mr. Vernon surely does not keep in line with the scientific way through use of the *facts*.

The text goes on and on: "The evolution of man has apparently favored individuals with larger brains." "The specialized functions of the (human) nervous system all evolved in terms of allowing the individual to respond to events rapidly and effectively in ways that maximize the chances for survival."

Indeed I could write twenty pages of examples from this text where evolution is an accepted *fact*. I am glad I've been taught the real picture so that I can more realistically study the psychological processes in man.

In contemplating my encounters with evolutionary ideas, it is hard to tell which encounter has been most influential to my way of thinking.

Perhaps, I became most aware of the evolutionary way of thinking through a series of specials produced by National Geographic featuring the famous evolutionist and archaeologist, Dr. Leakey. The productions expanded on his many treks to Africa in search of prehistoric human fossils. In considering the fossils that were unearthed, teeth, jaw bones, skulls, etc., I became most aware of the similarities as well as the differences of the cave man and modern man. I found that what evolutionists were saying was easy to believe, especially when considering similar bone structures of ancient and modern man.

The productions of National Geographic also included several proposed environments and their corresponding inhabitants. I found the evolutionary ideas of mutations arising to fit in, or to better adapt the human to his way of life to be easily acceptable, until this year.

I now find myself constantly questioning those same views, those views which I once held as fact, simply because they are just views and nothing more. I do not think the evolutionary ideas were forced on me here—I just was not offered an alternative—and I didn't need one—because everything I had learned in regard to evolution fitted into place. I had no reason to question it, until now.

Appendix B

ARGUMENTS AGAINST BIG BANG AND STEADY STATE THEORIES

1. The Big Bang Hypothesis is predicated on a Doppler shift interpretation of the red shift of light from galaxies. Moving galaxies can be interpreted in a variety of ways. There is no independent check of the Hubble law.
2. Rate of motion of galaxies is debatable.
3. Galaxies seem to be of different ages rather than of the same age as would be consistent with the idea of them coming from one explosion.
4. Expansion of material is contradictory to condensation of material to form galaxies and stars. Cosmic expansion makes condensation of matter very difficult if only gravitational attraction is considered.
5. Problem of nucleogenesis occurring for elements heavier than helium.
6. Formation of ordered arrangements seems contradictory to second law of thermodynamics that involves the concept that an unaltered system tends toward increasing disorder. How could all the gradients, differentiations, energy transforming processes and ordered bodies come about in a big bang without violation of the entropy law?
7. What caused the explosion of some cosmic egg?
8. Whether an atom of definite radius, or a cloud of infinite size, what caused propagation of some explosion throughout such original matter? Would the forces of attraction holding the matter together be greater than some explosive force?
9. How did the rotational motion of stars, galaxies and clusters of galaxies originate?

ARGUMENTS AGAINST THE STEADY STATE (or CONTINUOUS CREATION) HYPOTHESIS

1. What started supposed preestablished harmony of recession of nebulae into unobservability and the creation of isolated particles near at hand?

2. Every known process is not reversible, as nebulae expand but do not contract, gravitation is attraction and not repulsion, entropy of a closed system increases and does not decrease, every chemical process tends toward a state of equilibrium from which the substances involved do not depart if left undisturbed.

3. What is the source of new hydrogen atoms? Supposedly the formation of matter is not out of radiation but out of nothing, which is a violation of the first law of thermodynamics (that the total amount of energy and the total amount of matter in the universe is constant).

4. Any matter created in an already existing galaxy would result in increased mass of the galaxy, which is not known to occur.

5. The radio frequency radiation of 3°K coming to the earth from all directions cannot be explained by the steady state hypothesis.

6. Detected lack of homogeneity in the universe as evidenced from study of quasars (quasi-stellar radio objects) with regard to red-shifted spectral lines, calculated velocities and deduced distances, cannot be explained by the steady state hypothesis.

7. That the universe seems to be running down toward a state of maximum disorder and that the universe is finite in time as far as age is concerned are contradictory to the Steady State Hypothesis but consistent with the second law of thermodynamics.

—Modified from Harold S. Slusher, *The Origin of the Universe* (San Diego, Calif.: Institute for Creation Research, 1979).

Appendix C

ARGUMENTS FOR WORLDWIDE FLOOD

1. Worldwide distribution of flood traditions
2. Origin of civilization near Ararat-Babylon region in post flood time
3. Convergence of population growth statistics on date of flood
4. Dating of oldest living things at post flood time
5. Worldwide occurrence of water laid sediments and sedimentary rocks

6. Recent uplift of major mountain ranges
7. Marine fossils on crests of mountains
8. Evidence of former worldwide warm climate
9. Necessity of catastrophic burial and rapid lithification of fossil deposits
10. Recent origin of many datable geological processes

11. Worldwide distribution of all types of fossils
12. Uniform physical appearance of rocks from different ''ages''
13. Frequent mixing of fossils from different ''ages''
14. Near random deposition of formational sequences
15. Equivalence of total organic material in present world and fossil world

16. Wide distribution of recent volcanic rocks
17. Evidence of recent water bodies in present desert areas
18. Worldwide occurrence of raised shore lines and river terraces
19. Evidence of recent dramatic rise in sea level
20. Universal occurrence of rivers in valleys too large for the present stream

21. Sudden extinction of dinosaurs and other prehistoric animals
22. Rapid onset of glacial period
23. Existence of polystrate fossils
24. Preservation of tracks and other ephemeral markings throughout geologic column

25. Worldwide occurrence of sedimentary fossil graveyards in rocks of all "ages"

26. Absence of any physical evidence of chronologic boundary between rocks of successive "ages"

27. Occurrence of all rock types (shale, limestone, granite, etc.) in all "ages"

28. Parallel of supposed evolutionary sequence through different "ages" with modern ecological zonation in the one present age

29. Lack of correlation of most radiometric "ages" with assumed paleontologic "ages"

30. Absence of meteorites in geologic column

31. Absence of hail imprints in geologic column, despite abundance of fossil ripple marks and raindrop imprints

32. Evidence of man's existence during earliest of geologic "ages" (i.e., human footprints in Cambrian, Carboniferous and Cretaceous formations)

—Modified from H. M. Morris

Appendix D

THE OBJECTIVE STUDY OF ORIGINS

During confrontations between evolutionists and creationists the latter are often challenged to present a clear and understandable representation of the creation model. Fig. 51 summarizes the evolution model and the creation model as discrete explanatory systems of thought regarding first origin questions: origin of the universe, origin of life on the earth and origin of humankind. This diagram shows the contrast between supposed integrative and generative changes according to the evolution (megaevolution) model and disintegrative and degenerative changes according to the creation model.

Fig. 51: CREATION AND EVOLUTION

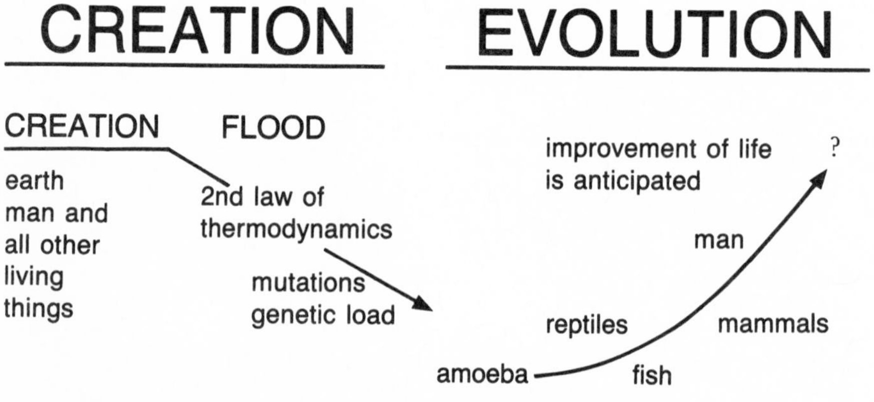

In the following two sections I have outlined what can be called the evolutionary uniformitarian model, and the scientific creationism and catastrophism model, with brief application of these models in the broad fields of physical sciences, earth sciences, life sciences and social sciences.

Outlines of Two Foundational Models of Origins

There are just two foundational viewpoints regarding first origins: the evolution (or evolutionary uniformitarianism) model, and the creation (or catastrophism and creationism) model. The first is a viewpoint or world-view generated by those with prior commitments to the philosophy of naturalism; the second is a viewpoint or world-view generated by those with prior commitments to the philosophy of theism.

In very brief and condensed form the primary points held by proponents of the two foundational viewpoints of models regarding first origins have been formulated in the two columns of the following chart.

Statements of Evolutionary Uniformitarianism Model of Origins	**Statements of Catastrophism and Creationism Model of Origins**
(based upon world-view of naturalism)	(based upon world-view of theism)

1. Matter has existed eternally (no cause).
  a. Matter continually appears (from energy?).
  b. Matter exploded and continues to expand.
	1. Universe was created essentially in present state. (Cause: eternal Creator)
	  a. Matter, plants, stars created complete.
	  b. Light rays created directly.

2. A whole series of elements was generated (evolved); and stars, planets have evolved by accretion.	2. Universe was created complete and basically stable.
3. Apparent land features resulted from specific causes of vulcanism, diastrophism, gradation (the present is the key to the past).	3. Causes seen in present were not causes of land features (the present is only the key to the present).
4. Forces of origination and integration exist.	4. Catastrophism, decay, and conservational activities prevail in antagonism.
5. Geologic column is evidence of vast "history" of the earth.	5. Only local sedimentary columns exist and world-wide destruction is evidenced by world-wide distribution of sedimentary rocks.
6. Because of innate propensity of matter, organic matter came from inorganic matter by spontaneous generation.	6. Since spontaneous generation of life is contradictory to Second Law of Thermodynamics, only special creation of life could be cause of life.

7. Changes in evolutionary sequence of life forms are due to random mutational changes in genes.

7. Mutations are evidence of increased disorder (entropy) and only changes *within* limits of kinds, group, or species result from mutations/recombination of genes.

8. Changes of complex forms or kinds from less complex kinds are the result of accumulation of random variations.

8. Conservative processes are involved in operation of genetic code resulting in essential stability (fixity) of basic kinds, groups, species, with no accumulation of random variations.

9. Mankind is related to the ape through an unknown common ancestor.

9. Mankind is a special creation.

10. Fossils of genus *Homo* are immediate ancestors of modern man.

10. "Ape-like" features of prehistoric man may be due to disease and degeneration.

11. Races of man resulted from mutations and segregation in early man-like forms.

11. Human beings all belong to one race and languages are merely tribal differences.

12. Evolutionary humanism can be a guiding faith.

12. Alienation, identity, and relevance can be answered in context of relation to Creator God.

Two Contrasting Explanations of Origins

Because primeval origins are completely beyond the limitations of scientific method, which involves observation, experimentation and repeatability, it will never be possible to say, a. "Scientists have proved that all things have evolved from a primeval common origin," or b. "Scientists have now proved the special creation of all things in the beginning."

Therefore the question as to which model of origins is ultimately the better explanation of origins can never be resolved scientifically, and one of the two models of ultimate origins must be accepted eventually on faith, not by any scientific proof or historic proof.

In the chart below, main features from certain scientific disciplines are related to the two possible models of origins:

Model of Evolutionary Uniformitarianism	Model of Scientific Creationism and Catastrophism

1. PHYSICAL SCIENCES:

Origin of Universe, Solar System (incl. elements, stars, galaxies)

a. Eternal existence of universe	a. Universe created essentially in present form
(1) Steady State Theory: continual appearance of matter with simultaneous decay of matter, resulting in constancy	(1) Light sources established
(2) Big-Bang Theory: explosively expanding from primeval state of extremely high density	(2) Light rays, with electromagnetic fields, created directly and light sources seen instantly
	(3) Whole universe created "full grown" and functioning perfectly with unique fitness of earth for life quite evident
b. Stellar and galactic evolution in some kind of evolutionary series	b. Essential stability of completed creation with concurrent principle of disintegration
c. Nucleogenesis of sub-nuclear and sub-atomic particles leading to ascending series of elements beginning with evolution of hydrogen	c. Creator was source of cosmic nucleosynthesis which He empowered

2. EARTH SCIENCES:

a. **Nature of Geologic Processes:**	a. **Nature of Geologic Processes:**
(1) Erosion, weathering, vulcanism, diastrophism, radioactive decay result in formation of land features of continental ice sheets, batholiths and lava plateaus, fault scarps and overthrusts, continental alluviation, multiple coal seams	(1) Present processes (in left col.) cannot be used to explain modern land features (given on right col.):

glacial processes ⟶ continental ice sheets

volcanic activity ⟶ batholiths and lava plateaus

earth movements ⟶ extensive fault scarps, overthrusts

modern rivers ⟶ continental alluviation, peneplanes, geosynclinal rocks

peat bogs ⟶ multiple coal seams

(2) Vast span of geologic "history" is assumed

(2) Catastrophism and processes of decay and of conservation of matter better fit data and methodologies of hydrology, petrology, mineralogy, geophysics, meteorology, sedimentology and geochemistry than so-called "historical" geology

b. Geologic column:
(1) Standard column erected by superposition of sedimentary rock formations containing animal and plant fossils, and divided into system of geologic ages
(2) Paleontological dates of fossils are then structured to agree with the same assumption of organic evolution

b. Geologic column:
(1) Since normally only a few thousand feet or a few miles of rock formations constitutes any local column, there is no such thing as a standard geologic column, and geologic ages never existed
(2) Because of world-wide distribution of sedimentary rocks (in various local orders and variety of physical and chemical composition) and many evidences of mass death in fossils, one great global catastrophe—followed by lesser regional catastrophes—can be used to explain actual sedimentary columns, involving rapid destruction and aqueous burial of living forms

3. LIFE SCIENCES:

a. Origin of Life:
(1) Spontaneous development of life from non-living chemicals

(2) Successful synthesis of living substance expected, but will be according to research plan and not blind chance

b. Nature of Biologic Change:
(1) Random changes in genes, called mutations, have resulted in a gigantic evolutionary sequence

a. Origin of Life:
(1) Spontaneous generation of life is contrary to Second Law of Thermodynamics
(2) Only special creation of life affords a "cause" for the beginning of life

b. Nature of Biologic Change:
(1) Extrapolation from trivial changes, due to gene recombinations and mutations *within* limits of kind, is not justified to explain supposed evolutionary changes *between* kinds.

(2) Accumulation of random variation due to recombinations and favorable mutations preserved by natural selection is the explanation of complex forms from less complex forms.

(2) Essential stability of basic kinds of living things is not altered by Mendelian variations, mutations, or hybridizations since genetic code is primarily a process of conservation.

(3) Mutations *exemplify* result in decrease in order with decrease in effectiveness in accordance with Second Law of Thermodynamics

4. SOCIAL SCIENCES:

a. Origin of Man:
  (1) Man is related to ape through unknown common ancestor.
  (2) Certain fossil remains are assigned to genus *Homo* as more immediate ancestors of modern man

a. Origin of Man:
  (1) Man is a separate creation from all other organisms.
  (2) "Ape-like" features of prehistoric men may have come from diseased or degenerate sources, or so-called ape-men may be from tribes, races, or varieties of men resulting from inbreeding and isolation.
  (3) No true transitional forms have been found between fossil apes and fossil men (who are being recognized more and more as human beings of genus *Homo*, rather than members of separate genera as some 30 years ago).

b. Races, Languages, and Behavior:
  (1) "Race" is solely a category of evolutionary biology.

  (2) Possibility is assumed that processes of mutation and segregation in early man-like forms led to establishment of different races

b. Races, Languages, and Behavior:
  (1) All present-day men are descendants of the first man and woman who came into existence through special creation.
  (2) "Racial" characteristics are merely characteristics of various nations and tribes and the only true race is the *human* race.

(3) No explanation is available for the origin of languages.

(3) Language was created with the first man and is merely a tribal characteristic as migration, conquests and in-breeding have occurred.

(4) The struggle for existence and survival of the fittest have caused evolution of man.

(4) Influences of evolutionary thinking have been pervasive and devastating as used by such as Nietzche, Hitler, Engels, and Marx. (See diagram of Impact of Modern Evolutionary Thought)

(5) Man is only part of a group.

(5) Man is not just an animal, nor is his social culture determined by processes of evolution.

(6) Evolutionary humanism can be the guiding faith as man tries to bring about a future utopian state through genetic engineering and social engineering.

(6) According to the real facts of human and cultural history, questions of alienation, identity and relevance can be answered in the context of man's relation to the God who created him.

—Based on Chapter I, "The Scientific Study of Origins" and Chapter III, "Creation and the Scientific Disciplines", (in) *Science and Creation* (A Handbook for Teachers) by Henry M. Morris, Ph.D.; William W. Boardman, Jr., Ph.D.; and Robert F. Koontz, Ph.D. 1971. Creation-Science Research Center, P.O. Box 23195, San Diego, CA 92123.

Appendix E

MODERN MAN AND APES COMPARED

Because evolutionists place such stress and emphasis upon the noteworthy similarities of skeletal patterns and bipedal gait between modern man and apes, I have found it very important in evolution/creation confrontation teaching to bring out significant differences. Such differences are evident from the following chart. Of course all fleshy aspects have not been fossilized; therefore, all reconstructions of so-called prehistoric forms are primarily deductions and are basically artist's conceptualizations.

A TABLE OF COMPARISONS

Modern Man	Apes
1. Large vaulted cranium	Flattened cranium
2. Mastoid process prominent	Mastoid process absent or inconspicuous
3. Dental arch parabolic	Dental arch U-shaped
4. Canines project little, if at all	Projecting canines
5. No diastema in upper jaw	Diastema present
6. No simian shelf	Simian shelf
*7. Lips prominent	Lips extremely thin
8. Vertebral column in 3 curves	Vertebral column in 2 curves
9. Short neural spines on cervical vertebrae	Long neural spines on cervical vertebrae
10. Relatively short arms	Relatively long arms
*11. Lower placed nipples	Higher placed nipples
*12. Female with prominent breasts	Female with flattened breasts
*13. Body relatively hairless	Body relatively hairy
*14. Body hair, when present, most prominent on ventral body surface	Body hair always present, most prominent on dorsal surface
15. No baculum (*os penis*)	Baculum present (*os penis*)
16. Deep, bowl-shaped pelvis	Shallow, flattened pelvis
*17. Bulging gluteus maximus (buttocks)	Flattened gluteus maximus

18.	Linea aspara present on femur	Linea aspara absent
19.	Feet different from hands	Feet similar to hands
20.	Vertebral column attached more or less at center of skull base	Vertebral column attached much toward dorsal portion of skull base

*Items so marked are fleshy aspects and not subject to fossilization. Of course, no record of behavior patterns nor physiology is available through study of the fossil material.

—Modified from W. H. Rusch, Sr.

Appendix F

HUMANS AND CHIMPANZEES COMPARED

Most commonly evolutionist thinkers hold that human behavior evolved from animal behavior. They are quite certain that human behavior is nothing but a refinement of animal behavior. In short, many evolutionists in psychology, ethology and sociology are quite confident that objective study of animal behavior is a *sufficient* grounds for understanding much of human behavior. A restricted number of evolutionists would even take the position that studies of animal behavior are a *necessary* basis for understanding human behavior. Of course such an outlook or point of view is quite consistent with the assumed animal origin of humankind proposed by megaevolutionists.

As a part of my confrontation approach I have prepared a terse summary of main points garnered from three chapters of *On Being Human* by Dr. G. Marion Kinget.[1] Key words are emphasized in italics, but the evolution/creation teacher should call particular attention to the numbered statements about signs and symbols, perceptual and conceptual thinking, methodological and ontological determinism, and empirical and experimental approaches.

Although the chimpanzee Washoe has been taught the American Sign Language, such an accomplishment is *primarily* an increase in an ability of the anthropoid to respond to direct presentation of *signs*. And, further, the learned capability of the chimpanzee Lana to utilize push buttons connected with a computer to ''converse'' with a human trainer depends fundamentally upon increased conditioned reflex response to *signs*.

After several exerpted portions from the Kinget book I have provided charts to bring out further details of contrast and differences between the language and speech facilities of human beings and that of chimpanzees.

CHARACTERISTICALLY HUMAN DIMENSIONS

1. Languages: propositional, organized according to rules
2. Toolmaking: manufacture of clothing, food; technology
3. Culture making: socially determined modes

4. Reflective awareness: to know that one knows
5. Ethical concern: sense of right and wrong
6. Esthetic urges: decorates self; makes scents, patterns of sounds
7. Historical awareness: as sense of time
8. Metaphysical concern: questions transcending visible or sensory

All specific, exclusive capacities of human beings are traceable to the symbolic activity: to know, to know that one knows, to reflect, to conclude

1. Symbolic capacity of human beings is an extraordinary capacity unmatched by any other species.
2. Reductionist social scientists have failed to distinguish between *perceptual* and *conceptual* thinking.
3. Reductionist social scientists have failed to distinguish between *methodological* and *ontological* determinism. (See Mortimer Adler, *The Difference of Man and the Difference It Makes* (New York: Holt, Rinehart and Winston, 1967.)
4. Reductionist social scientists have failed to distinguish between *empirical* and *experimental* approaches. (See David Bakan, "Psychology's Research Crisis", *The Michigan Psychologist*, 26: 20-33, 1967.)
5 Reductionist social scientists have failed to distinguish between *signs* and *symbols* with differential meaning, which are both terms for "signifiers".

THE REALM OF SIGNIFIERS

Signs and signals (operator symbols)	Symbols (designator symbols)
are *operators*: their significance is functional; they tell subject to *do* or *not to do* something	are designators: their significance is referential; they tell *what* or *how* a thing is
stand in a *one-to-one relationship* to the object represented	stand in a *one-to-many relationship* to object referred to; can stand for wide variety of things at different times and places
are *stimulus bound*; that is, tied to perception by the senses	are *independent* of the presence of *sensory stimulation*
are *time-bound*, confined within the present	*transcend time*, are conceptual in nature
are *subject oriented*	can be *object oriented*; that is, can be independent of subjective need or reference

CHAPTER 1   The Symbolic Animal[2]

A Qualitative or A Quantitative Difference?

Where the expert's unanimity about man's symbolic capacity breaks down is over the question of *the nature of the difference*: Is man simply excelling along the symbolic dimension, or is he the only organism to have specifically symbolic capacity? (p. 12) (emphasis in book)

The Key Issue: Symbols Versus Signs

See previous page of Characteristically Human Dimensions concerning "signifiers" for clear basis for differential meaning between SIGNS, SIGNALS, and SYMBOLS. (pp. 13, 15)

"Minimal Man" Versus Nonman

A clear understanding . . . of the difference between sign and symbol is, at the present time, the only empirically valid way to distinguish between specifically human behavior and certain forms of animal behavior that appear similar. (p. 16)

CHAPTER 2   Reflective Consciousness

Man owes his superior cognitive ability to two species-specific attributes: reflective awareness and conceptual thought. (p. 23)

Reflective Awareness

Reflection—the capacity of human consciousness for turning in upon itself—allows him not only to know but to know he knows; to emit and receive the same symbolic content; to re-flect it. (p. 23)

First-Person Statements

Reflective thought and the resulting self-concept enable man, and only man, to make first-person statements—a typical form of human expression. (p. 25)

How Do We Know That Animals Don't?

Granted, reflective awareness is clearly not a datum of external observation; it is part of the private world of the subject . . . Thus it is not only permissible to infer the operation of reflection and conceptual thought in man, but as William James, Henri Bergson, Mortimer Adler and others have made amply clear, it is *necessary* to do so in order to account for the kind of behavior man exhibits over a span of time. The existence of an

internal process *must* be inferred for most of man's initiatives to make sense.
. . . Conversely, in the case of subhuman animals, one *need not* infer reflective and conceptual thought because their behavior—which does not transcend the level of elementary associations elicited by an immediate
stimulus—does not call for nonobservable explanatory mechanism. (p. 26
emphasis in book)

Conceptual Thought

The purest and most complex manifestation of man's symbolic nature
is his capacity for conceptual thought, that is, for thought involving sus-
tained and high order abstraction and generalization. Conceptual thought
enables man to make himself independent of stimulus boundness that
characterizes animal thinking. Animals, especially primates, give undeniable
evidence of something *analogous* to human thought—*analogous* yet medical-
ly different in that their thought is bound to the immediate stimulus situation and to the felt impulse of the organism. (Emphasis added) Animal
thinking, too, is riveted to the realm of survival (broadly taken) and therefore
encompasses a variety of needs pertinent to the species as well as to the
individual. These differences account for the distinction between *conceptual* thought, which is the exclusive prerogative of man, and *perceptual*
thought, a cognitive function based directly upon sense perception, which
man shares with other animals. (pp. 23, 24, emphasis in book)

Do Animals Think?

Animals can think in several ways . . . though only on the perceptual,
not on the conceptual level. (p. 30) The key difference here is one between
conceptual and perceptual thinking. The latter, which is typical of animal
thinking, requires the actual or nearly immediate presence of the pertinent objects. Man's thinking, on the other hand, is independent of the
presence of pertinent objects. It is, in fact, independent of objects altogether,
as is the case with logical or mathematical exercises. Secondly, the difference
between human and animal thinking resides in the fact that, whether or
not the object of the mental operation is present, animals cannot make
judgments or engage in reasoning. For example, animals are unable to
conclude that such and such *is* or *is not* the case in a given situation or
that *if* such and such is the case, *then* so and so is not.

Conclusion

In conclusion, the key issue here again is not whether animals can think, but whether they can think *in the way that people do*. The answer is clearly no. To conclude otherwise, as behaviorists do, is to violate the principle of parsimony—the precise principle on which these psychologists are so insistent. (pp. 30, 31, emphasis in book)

HUMANS	CHIMPANZEES
1. Human vocal apparatus is suitable for the production of spoken words.	Chimpanzees' vocal apparatus is not suitable for the production of spoken words.
2. The auditory processes are primary for the reception of language, that language itself primarily being spoken words.	The visual processes are primary for communication, though responses can be learned for a limited number of spoken words.
3. Exposure to human speech, and interaction with it, will lead to speech as appropriate maturational points are reached.	Exposure to human speech, and interaction with it, will not lead to speech, and "maturational points" are not relevant.
4. Language is spontaneous where the conditions in 3 above are met, and it is primarily acquired rather than learned.	Language is not spontaneous and is not acquired. Any language learning is a very difficult and unnatural process.
5. Imitation is important, but is a secondary language factor.	Imitation is the primary factor where language expression is to be attempted.
6. No reward-reinforcement is necessary.	Reward-reinforcement is a necessity.
7. Humans can discuss their own language functions and practices.	There is no indication that chimpanzees have any interest in discussing human language.
8. Abstract concepts can be understood and discussed.	Abstract concepts cannot be understood or described.
9. Situations removed from the immediate present can be understood and discussed.	Situations removed from the immediate present cannot be understood or discussed.
10. Human speech has the potential to deal with past-present-future.	Chimpanzees learn associative patterns applicable only to the present.
11. Human speech is rule oriented, with words formed into sentences.	Chimpanzees using "word-signs" utilize an order only for reward-gaining.

12. Human language acquisition and word association does not involve problem solving techniques.

Chimpanzees learn word associations only by problem solving techniques.

13. It is natural for humans to acquire and learn linguistic skills over a period of time, mainly between the ages of one and five.

It is normal for chimpanzees to communicate, but their natural processes and skills are greatly restricted and are acquired in a much shorter period of time than is normally required for humans to acquire language skills.

14. Humans utilize their tongues in the formation of speech sounds.

Chimpanzees make little use of their tongues in the production of their normal sounds.

15. Humans can both receive and transmit vocal speech sounds.

To a limited degree chimpanzees can receive, but not transmit, speech sounds vocally.

16. Humans normally use their hands only to supplement vocal speech sounds.

Chimpanzees use their hands as the primary component of their manual diction.

17. Humans can make arbitrary decisions as to the different meanings of words having similar sounds (e.g., "one" and "won") according to the context.

Chimpanzees display no ability for such arbitrary distinctions.

18. Humans can create entirely new messages by fresh combinations of the same words: the order of words is not necessarily rigidly established.

Chimpanzees are limited to the learned constructions for which rewards were originally forthcoming.

19. Words can be changed in their external form, by abbreviation or by the addition of a suffix, and can still be understood as having the same basic meaning.

Words and the object they signify can be interchanged, but there is no indication that the words themselves would be understood in different forms without separate learning of the new forms.

20. Suprasegmental features such as pitch, stress, inflection, tone and juncture are interwoven with human language.

In the use of human word-signs, suprasegmental features are irrelevant to chimpanzees.

—After C. F. Hockett

Figure 52
HUMANS AND CHIMPANZEES COMPARED - C. Wilson

PROCESS	FOR HUMANS		FOR CHIMPANZEES	
	Primary	Secondary	Primary	Secondary
	(for Language Acquisition)	or nonexistent (for Language Learning)	(for Communication Development	or nonexistent
1. Manual Dexterity		X	X	
2. Imitation of Others		X	X	
3. Vocal Expression	X			X
4. Visual Functioning		X	X	
5. Auditory Rehearsal	X			X
6. Exposure to speech	X			X
7. Spontaneous Acquisition	X			X
8. Sequential Development	X			X
9. Immediacy of Application		X	X	
10. Information processing	X			X
11. Special Conditions Necessary		X	X	
12. Reward-Reinforcement Necessary		X	X	
13. One Unit At A Time		X	X	
14. Regression to Poor Diction		X	X	
15. Quantitative Restriction on Learning		X	X	
16. Labeling of Objects Natural	X			X
17. Vocabulary Usually Controlled Externally		X	X	
18. Creative Skill Demonstrated	X			X
19. Nouns Initially Predominate as Sentences	X			X
20. First Joining of Two Words	X			X
Extends 1 concept	X			X
21. Word Order Systematic	X			X
22. Morphological Principles Important	X			X
23. A Phonological System Utilized	X			X
24. Syntax is Rule Oriented	X			X
25. Universals World Wide	X			X
26. An Inherent Capacity for Speech/Language	X			X

FOOTNOTES

[1] G. Marian Kinget, *On Being Human* (N.Y.: Harcourt Brace Jovanovich, Inc., 1975).
[2] Excerpted and reprinted by permission of Harcourt Brace Jovanovich, Inc., from *On Being Human: A Systematic View* by G. Marian Kinget, Copyright 1975 by Harcourt Brace Jovanovich, Inc.

Appendix G

QUOTES BY EVOLUTIONISTS

Here is a sample of statements by evolutionists who are qualified to write in this area, showing that scientists *do* believe man evolved from apes or monkeys or both. When statements to the contrary are examined, it is found that the authors are saying that man has not evolved from any of the *living* apes. This is not an issue because as the outstanding evolutionist George Gaylord Simpson says, that man did not evolve from any living ape "is obvious to the verge of imbecility."

"On this subject, by the way, there has been too much pussyfooting. Apologists emphasize that man cannot be descendant of any living ape—a statement that is obvious to the verge of imbecility—and go on to state or imply that man is not really descended from an ape or monkey at all, but from an earlier common ancestor. In fact, that earlier ancestor would certainly be called an ape or monkey in popular speech by anyone who saw it. Since the terms *ape* and *monkey* are defined by popular usage, man's ancestors were apes or monkeys (or successively both). It is pusillanimous (cowardly) if not dishonest for an informed investigator to say otherwise." George Gaylord Simpson, formerly Professor of Paleontology, Harvard University, "The World Into Which Darwin Led Us," *Science*, 131:3405:966, April 1, 1960, p. 969, from his book *This View of Life* (Harcourt, Brace and World, printing of 1964), p. 12. Dr. Simpson is one of the most distinguished and highly respected American evolutionists.

"It is fashionable in some circles to refer slurringly to the inference that apes were ancestral to man, and to insinuate that it is more proper to say that men and apes, perhaps even men, apes, and monkeys, diverged long ago from a stem form that was more primitive than any of these. This is mere wishful thinking on the part of those who resent too vivid a visualization of their lowly origin and their presentday poor relations." H. J. Muller, Nobel Prize-winning geneticist of Indiana University. "Man's Place in Living Nature," *Scientific Monthly*, 84:5:245, May 1957, p. 250.

". . . perhaps the majority of anthropologists and comparative anatomists . . . believe that man has evolved from a true anthropoid ape at a relatively late geological date." William L. Straus Jr., famous anthropologist of the Johns Hopkins University, "The Riddle of Man's Ancestry," *Quarterly Review of Biology*, 23:3:200, Sept. 1949, p. 203.

"That man has been derived from a form which—without any strain on commonly recognized definitions—can be properly called an 'anthropoid ape' is a statement which no longer admits doubt." Wilfred Le Gros Clark, famous evolutionist of the University of Oxford, quoted by William Straus Jr., loc. cit., p. 208.

"The evolution of our ancestral Forest Apes took place in widely separated areas." Roy Chapman Andrews, noted paleontologist of the American Museum of Natural History, *Meet Your Ancestors* (Viking Press, 1956), p. 17.

". . . it was from the Old World, Eastern Hemisphere monkey stock that the early anthropoids arose, and from these, in turn, that the line which led to man came into being." M. F. Ashley Montagu, well-known anthropologist, formerly of Rutgers University, *The Science of Man* (Odessy Press, 1964), p.14.

"About a million years ago . . . the curtain rose on man . . . a creature with a small skull, a massive mandible, and trailing in many parts of his anatomy evidences of his recent emergence from the world of apes." Harry L. Shapiro, anthropologist of the American Museum of Natural History, *Man, Culture, and Society* (Oxford University Press, 1956), page 5.

"Man, it seems, could only have evolved from a tree-living mammal which came down from the trees. Tree life as a monkey gave him grasping hands able to manipulate objects, and binocular vision." Professor Julian Huxley, Lecturer at the University of London, famous biologist and grandson of Thomas Henry Huxley, chief disciple of Charles Darwin, and who called himself "Darwin's bulldog." *The Wonderful World of Life* (Garden City Books, 1958), p. 36.

"From everything we know, it seems that our remote ancestors were monkeys." Ralph Linton, anthropologist of the University of Pennsylvania, *The Tree of Culture* (Alfred A. Knopf, 1957), p. 4.

"For the student of human evolution the new finds make it possible to more clearly discern the evolutionary pathway traversing the past fourteen million years. . . . The pathway begins in Miocene times with an Old World population of apes . . ." Elwyn L. Simons, Professor of Geology, Yale University and Head of the Division of Vertebrate Paleontology at the Yale Peobody Museum, "Ramapithecus," *Scientific American*, 236:5:28, May, 1977, p. 28.

". . . fossil material of apes, ape-men, and men have been gathered from a wide variety of sources, and both the cumulative evidence and recent finds unequivocally support the theory of human origin from the higher apes." Jay M. Savage, Professor of Biology, the University of Southern California, *Evolution* (Holt, Rinehart, and Winston, Modern Biology Series, 1965), p. 110.

"Some of the descendants of the monkeys that had learned to walk upright went back to the forest, where they became the ancestors of the apes. Only those upright ones that stayed out in the open grew to be men." Carleton Coon, Harvard anthropologist, *The Story of Man* (Borzoi Books, 1954), p. 11.

"As Elliot Smith put it: 'The question of speech was, in fact, an essential part of the process of transforming an ape into a human being.' " Raymond Dart, discoverer of the Australopithecines, *Adventures With the Missing Link* (Harper and Brothers, 1959), p. 215.

"Once he was thought a fallen angel; then we found him to be an ascended ape . . . apes whose cultural remains at the beginning of the first glaciation can scarcely be distinguished from chance bits of stone has, by the end of the fourth ice age, become artist and world rover, penetrator of five continents, and master of all." Loren Eiseley of the University of Pennsylvania, famous writer on evolution, "The Time of Man," *Horizon*, 4:4:4, Mar. 1962, p. 4.

"From some such early ancestor as *Dryopithecus*, the primitive ape, appeared the earliest man . . ." Professor John S. Hensill of San Francisco State College, *The Biology of Man* (The Blakiston Co., 1954), p. 126.

"This paper will attempt to reconstruct the transition from ape to man . . ." Frank B. Livingstone of the University of Michigan, "Rediscovering Man's Pongid Ancestor," *American Anthropologist*, 64:2:301, Apr. 1962, p. 301.

"Either he diverged from the apes at a relatively late time and is a made over ape, or he split off from the primates much earlier at the evolutionary state represented by the tarsiers or lower monkeys." William Lee Stokes of the University of Utah, *Essentials of Earth History* (Prentice-Hall, 1960), p. 361.

"Man began when populations of apes . . . started the bipedal, tool-using way of life that gave rise to the man-apes of the genus *Australopithecus*." Sherwood L. Washburn, anthropologist of the University of California, "Tools and Human Evolution," *Scientific American*, 203:3:63, Sept. 1960, p. 68.

"By the next epoch, the Miocene, so many forms of extinct apes abound that it is impossible to tell which were directly ancestral to man and which were not." Mischa Titiev, Professor of Anthropology, University of Michigan, *The Science of Man*, Revised Edition (Holt, Rinehart, and Winston, 1963), p. 68.

Appendix H

THE YALE LAW JOURNAL

"Freedom of Religion and Science Instruction in Public Schools"
87 *Yale Law Journal* 515-70 (Jan. 1978)
by Wendell R. Bird

SUMMARY

This Note discusses the construction of the free exercise clause of the First Amendment, and scrutinizes the burdens and coercion against free religious exercise arising in public schools.

The author concludes that the free exercise protection is denied by presentation of only the general theory of evolution in public schools, because that undermines creationist beliefs, compels unconscionable affirmations, violates separatist practices, and hinders parental guidance of childrens' religious upbringing. The article argues that this unconstitutional situation can be remedied either by neutralization through adding instruction in scientific creationism or by elimination of exclusive instruction in the evolutionary theory.

TABLE OF CONTENTS

Appendix I

HARVARD JOURNAL OF
LAW AND PUBLIC POLICY

''Freedom from Establishment and Unneutrality in Public School
Instruction and Religious School Regulation''
1979 *Harvard Journal of Law & Public Policy* 125-205 (June 1979)
by Wendell R. Bird

SUMMARY
This article analyzes the meaning of the establishment clause of the First
Amendment of the Constitution.
The author concludes that the establishment clause permits public school
instruction in scientific creationism along with evolution and permits
legislative restrictions on government funded abortions. He demonstrates
that the establishment clause prohibits public school instruction in evolution alone without scientific creationism and prohibits intrusive regulation of religious schools.

TABLE OF CONTENTS

FURTHER INFORMATION

For copies of the Harvard Journal of Law & Public Policy article on the eatablishment clause, send $1.95 plus $.95 postage and handling to:
Wendell R. Bird, Harvard Journal of Law & P.P.; 200 Chandler Building, 127 Peachtree St., N.E.; Atlanta, GA 30303.

For copies of the Yale Law Journal article on free religious exercise, send $2.50 to:

Yale Law Journal, 401A Yale Station,
New Haven, Conn. 06520

For a scientific analysis of creation, order *Scientific Creationism* (Pub. Sch. Ed.) in paperback or hardback from:

Creation-Life Publishers, P.O. Box 15666,
San Diego, Cal. 92115

For suggestions for introducing scientific creationism into public schools, send a stamped and addressed envelope requesting Impact Series 69 and 70, or

For a resolution to give to school authorities to request balanced treatment of evolution and creation, send a stamped and addressed envelope requesting Impact Series 71 to:

Institute for Creation Research, 2716 Madison Ave.,
San Diego, Cal. 92116

Appendix J

METHODS OF DEALING WITH CONTRADICTIONS IN SCIENTIFIC STUDIES

The next page might be used during an evolution/creation confrontation session. It is drawn up as a multiple choice test item, with documentation supplied for each statement, which can be matched with one of the seven choices listed in the *key*. Students should notice that the seven entries in the *key* include representative methods for meeting contradictions between fact and theory as practiced by scientists. Actually the correct or expected answer for each statement, according to the directions, is the first choice in the *key*. Of course this is another way of stimulating discussion of the concept of fixity of kinds.

Most of the statements relate to plant materials, but statement number one involves manlike tracks and dinosaur tracks reported in the same sedimentary layer in the Paluxy River bed in Texas, southwest of the Dallas-Fort Worth complex. A significant addition to evolution/creation confrontation teaching would be screening of the documentary film, ''Footprints in Stone'', produced and distributed by Eden Films (N. Eden Road, Elmwood, IL 61529). The narrator considers implications of the possible contemporaniety of dinosaurs and human beings with regard to the evolution model and the creation model. Of course only circumstantial evidence is presented, but the topic is most provocative and much classroom discussion can be stimulated through use of the film. The same producers also have the film, ''The Great Dinosaur Mystery'', that contains a totally new perspective on how dinosaurs fit into the history of the human race.

During recent centuries scientists have used various methods for handling contradictions between fact and theory. For items 1 through 4, associate a specific method for meeting contradictions in scientific studies, as given in the *key* below, with each statement.

KEY: 1. Ignore contradictions
        2. Allow coexistence of theories
        3. Develop *ad hoc* hypotheses
        4. Change part of the theory
        5. Replacement of part or all of the theory
        6. Absorb one theory into another theory
        7. Claim contradictions due to error of observation
           (error of measurement)

1. Manlike tracks (Cenozoic) have been found reportedly in Texas in exactly the same type of stone or rock layers as tracks of three-toed dinosaurs (Mesozoic).

    (Roland T. Bird, "Thunder in His Footstep", *Natural History*, Vol. 43, May, 1939, pp. 255-261, 302.)

2. Spore of Angiosperms (flowering plants) and Gymnosperms (evergreens) have been found reportedly in four shale formations of the Grand Canyon, beginning with the Permian Supai on down to the pre-Cambrian Hakati.

    (Interim Research Report #3, "Preliminary Investigation of the microenvironment of the Chinle formation," Petrified Forest National Park, Arizona. Jack Roadifer, Joseph Schreiber, Jr., David Peabody, Gerhard Kremp, Terah L. Smiley. Geochronology Laboratories, University of Arizona. Other plates in Clifford Burdick, "Microflora of the Grand Canyon", *Creation Research Society* Annual, Vol. 3, May, 1966).

3. Remains of vascular plants have been found reportedly in Cambrian formations.

    (S. Leclercq, "Evidences of Vascular Plants in the Cambrian", *Evolution*, Vol. 10, June, 1956, pp. 109-113. See also Daniel Axelrod, "Evolution of the Psilophyte", *Evolution*, Vol. 13, pp. 264-275, 1959).

4. In spite of prevailing hypotheses of gradual deposition of sedimentary layers, many instances have been recorded of fossil remains of huge animals and petrified tree trunks which extend through several meters of sedimentary rock.

    (A. Geikie, Textbook of Geology (London: MacMillan, 4th ed., 1903): M. C. Grand-Eury, *Geologic of paleontologie du bassin houiller du Gard* (with atlas). (Saint-Etiennem Theolier, 1890): H. Kluse-mann and R. Tsichmuller, "Begrabene Walder im Ruhrkolen-becken", *Natur u. Volk*, 84: 373-382, 1954: H. Nilsson, *Synthetische Artbildung. Grundlinien einer exaten Biologie.* (Lund: Gleerups, 1953); R. R. Shrock, *Sequence in Layered Rocks.* (New York: McGraw-Hill, 1948): and I. M. van der Vlerk and Ph. H. Kuenen, *Geheimschrift der aarde.* (Zeist, de Haan, Arnhem, van Loghun Slaterus, 7th impr., 1962.)

GLOSSARY

Agnosticism: The point of view that an individual cannot know anything about spiritual existences or about future life.

Analogy: An expression or comparison of like or similar aspects of known objects, events, concepts and/or ideas.

Animism: The point of view that involves personification of all phenomena.

Anthropocentrism: The point of view regarding man as the central fact, or final aim, of the universe.

Anthropomorphism: The point of view attributing human shape or characteristics to gods, objects, or animals.

Assumption (Postulate): A statement of a concept taken for granted and not tested during particular scientific activity (explicated as basic assumptions, experimental assumptions, or theoretical assumptions).

Atheism: The point of view that involves denial of the existence of God and an account of existence of the universe without a self-existent and self-conscious God.

Basic Assumption: A statement taken for granted as an untestable given upon which scientific activities and intellectual discourse are based such as:
1. Objectivity of study is possible.
2. Objects and/or events exist independent of observers.
3. Cause and effect relationships exist that may be identified.
4. Scientific ideas are testable, i.e., falsifiable, or not.
5. There is uniformity in the natural environment.

Calculation: Some arithmetic and/or mathematical manipulation of abstract and numerical symbols.

Christian Theism: The point of view that the Eternal, triune personal God of the Bible created the universe and all therein, and can be known because He has revealed Himself to man, who was His special creation.

Christotheism: The point of view that the Creator of the universe and all that is therein was the Person of Christ Jesus.

Classification: The end result of ordering of objects and/or events according to stated criteria; the process of ordering objects and/or events according to stated criteria.

Cosmogony: A list of ideas or formulations centered on origination and generation of the universe. (Such conceptual patterns or models do not qualify as scientific theories since no prior observations or testable predictions about origins are possible.)

Cosmology: The study of the nature of the universe; use of tools and technology to describe aspects of the observable and physical universe.

Creationism: The point of view that all existing reality came into existence initially as the consequence of creative acts of the Supreme Being such that all aspects of the universe and life were completely functional.

Creation Model: An explanatory belief system based upon existence of an eternal Creator who established a completed, finished and functional universe in all aspects regarding elements, galaxies, stars, planets (especially the earth with mutually exclusive groups of animals and plants); ideas have to do with conservation of known conditions; yet, changes of decay and degeneration are evident and easily documented.

Communism: The point of view that the means of production and distribution are owned and controlled by the community, though in modern Communism advocates use a strategy of power by the proletariat to establish a transitional socialist state supposedly preliminary to gradual abolition of state control.

Darwinism: The point of view that all present variety of living things came from previously existing living things through survival of favored varieties as a result of natural selection.

Deism: The point of view that a personal transcendent God exists Who created the universe and all therein but does not intervene in ongoing existence or affairs of men.

Description: A statement about some object and/or event in space-time; the lowest (basic) level of scientific explanation.

Determinism: The point of view that involves universal application of causality such that no event is without a specific antecedent cause.

Empiricism: The point of view that valid ideas can be derived from observation and experimentation.

Environmentalism: The point of view that human behavior is mainly the consequence of the physical influences experienced by an individual.

Evolutionism: The point of view that all present variety of living things has come into existence through changes of previously existing living things; the concept has been extended back through time to include organic life coming from the inorganic and the whole universe coming from eternally existing matter; also applied to future changes of human society.

Evolution Model: An explanatory belief system based upon eternal existence of matter from which have come an ascending series of elements by nucleogenesis, changes by stellar evolution of young stars into old stars, galaxies, planets (especially the earth with life that appeared spontaneously through molecular evolution followed by organic evolution, including human evolution); ideas have to do with origination of order out of disorder and integration of more complex patterns out of less complex patterns.

Existentialism: The point of view that reality is defined by the mind and the responsibility for man's life is in man's hands with fullest hope being found in self-realization.

Experiment: A specifically designed use of equipment, tools of measurement and controlled variable components to gain observations and descriptions usually otherwise unobtainable.

Experimental Assumption: A statement about that aspect of experimentation (controlled or of trial and error category) that is taken for granted as noncritical and not measured in any way.

Explanation: A particular frame of reference used to provide meaning for particular facts.

Fabian Socialists: Members of the Fabian Society who worked for the rejection of capitalism and advocacy of socialism and reliance upon continual political pressures to accomplish their goals.

Fabian Society: An English socialist educational organization important in the development of English socialist and labor movements.

Fact: An object and/or event in space at some time.

Freudianism: The point of view that involves understanding human personality and mental disorders by the study of the unconscious and psychoanalysis with emphasis upon the role of sexuality in the origin of neuroses.

Generalization: A statement of common aspects of similar objects and/or events; an assertion that something is true about all members of a certain class of objects and/or events.

Geocentric (Geostatic): The point of view attributed primarily to Ptolemy that the earth is the center of the universe.

Heliocentric (Heliostatic): The point of view attributed primarily to Copernicus that the sun is the center of the Solar System.

Humanism: The point of view of placing faith in man rather than faith in God.

Hypothesis: A tentative answer to a problem; a hypothesis is most properly expressed as an assertive statement in form suitable for testing.

Logical Positivism: The point of view that the criterion of meaning is verification or falsification, that is, an empirical statement is significant or meaningful only if it is verifiable by direct experience.

Marxism: (or Scientific Socialism): The point of view of analysis of capitalist economy, historical materialism, the class struggle, and surplus value as the basis of modern socialist doctrine.

Materialism: The point of view through which all things are described in terms of matter in accordance with mechanical laws.

Model: A physical object designed to show analogical representation of some larger object and/or event; or a conceptual pattern involving listed statements about imaginary objects and/or events and supposed relationships, especially associated with concepts of origination and generation.

Modern Synthetic Theory: The point of view that all present variety of living things came into existence through Mendelian variation and natural selection and can be explained according to population genetics.

Mysticism: The point of view that knowledge can be obtained by revelation, often accompanied by intense emotional experiences which transcend time, space, and morality.

Naturalism: The point of view that God does not exist and eternal matter is all there is in a cosmos that is a closed system.

Neo-Darwinism: The point of view that all present variety of living things came into existence through variation according to Mendelian genetics plus natural selection of favored varieties.

New Consciousness: The point of view (a sort of mystical occult) that involves altered states of consciousness such that a transcendent God is denied and the self-conscious person is the prime reality.

Nihilism: The point of view (mainly an attitude or feeling) that involves the negation of everything: knowledge, values, and ethics such that there is no valid statement and nothing has meaning.

Observation: A written or spoken record as communication to self or another of an awareness (perception) of an object and/or event.

Postulate: A scientific assumption or statement based upon prior observations of relevant objects and/or events; and, in turn, are basis of predictions testable by experience, directly or indirectly.

Pragmatism: The point of view that only useful ideas are valid.

Prediction (Expectation): That expected or projected state of affairs or relationship of objects and/or events based upon known or understood conditions; often found in an if-then expression.

Problem: An interrogation or stated perplexity for which an answer is sought; a problem is most properly expressed in question form.

Rationalism: The point of view that there are some things man can know from reason alone.

Relativism: The point of view that ''correctness'' or ''rightness'' is dependent upon the situation, or that right or wrong must be judged by the circumstances.

Science: An interconnected series of concepts and conceptual schemes that have been developed as a result of experimentation and observation and are fruitful of further experimentation and observation; or the body of knowledge obtained by methods based upon the authority of observation. (Science is limited to the study of nature: that is, study of matter and energy, because of limiting principles of being empirical, quantitative, mechanical and correctable.)

Scientific Creationism: The point of view that existing proper scientific data gained from the study of natural objects and/or events can be used validly to support the creationist viewpoint on origin questions.

Scientific Law: A repeatedly tested and well supported or substantiated generalization of seemingly universal application regarding a certain set of facts; a level of scientific explanation between description and scientific theory.

Scientific Theory: A list of postulates or theoretical assumptions usually specifying existence, relationship and events concerning an imaginary entity (such as an atom, gene or molecule) whereby a meaningful system for a range of rather diverse facts is made available; the highest level of scientific explanation.

Scientism: The point of view that matter and energy are the only reality with stress upon the position that the only knowledge of any real value is that gained through methods of scientists.

Secular Humanism: The point of view that deifies man and denies the existence of a supernatural prayer-hearing God.

Secularism: The point of view that places emphasis upon the present life according to principles of ethics not dependent upon any religion.

Theism: The point of view that a Supreme Being created the universe, the earth and all life.

Theorem: A statement derived from assumptions of scientific theory more or less in the form of testable predictions or expectations.

Utilitarianism: The point of view that what is useful is good so that the ethical value of conduct is determined by the usefulness of results; or the achievement of the greatest happiness for the greatest number.

Utopianism: The point of view that an ideal human society is possible.

World View: A point of view that is essentially a set of assumptions (presuppositions) which an individual accepts (consciously or unconsciously) about the basic makeup of the world and all existence.

BASIC
ANNOTATED BIBLIOGRAPHY
OF CREATIONIST BOOKS

Barnes, Thomas G., *Origin and Destiny of the Earth's Magnetic Field* (San Diego: Institute for Creation Research, 1973).
Contains well-reasoned argument for a young earth on the basis of one physical factor. The author purposely used uniformitarian pattern of thought of evolutionists to show logical consequences in this case.

Bliss, Richard B., *Origins: Two Models* (San Diego: Creation-Life Publishers, 1976).
Special student workbook for lucid and careful consideration of two points of view about first origins. Planned for high school level but might be used with college students as well.

Clark, R. T. and Bales, James D., *Why Scientists Accept Evolution.* (Nutley, N. J.: Presbyterian and Reformed Publishers Company, 1966).
Five contemporaries and Charles Darwin are examined to show that they first turned away from belief in God the Creator and accepted belief in evolution as a substitute.

Coppedge, James, *Evolution: Possible or Impossible?* (Grand Rapids, MI: Zondervan, 1973).
Written by a specialist on probability who shows very clearly the high improbability of amino acid formation by chance combination of molecular portions (that is, spontaneous generation at submicroscopic level).

Culp, G. Richard, *Remember Thy Creator* (Grand Rapids, MI: Baker Book House, 1975).
Written by a scientist who was once an evolutionist. The author provides specific support from scientific findings for his belief in a creationist point of view.

Custance, Arthur C., *Genesis and Early Man* (Grand Rapids, MI: Zondervan Publishing House, 1975).
Valuable treatment of so-called prehistoric fossil men which the author places most logically into a possible biblical frame of reference.

_____ *Noah's Three Sons: Human History in Three Dimensions* (Grand
Rapids, MI: Zondervan Publishing House, 1975).
An examination of much cultural information relevant to the Table
of Nations in Genesis.

_____ *Evolution or Creation?* (Grand Rapids, MI: Zondervan Publishing House, 1976).
A continuation of the reasoned approach of this fine scientist consistent
with his position in the previous two books.

Davidheiser, Bolton, *Evolution and Christian Faith* (Nutley, N. J.: Presbyterian & Reformed Publishing Company, 1969).
Written by a scientist who was once an evolutionist but who now
marshalls chapter after chapter of thorough examination of facts
against evolution and for a creationist point of view.

Frair, Wayne and Davis, P. William, *The Case for Creation*, revised ed.,
Chicago: Moody Press, 1972).
An expanded edition of a plainly worded case for creation in clear
irenic exposition.

Gish, Duane T., *Speculations and Experiments on the Origin of Life.* (San
Diego: Institute for Creation Research, 1972).
A technical monograph containing pointed analysis of the unscientific
nature of the speculations some scientists propose about ultimate origin
of life on the earth.

_____ *Evidence Against Evolution* (Wheaton, Ill.: Tyndale House,
1972).
Handy pocket sized compilation of concise arguments against evolution written for nonspecialists.

_____ "Creation, Evolution, and the Historical Evidence", *American
Biology Teacher*, March 1973, pp. 132-141.
A printed form of a talk presented in September 1972 in San
Francisco before over 1500 members of the National Association
of Biology Teachers. Useful reference in a noncreationist publication.

_____ *Evolution, The Fossils Say NO!* 2nd ed. (San Diego: Institute
for Creation Research, 1973).
An expanded edition of this classic work by a most eminent spokesman and writer for scientific creationism. Contains a specially unique
combination of illustrations and discussion of so-called human evolution.

_____ *Dinosaurs: Those Terrible Lizards* (San Diego: Creation-Life Publishers, 1977).
A book for young people, illustrated in color, on those intriguing dinosaurs from a creationist perspective.

Howe, George F., Editor, *Speak to the Earth: Creation Studies in Geoscience* (Nutley, N. J.: Presbyterian & Reformed Publishing Company, 1975).
A classified anthology of articles from *Creation Research Society Quarterly* from second five-year period, 1969-1974.

Klotz, John W., *Genes, Genesis and Evolution* 2nd ed., (St. Louis: Concordia Publishing House, 1970).
A fine standard textbook treatment of this complex subject matter area.

Kofahl, Robert E. and Seagraves, Kelly L., *The Creation Explanation* Wheaton, Ill.: Harold Shaw Publishers, 1975).
A very readable presentation of a creation point of view with noticeable emphasis on physical science aspects.

Lammerts, Walter E., Editor, *Why Not Creation?* (Nutley, N. J.: Presbyterian & Reformed Publishing Company, 1970).
A classified anthology of articles from *Creation Research Society Quarterly* from the first five-year period, 1964-1969.

_____ *Scientific Studies in Special Creation* (Nutley, N.J.: Presbyterian Reformed Publishing Company, 1971).
A second classified anthology of articles from *Creation Research Society Quarterly*, 1964-1969.

Lester, Lane P.; Anderson, Wyatt W.; Moore, John N.; and Simpson, Ronald D., "Evolutionist-Creationist Roundtable", *The Science Teacher,* November 1976, pp. 34-39.
A provocative handling in a noncreationist publication of the evolution/creation confrontation.

Levitt, Zola, *Creation: A Scientists Choice* (San Diego: Creation-Life Publishers, 1981).
A journalist's interview with Dr. John N. Moore regarding his strong case for creationism.

Macbeth, Norman, *Darwin Retried: An Appeal to Reason* New York: Dell Publishing, 1973).
Written by a lawyer who was interested in a critical examination

of the case for evolution, which he shows is without substance.

Moore, John N., "Evolution, Creation, and the Scientific Method", *American Biology Teacher*, January 1973, pp. 23-26.

A printed form of a talk presented in September 1972 in San Francisco before over 1500 members of the National Association of Biology Teachers. Useful reference in a noncreationist publication.

_____ *Should Evolution Be Taught?* (San Diego: Creation-Life Publishers, 1974).

Small booklet containing a case against evolution with suggestions on how evolution should be taught: not as if observed, but as an idea of some scientists.

_____ *Questions and Answers on Creation/Evolution* (Grand Rapids: Baker Book House, 1976).

A comprehensive, yet popularly written, handbook for nonspecialists about the questions most often raised about origins.

Moore, John N. and Slusher, Harold S. Co-Editors, *Biology: A Search for Order in Complexity.* revised ed. (Grand Rapids, MI: Zondervan Publishing House, 1974).

Only high school biology textbook yet published in which chapter authors (over a dozen scientifically trained creationist biologists) present biology as a science, and then consider questions of origins of life (and human beings) on the earth from creation as well as evolution point of view.

Morris, Henry M., *Biblical Cosmology and Modern Science* (Grand Rapids, MI: Baker Book House, 1970).

Excellent classic on relationship of the Bible and proper science.

_____ *The Troubled Waters of Evolution* (San Diego: Creation-Life Publishers, 1974).

Important effort to present in very readable style some of the wide ranging consequences of acceptance of evolutionary thinking by natural sciences, social studies and humanities specialists.

_____ *Evolution in Turmoil* (San Diego: Creation-Life Publishers, 1982).

The evolutionary establishment is in turmoil because of internal disagreements and because of creationist pressures. Developments in 1975-1982 are surveyed in this book.

_____ *The Genesis Record* (Grand Rapids, MI: Baker Book House, 1976).

This is the only commentary (with devotional suggestions) on the complete book of Genesis written by a creationist scientist. Convincing treatments are given to the record of an actual six-day special creation, the worldwide flood, the dispersion, and the lives of the patriarchs exactly as written in Genesis.

Morris, Henry M., Editor, *Scientific Creationism* (San Diego: Creation-Life Publishers, 1974).

This is a valuable scientific handbook for the subject of origins and early earth history, and the entire field of the creationist alternative to evolution.

Riegle, David D., *Creation or Evolution?* (Grand Rapids, MI: Zondervan Publishing House, 1971).

Specially written by a high school biology teacher for high school students in which the author presents first the evolutionist position and then the creationist position in alternating chapters.

Siegler, H. R., *Evolution or Degeneration Which?* Milwaukee, Wis.: Northwestern Publishing Company House, 1972).

Written by a keen observer of nature who is a scientist. This book contains excellent tables of Mammalian and Avian hybrids in addition to critical treatment of usual circumstantial support offered for the evolution position.

Slusher, Harold S., *Critique of Radiometric Dating* (San Diego: Institute for Creation Research, 1973).

A technical monograph in which each of the major radiometric methods of estimating time are critically examined against specific criteria applicable to any reliable chronometer.

Smith, A. E. Wilder, *Man's Origin and Man's Destiny* (Wheaton, Ill.: Harold Shaw Publishers, 1968).

The initial work by this prolific creationist scientist in which he meticulously dissects the evolutionist position.

_____ *The Creation of Life* (Wheaton, Ill.: Harold Shaw Publishers, 1970).

A rather technical study of cybernetics, communication theory and codes (DNA) for life in which the author shows the utter bankruptcy of ideas of evolutionists about ultimate origin of life on the earth.

Tiner, John, *When Science Fails* (Grand Rapids, MI: Baker Book House, 1974).

A popular account of documented cases in which strongly held scientific theories were shown to be incorrect.

Whitcomb, John C., Jr., *The Origin of the Solar System* (Nutley, N. J.: Presbyterian & Reformed Publishing Company, 1964).

This small pamphlet is richly loaded with concise argumentations against the imaginative ideas of some astronomers about ultimate origins of the solar system.

_____ *The Early Earth* (Grand Rapids, MI: Baker Book House, 1972).

The author shows that secular evolution and theistic evolution can be rejected on the basis of true findings of scientists.

_____ *The World That Perished* (Grand Rapids, MI: Baker Book House, 1973).

In this forceful sequel to *The Genesis Flood* the author restates, updates, and defends in less specialized language the scientific evidence for the global catastrophe, the Noachian Flood.

Whitcomb, John C., Jr., and Morris, Henry M., *The Genesis Flood* (Nutley, N. J.: Presbyterian & Reformed Publishing Company, 1961).

A scholarly, detailed, thoroughly documented statement of the biblical and scientific evidence for the Noachian Flood.

Wysong, R. L., *The Creation-Evolution Controversy* (Midland, MI: Inquiry Press, 1976).

This is a daring reading adventure between two emotionally charged spheres of thought involving disciplines from chemistry to geology to philosophy with 138 very instructional illustrations.

Zimmerman, Paul A., Ed., *Darwin, Evolution and Creation* (St. Louis: Concordia Publishing House, 1959).

One of the earliest collections of careful analyses of these topics by creationist scientists.

_____ *Creation, Evolution, and God's Word* (St. Louis: Concordia Publishing House, 1972).

A broader, updated treatment of subject matter similar to the chapters by creationist scientists included in the previous book.

SOURCES OF CREATION MATERIALS

U.S.A.

Bible-Science Association
2911 East 42nd Street
Minneapolis, MN 55406

Creation Research Society
2717 Cranbrook Road
Ann Arbor, MI 48104

Creation Science Association
18346 Beverly Road
Birmingham, MI 48009

Creation Science Association
2825 Riva Ridge Circle
Cottage Grove, WI 53527

Creation-Science Research Center
P.O. Box 23195
San Diego, CA 92123

Creation Social Science & Humanities Society
1429 North Holyoke
Wichita, KS 67208

Geoscience Research Institute
Andrews University
Berrien Springs, MI 49104

Center for Scientific Creation
1319 Brush Hill Circle
Naperville, IL 60540

Institute for Creation Research
2100 Greenfield Drive
P.O. Box 2666
El Cajon, CA 92021

Lutheran Science Institute
8830 West Bluemound Road
Milwaukee, WI 53226
(Membership restricted
to Wisc. Ev. Lutherans)

Maxwell Society of Shoreland
Shoreland Lutheran High
School
5043 20th Avenue
Kenosha, WI 53140

Missouri Association for Creation
2111 Princeton
St. Louis, MO 63117

Origins
Geoscience Research Institute
Loma Linda University
Loma Linda, CA 92350

Pittsburgh Creation Society
208 S. Magnolia Drive
Glenshaw, PA 15116

Students for Origins Research
P.O. Box 203
Goleta, CA 93116

OVERSEAS

Biblical Creation Society
51 Cloan Crescent
Bishopbriggs
Glasgow, Scotland G64 2HN

(Dr. David Lackman
North American Agent
316 Hamel Avenue
North Hills, PA 19038)

**Creation Science Assoc.
of Australia**
P.O. Box 302
Sunnybank, Queensland
Australia 4109

**Creation Scientist Forum of
India**
Chalukunnu
Kottayam
Kerala 686001

**A. Radcliffe-Smith, Hon. Sec.
Evolution Protest Movement**
13 Argyle Avenue
Hounslow, Middlesex
England, TW3 2LE

**Forening for Biblisk
Skapelesetro**
Box 50
424 21 Angered
Sweden

Newton Scientific Association
2 Westoe Road
Edmonton
London, England N9 OSH

CANADA
**Creation Science Association
of Canada**
P.O. Box 34006
Vancouver, B.C. V6J 4M1

**Creation Science Association
of Alberta**
P.O. Box 9075, Station "E"
Edmonton, Alta. T5P 4K1

**Creation Science Association
of Saskatchewan**
Box 1821
Prince Albert, Sask. S6V 6J9

**Creation Science Association
of Ontario**
P.O. Box 821, Station "A"
Scarborough, Ont. M1K 5C8

**International Christian
Crusade**
205 Yonge Street, Room 31
Toronto, Ont. M5B 1N2

**North American Creation
Movement**
P.O. Box 5083, Station "B"
Victoria, B.C. V8R 6N3

PUBLISHERS
Baker Book House
P.O. Box 6287
Grand Rapids, MI 49506

Concordia Publishing House
3558 South Jefferson
St. Louis, MO 63118

Creation-Life Publishers, Inc.
Box 15666
San Diego, CA 92115

Mott Media
1000 E. Huron
Milford, MI 48042

AUDIO-VISUAL SUPPLIERS
Eden Films
  North Eden Road
  Elmwood, IL 61529
Crossroads (Ian Taylor)
  100 Huntley Street
  Toronto, Ontario
  Canada M4Y 2L1
Creation Filmstrip Center
  Route 1
  Haviland, KS 67059
CLP VIDEO
  P.O. Box 15666
  San Diego, CA 92115

Topical Index